DRILLS AND

Precious Metal Mining and Milling Methods of the Frontier West

WILL MEYERRIECKS

Second Edition · Revised and Expanded

Drills And Mills
Precious Metal Mining and Milling Methods of the Frontier West

Second Edition
First Printing   **June 2003, first 100 copies hand-numbered.**

First Edition
Third Printing   December 2002
Second Printing   February 2002
First Printing   June 2001, limited to 500 hand-numbered copies.

This book is printed on neutral pH paper. Manufactured in the United States of America.

Library of Congress Cataloging – Publication Data

Meyerriecks, Will
    Drills And Mills : Precious Metal Mining and Milling Methods of the Frontier West

    Description: viii, 264 p. : ill. · 28cm.
    Subjects: Mines and mineral resources—West (U.S)—History—19th century.
                 Mining engineering—West (U.S.)—History—19th century.
                 Ore-dressing—West (U.S.)—History—19th century.
                 Ore-dressing plants—West (U.S.)—History—19th century.
    Notes: Includes bibliographical references (p. 250-258) and indexes.

    ISBN: 0-9714383-1-5

    LC Classification: TN23.6 .M49 2001
    Dewey Class No.:   622/.342/0978 21

Questions? Comments? Suggestions? Corrections? The author may be reached at:

Will Meyerriecks
702 Leisure Avenue
Tampa, Florida
33613-1835USA

wmeyerriecks@yahoo.com

Cover Image:

Humphrey Concentration Mill, Creede, Mineral County, Colorado, ca 1905
Courtesy USGS

Title Page Image:

Silver King Mine and Mill, Park City District, Summit County, Utah, 1902
Courtesy USGS

This book is dedicated to Sunshine and Sampson.

*It would not have been possible without their
support, encouragement, and enthusiasm.*

Molas Pass, Colorado

June 2001

TABLE OF CONTENTS

The Gold Rush...1

North Carolina 1
California 1

Placer Mining...2

Boomtowns 2
Panning 4
Rockers 5
Sluices and Long Toms...........................7
River Mining 8
Hydraulic Mining 9
Dredging 12
Drift Mining 14
California Placer Gold Résumé..............15
Ditches and Flumes 16
    Notable Failures 17
Endnotes 18

Hardrock Mining 21

Luck: The Good, the Bad, and the Sneaky 22
    The Good 22
    The Bad 23
    The Sneaky 23
Claims 23
Mining 26
    Terminology 27
    Drilling 27
    Blasting 30
        Blasting Sequence 32
    Loading 33
    Hauling 35
    Hoisting 36
        Rope and Cable.......................38
        Buckets, Cages, and Skips.....39
        Hoisting Safety 40
    Illumination 41
    Ventilation 43
        Heat 44
    Changing Ore with Depth.................45
    Tunnels 46
        The Revenue Tunnel...............46
        The Sutro Tunnel....................47
        The Newhouse (Argo) Tunnel 48
    Mining Costs.....................................50
Endnotes 52

**Timbering, Pumping
Explosives, Machine Drills**......................55

Timbering 56
    Spiling 56
    Pig-stying 57
    Square Sets 57
        Ore Exploitation Using Square Sets.......60
        Dimensions and Framing.........61

    Decay 61
    Fire 61
    Collapse....................................62
    Reuse 63
Dewatering & Pumps 63
    Pump Primer 65
    Cornish Pumps 66
        Pumps 66
        Pump Rods 67
        Directional Changes 69
        Balance Bobs 69
        Operation............................69
        Man Engines 71
Explosives 72
    Rackarock 76
Machine Drills & Compressors.................77
Endnotes 87

**Transportation, Power
And Fuel, Assays** 91

Transportation 92
    Four-footed Friends:
    Mules, Burros, and Horses.............93
        Prunes 94
        Weights and Distances.......94
    Ore Wagons 97
    Underground Horses and Mules 99
        How to get a Mule in the Mine.............100
    Arabian Nights..........................100
    Railroads 101
    Aerial Trams 103
    The Botched Jig-Back Inclined Tramway 106
Power and Fuel 107
    Steam Engines 107
    The Pelton Wheel......................108
    Electricity 110
    Wood 111
        Sawmills 112
        Log Chutes 113
        The V-Flume.......................113
    Charcoal 113
    Coke 115
    Fire 116
Assays 117
    Field Assay 118
    The Fire Assay 118
        Preparation........................119
        Inquartation........................120
        Classic Lead Assay 121
        Cupellation.........................121
        Parting 122
    Samplers 122
    Metalliferous Murphy 123
Endnotes 124

Mill Processes 127

Mill Processes 128
Amalgamation 128
    Retorting 129
    Melting 130
The Patio Process.................................131
The Washoe Process.................................133
    The Sagebrush Process.................................134
    Consolidated Virginia Mill.................................134
    Stanford Mill 136
    Quicksilver Loss 138
    Washoe Process Résumé.................................138
Roasting 140
The Reese River Process 142
The Freiberg and Augustin Processes.................................143
The Chlorination Process.................................143
    Leaching Vats and Charging.................................144
    Chlorine Gas Generation.................................145
    Chlorination 146
    Settling and Precipitation.................................147
    Refining 148
    Process Improvements: Barrels 148
        The Mears Process 148
        The Thies Process.................................149
    Precipitation Improvements.................................150
    The Rothwell and
    Newberry-Vautin Processes.................................151
    Chlorination Résumé.................................152
        Cripple Creek.................................152
The Kiss Process 153
The Cyanide Process.................................154
    The Process 156
    Cyanide Résumé 157
Endnotes 159

Smelters and Refineries
Quicksilver and Zinc 163

Eureka 164
    Smelter Operation 166
    The Campaign.................................167
    The Arents Tap.................................168
    Eureka Production 168
Black Hawk and Denver.................................169
    The Ziervogel Process 171
Durango 171
Leadville 172
    Smelting Fees 172
    Ore Beds 173
    Flue Dust 174
    Decline 175
    Leadville Production 176
Pyritic Smelting 177
Refineries 177
    The Flach Process 178
    The Parkes Process 178
    The Pattinson Process 179
Carson Mint 180
Quicksilver 181
    The Scott Furnace 184
Zinc 186
Endnotes 187

Mill Machinery.................................191

Grinding and Crushing 192
    The Arrastra 192
    Stamps 194
        Stamp Battery.................................195
        Automatic Ore Feeders 197
        Stamp Summary.................................198
    Pans 199
        Varney and Wheeler Pans.................................199
    Blake Jaw Crusher 201
Concentrating 203
    The Buddle 203
    Hendy's Concentrator.................................204
    The Gilpin County Concentrator
    and the Rittinger Table 205
    The Wilfley Table.................................205
    The Frue Vanner 207
Roasting Furnaces 210
    Brückner Cylinder 210
    White-Howell Furnace 211
Endnotes 212

Mines and Mills
Occupational Hazards.................................215

Mills 217
    Disasters 219
Mines and Mining Districts 219
    The Elkhorn 219
    Mercur 220
    Philipsburg 221
    Butte 222
    The Horn Silver.................................225
Are Stamp Mills Extinct? 226
Occupational Hazards.................................228
    Diseases & Sanitation 228
        Ver ist der *Krappen Hausen*? 229
    Drug Abuse 230
    Poisoning 230
    Silicosis 232
    Explosions and Explosives.................................233
    Falls 234
    Cave-ins, Rock Falls,
    Falling Objects, and Hoisting.................................235
    Mine and Mill Machinery.................................236
    Nature 237
    Accident Statistics 237
Endnotes 239

Appendices 241

The Welsh (Swansea) Copper Process 241
Smelting Chemistry 242
Pelton Wheel Power Output.................................242
The Environment.................................243
Wages and the Cost of Living 245
Annual Metal Production and Average Price.................................247
Endnotes 249

References 250

Index 259

Author's Notes

Welcome to the Second Edition of Drills And Mills, which has been extensively revised and expanded. Readers of the First Edition will immediately notice the new lay-flat style binding and cover graphics. Inside are hundreds of new facts and figures, and dozens of new references, photographs, charts, and tables. Additional metallurgical processes and sections about refineries have been added, as have vignettes outlining a selection of mines and mining districts in the West. Did you ever wonder how a mule was hoisted into a mine? Now there are photographs that illustrate just such an event. Other new photographs depict diverting an entire river with a flume, undercurrent sluices, the Patio process on the Comstock, blanket sluices, and diamond drilling in action to name but a few.

Every effort has been made to keep Drills And Mills accurate. This is not always an easy task. For example, one reference states that the discovery of gold by Marshall was in 1847, and this same reference states that 256 million pounds of gold had been recovered in the U.S. through 1888. Closer inspection reveals that the author intended to state that £256 million had been recovered, which is itself an overstated figure, but far closer to the facts. Another reference states that Senator Horace Tabor was involved in a mining venture in Montana in the early 1900's... years after his death! Statistical details suffer from similar issues too. A good example is the production of the Reese River mining district of Nevada. The following table illustrates this point rather well.

For 1866, 69, and 71-87	Tons	Dollars	Dollars per Ton
County Assessor's Records	79,639	$11,713,732	$147
Reese River Reveille	1,341,510	$18,602,300	$14
State Production Figures	92,622	$12,332,123	$133

Interesting, isn't it? Which figures do you believe? Apparently the Reveille puffed the district's production to the point of bursting. The average ore value of $14 per ton simply could not have been mined *or* milled (let alone both) at a profit by the processes then in use. In this instance (and in others) economic geologists have critically evaluated the available details culled from numerous sources, and from this have compiled the best and most meaningful values. The state production figures are the ones selected for facts and figures, in this case.

The trends seen in historic production figures, when graphed, often convey more information than tabulated figures do, especially in regards to the inevitable decline of the various mining districts. The extensive "low-grade period" of the Comstock, followed by a brief flurry of lucrative cyanidation at the turn of the century, tells such a tale. For this reason, charts are used wherever appropriate. The charts sometimes reflect drastic events, such as the massive caving-in of the Horn Silver mine in 1885. Equally important are economic effects and government policies, some of which caved-in the economy. A few such events of the many that spelled change for the western mining industries follow.

1849	The "sixteen to one" ratio · silver and gold are minted at the ratio of 16 to 1
1873	"Coinage Act" passed · silver demonetized · silver price declines · Panic of 1873 begins · later this was called "The Crime of 1873"
1875	The Coinage Act was modified by the "Resumption of Species Payment Act"
1876	"Joint Resolution for the Issue of Silver Coin" was passed
1878	Bland-Allison Act ("Coinage of Standard Silver Dollar Act") passed silver mining resumes · price of silver steadily rises · value of silver dollar drops · inflation follows
1889	Price of silver declines · Panic of 1889 begins
1890	(Sherman) "Silver Purchase Act" passed (Bland-Allison Act rescinded) · silver price briefly rises, then declines
1893	Silver Purchase Act repealed · silver price declines rapidly · mines close British Crown Colony of India ceases purchase of silver for coinage · Panic of 1893 begins
1896	William Jennings Bryan's famous "Cross of Gold" speech of July 9 · "You shall not press down upon the brow of labor this crown of thorns, you shall not crucify mankind upon a cross of gold."
1900	Gold Standard Act passed

Many books are available that feature ghost towns, frontier life, boomtowns, saloons, brothels, and gunfights in the Old West. Very few describe in detail the economic backbone of the frontier West: mining and milling. Those books that do provide such details generally focus on a specific town or mining district, or are targeted towards the mining engineer or professional. Drills and Mills is written for a general audience, though the student or historian will find the facts, figures, and endnotes helpful for further studies, research, and as a reference. Please enjoy Drills and Mills and the fascinating 19th century mining and milling methods, processes, and history that it brings to life!

Acknowledgements

The author wishes to express a sincere appreciation for the efforts put forth by the various parks and agencies, historic societies, museums, and staff and volunteers that help preserve our history and heritage in all of its forms. Also, to the miners and enthusiasts that keep the techniques used by the old-timers alive, single- and double-jacking, at mining heritage events.

The author thanks the following individuals, museums, libraries, organizations, agencies, societies, and parks for all of their help in making this book possible. Hopefully nobody has been left out...

Joyce Achtschin · Dr. Earle B. Amey · Corby Anderson · Ron Balazik · Ray Boyle · Scott Brady
Janell Brimhall · Jed Bullard · Mary C. Dale · Daniel Edelstein · Scott Fetchenhier · Bob Gardner
Murphy Givens · Shawn Hall · Wendy Hall · Tom Hash · Henry E. Hilliard · Ron Hopkins
Michael P. Hunerlach · Chris Kiechler · Ken and Bonnie Kosanke · Richard and Diann Kuzma
Dennis and Christine Lanning · Wilbur Lewis · Tom Lowe · Michael J. McKinley
Andrew and Norma Meyerriecks · Doug Misner · Kitty Monahan · Alvin Mosch
Garry and Monika Mullan · Bob Neal · Carl Nesbitt · Bethany Perez · Beth Price · Robert Reese
Sampson (who still dreams about where that chipmunk scampered off to at the Yankee Girl)
Robin Schaut · Ted Shaw · Beth Simmons · Gerald Smith · Jennifer Sotelo · Susan Snyder
Charlotte Stock · Robert Stoufer · Erik Swanson · Doug Tomlinson · Al Turner · Linda Ulbricht
Robin Urban · and last but definitely not least, Dan Wilson

Argo Mill, Idaho Springs, CO · Arthur Lakes Library, Colorado School of Mines, Golden, CO
Bachelor-Syracuse Mine, Ouray, CO · Bancroft Library, University of California, Berkeley, CA
The Bannack Association, Dillon, MT · Berlin Ichthyosaur Sate Park, Berlin, NV
Bodie State Historic Park, Bodie, CA · Carnegie Branch Library for Local History, Boulder, CO
Chollar Mine, Virginia City, NV · Creede Underground Mining Museum, Creede, CO
Cripple Creek District Museum, Cripple Creek, CO · Country Boy Mine, Breckenridge, CO
Department of Conservation, Division of Mines and Geology Library, Sacramento, CA
Early Mining Heritage Museum (online) · Empire Mine Historic Park, Grass Valley, CA
Fire, Arson and Explosion Investigation Program, Eastern Kentucky University, KY
Florida State Fair, Tampa, FL · Friends of Bodie, Bridgeport, CA · Friends of Rhyolite, Beatty, NV
Gilpin County Historical Society, Central City, CO · Golden Spike National Historic Site, Promontory, UT
Hard Tack Mine & Museum, Lake City, CO · Hinsdale County Museum, Lake City, CO
Jerome State Park, Jerome, AZ · Lincoln County Historical Museum, Pioche, NV
Malakoff Diggins State Park, North Bloomfield, CA · Marshall Gold Discovery State Park, Coloma, CA
Mayflower Mill, Silverton, CO · Mollie Kathleen Mine, Cripple Creek, CO
Montana Historical Society Museum, Helena, MT · Mount Morgan Historical Museum, Inc., Australia
Nevada Bureau of Mines and Geology, Reno, NV
New Almaden Quicksilver Mining Museum, Santa Clara County, CA
North Star Mining Museum, Grass Valley, CA · Old Irontown State Park, Little Pinto, UT
Phoenix Gold Mine, Idaho Springs, CO · Pioneer Tunnel, Ashland, PA
San Juan County Historical Society, Silverton, CO · Santa Clara County Parks and Recreation Department, CA
South Park City, (Fairplay) CO · South Pass City Historical Site, South Pass, WY
Tonopah Mining Park, Tonopah, NV · Utah State Historical Society, Salt Lake City, UT
Victor/Lowell Thomas Museum, Victor, CO · Ward Charcoal Ovens State Park, Ward, NV
Western Museum of Mining and Industry, Colorado Springs, CO · Wolverton Mill, Hanksville, UT
World Museum of Mining, Butte, MT · Yankee Fork Gold Dredge Association, Challis, ID

Library of Congress, Prints and Photographs Division: Detroit Publishing Company Collection, John C. Grabill Collection, HABS-HAER, Lawrence & Houseworth Collection, and Panoramic Photographs Collection

National Archives and Records Administration (NARA)

United States Geological Survey · Metals Section - Minerals Information Team

THE GOLD RUSH

North Carolina

In 1799, twelve-year-old Conrad Reed was babysitting his younger siblings as all were playing around Little Meadow Creek, which ran across the Reed farm in Cabarrus County, North Carolina. A yellow rock – about the size of a shoe, caught his attention. He hefted the rock and found it to be surprisingly heavy, and decided to take it home. His father found the rock curious, and brought it to a local silversmith. The silversmith told him that it was worthless, so John Reed took it home and found practical use for the rock as a doorstop. There it sat for three years. In 1802, on a trip to Fayetteville, a jeweler purchased the rock from Reed for $3.50… a *seventeen-pound* gold nugget! Reed reportedly bought coffee beans and a calico dress for his wife with the proceeds. The First Gold Rush began in the U.S.[1]

Between 1804-1827, the only reported gold production was in North Carolina. Through 1828, gold worth $110,000 had been produced. By the end of the 1820's, Gold Fever found its way into Georgia, Virginia, and South Carolina.[2] Through the end of 1894, nearly $12 million in gold had been produced in North Carolina.[3]

California

On January 24, 1848 – 3000 miles from North Carolina, James Marshall was inspecting the millrace of a sawmill that he built as part of a partnership with John Sutter, the mill located on the south fork of the American River in the Sierra foothills. Each evening he diverted river water through the millrace to flush out the day's debris, the action of the water also deepening the channel. Something in the ditch caught his eye. He scooped up a handful of the dirt and gravels from the ditch, and forever changed the course of history. It too had the yellow metal, which on close examination he decided was gold. He trusted his men to keep the secret, which they did. But the secret could not be contained forever. Word spread like wildfire when merchant Sam Brannan waved a bottle filled with gold dust around San Francisco in May 1848. Soon, tens of thousands of gold-seekers – *Argonauts,* would find their way to California to participate in the greatest Gold Rush ever.[4]

Figure 1   Sutter's Mill (recreation), Coloma, California 2002   Author

PLACER MINING

A '49er reporting on the discovery of Discovery Bar, Idaho, May 18, 1863

The deposits of gold first worked by the Argonauts were *placers*. Placer deposits are natural accumulations of precious metal dust, flakes, grains, and nuggets, weathered free from the host rock that originally contained the metals.

Exposure to ice and temperature extremes – mechanical action, and to air, water, and naturally occurring dissolved acids and minerals – chemical action, slowly break down and oxidize the rocks that are exposed on or near the surface of the hills and mountains. Melting snow and rains wash away and erode the steeper slopes of the mountains, transporting the sand, gravel, and rocks to streams and rivers. The endless grinding and tumbling of the weathered rock fragments takes its toll, as it has for millennia; mountains crumble into the sea.

As the rock, some of which hold prisoner threads and flakes of precious metals, is subjected to mechanical and chemical action in the stream, it is slowly reduced until the bits of metal are exposed and ultimately set free. Gold and platinum, and to a lesser degree silver, are relatively impervious to natural chemical actions, however. The mechanical action of the streams round and blunt the edges of the larger metal bits, forming nuggets that range in size from pinheads up to, well, 17-pounders… and then some! These metals are also quite heavy – dense, and slowly seek the lowest parts of the stream or riverbed as the lighter – less dense, rocks such as quartz move towards the upper layers. Gold is very often found concentrated at or just above the bedrock level of streams.

Mother Nature – a *lot* of time, water, and gravity for the most part, did the bulk of the work. It ice-wedged, fractured, oxidized, and dissolved the rock that makes up the mountains. It transported the rocks along the streams and rivers, reducing giant boulders to cloudy silt, all the while unlocking the hidden treasures contained within. It separated and stratified the dense, precious metals from the valueless rock, and in the process rather conveniently concentrated the valuable parts – the *values,* along the stream channel bedrock, in cracks in the bedrock, and along some of the banks and bars.

Mother Nature did almost all of the work in making the gold readily available for Conrad and James and the tens of thousands of Argonauts. All they had to do was a bit of digging and washing, for the most part.

Boomtowns

Tent camps and boomtowns sprung up like mushrooms as new diggings were found, continuously replenished as thousands of fresh and wild-eyed Argonauts spilled onto the scene. On March 27, 1850, Dr. Thaddeus Hildreth and his party collected 30 *pounds* of gold nuggets in two days. Within two months 5000 argonauts were swarming over the area, and Hildreth's Diggin's became American Camp, later renamed Columbia, California.[6]

William Fairweather, Henry Edgar, and Barney Hughes discovered gold in Alder Gulch, Montana Territory, on May 22, 1863. They were enroute to Bannack when they discovered what would be the richest strike in Montana's history. Try as they might, the secret could not be kept, and the rush was on to Alder. Within a year, an estimated 10,000 miners stampeded to the area. Virginia City was established, which took the territorial capital away from Bannack in 1865, and kept it until 1875. During the first five years of this boom, an estimated $30-$40 million in gold was recovered by placer mining, with another $10 million recovered during the following 23 years.[7]

The boomtowns were hastily constructed, often in places where only primitive transportation and building materials were available. By the summer of 1863 – the first year of the great Reese River Rush, there were about 1450 people in the area, with 34 stone, 45 brush, 51 tent, 55 canvas, 58 frame, 61 adobe, and 62 log structures.[8]

Some miners proved very creative and resourceful, utilizing raw materials readily at hand. In the parched desert of western Nevada, Tom Kelly, a 76-year-old Australian, used that which was extremely abundant in any booming mining camp to build his house: *beer bottles!* His house – seen in figure 3, constructed primarily from bottles and adobe mortar, was started in September 1905 and was completed in February 1906.[9] Roofs of many of the houses in Terraville – a suburb of Lead, South Dakota, used cyanide can lids as shingles. These cans were found in great abundance in the nearby gold mills.[10]

Most of the boomtowns only lasted as long as the gold did – the irreverent and humorous names that were often used did not lend themselves to permanency. See the box below.[11] A few underwent name changes as they matured and gained both permanency and respectability. Marysville, California, for example, was "a little town, built mostly of canvas" in 1851. It had two brick buildings. Marysville didn't fade away like so many other camps, however. In 1852, there were 17 brick buildings; in 1853, 39, in 1854, 43, and by 1855 there were 54.[12]

Figure 2   Deadwood, SD ca 1876
                    Courtesy NARA

Figure 3   Tom Kelly's bottle house   Author
                    Rhyolite, Nevada 2002

Gold Rush Amusing Placenames

Barefoot Diggings · Bedbug (Ione) · Bloomer Hill · Chucklehead Diggings · Dead Broke
Delirium Tremens (Omega) · Dogtown · Donkeyville · Flea Valley · Forlorn Hope · Git-up-and-Git
Gouge Eye (Pleasant Grove) · Hangtown (Placerville) · Hell-Out-for-Noon City · Henpeck City
Mad Mule Gulch · Nut-cake Camp · One Horse Town · Petticoat Slide · Poodletown
Puke Ravine · Puppytown · Rot Gut · Rough and Ready · Salt Pork Ridge · Sucker Flat
Swellhead Diggings · Tin Cup Diggings · You Bet · You-be-damned

Panning

The places where the Argonauts dug up the ground in their pursuits for gold became known as *diggings* or *diggins*. At first it was easy enough to find good diggings as the ground was untouched, rich, and there was more than enough for everybody. That, of course, would change rapidly with the onslaught of the rush. The only equipment that was required in the most basic of recovery methods was a shovel and a pan – a process called *panning* for gold. It had the virtue of being extremely cheap, and something that a single person could do on their own. See figure 4.[13]

Gravel was dug up from the streambed or riverbank – rather arbitrarily at first, as nobody really knew what they were doing except those few with experience from Georgia or Carolina. A small amount of the gravel or dirt, perhaps two or three measuring cups worth, was placed in a large, shallow pan that had a flat bottom. The pan was submerged in a relatively calm portion of the stream. First, any clumps of dirt were broken apart. Next, a fairly vigorous side-to-side motion of the pan was begun. This had the effect of quickly settling the heavier contents while washing the pan free of the muddy contents. The larger stones and pebbles – down to, say, fingernail-sized, were quickly examined and thrown aside. One wouldn't want to miss a large nugget! All that remained in the pan was gravel and sand.

Figure 4   *"We Have it Rich"* 1889
Courtesy Library of Congress

The panning was then continued, but now with a more gentle side-to-side and very slightly circular motion, with the pan held at an angle and partially submerged in the water. It is interesting to watch how the gravel separates itself – floats. With the pan held at the correct depth and angle in the water, it is easy to float the unwanted (and lower density) gravel right over the edge of the pan, all the while keeping a sharp eye out for anything yellow or dull-metallic looking.

After a few minutes, a small crescent-shaped swirl of heavy sands would be left in the pan – the few cups of gravel reduced and concentrated to about that of a shot glass in volume. The miner would pan very cautiously at this point, and make frequent examinations of the contents of the pan. He would then carefully empty the pan of almost all of its water, then swirl the sands into a drawn-out streak around the crease of the pan. If gold were present, it would leave a trace of *colors* – small, visible flakes and dust, following beneath and behind a swirl of *black sands* – mostly *magnetite* (Fe_3O_4), in the crease of the pan.[14]

If there were no colors, the miner would move on, prospecting other areas of the stream in this fashion, keeping at least mental notes of the *indications* along the stream he worked. If the colors looked good, he would dig deeper, because, as a general rule, colors found from a shallow depth indicate a heavy *pay streak* near the bedrock below. This was (and is) not always the case, but more often than not it was.

BLUE GOLD?

Gold wasn't always the most profitable mineral to be found while placer mining. Miners working the Eldorado Bar on the Missouri River in 1865 made an interesting find: small, hard stones at first thought to be diamonds, and later determined to be sapphires.

It was reported that one man could collect from one to two pounds of sapphires per day from the bar in 1873, with perfect specimens in the four to six carat range frequently found.[15]

A placer miner might work one pan every 4-5 minutes, perhaps a little longer if the colors were good, perhaps a little shorter if the indications were poor. Panning may have been simple and inexpensive, but the quantity of gravel that could be worked was sorely limited. Too much time was spent alternating between digging for the rich placers and then panning what was dug.

It became difficult for men to work by themselves – those miners that happened to be near the newest discoveries and managed to get there first quickly claimed the richest diggings, the latecomers generally being crowded out, or left to rework abandoned claims. They either rushed off on the first news to new diggings – no matter how wild or unfounded the rumors might be, struck out on their own and prospected for new diggings, or worked with or for others in small partnerships or companies of miners.

What was needed was a way of streamlining and improving the gold recovery process, and the ability to work lower-grade placers at a profit.

Rockers

The *rocker* – sometimes called a *rocker-box* or *cradle*, increased the quantity of gravel that could be worked in a given time. The rocker had been used back in the east, long before the California Rush.[16] Isaac Humphrey was perhaps the first to use one in California about March 1848.[17] See figure 5.

A rocker was constructed not unlike an infant's cradle. It consisted of a hopper in which a shovel full of gravel was dumped. The base of the hopper had a perforated iron plate or screen. Water was poured through the hopper, and the rocker was – you guessed it, rocked from side to side by pushing and pulling on a handle. The larger stones were rinsed free of mud and silt, and were inspected and discarded... could be a nugget!

The small pieces of gravel and sands made their way through the perforated plate. They fell onto an apron, which was made of a small frame with a rectangular piece of canvas or fabric attached to it, and placed at about a 30° angle to the hopper. It had the effect of moderating the gush of water and sands falling from the hopper, and diverting this flow to the top of a small *sluice* mounted at the base of the rocker.

Figure 5   Miner with a Rocker
Columbia, Tuolumne County, California ca 1866
Courtesy Library of Congress

The water carrying this fine debris washed over the surface of the sluice, which was arranged with a slight downhill slope. The sluice had small strips of wood – *riffles*, nailed to its surface, oriented perpendicular to the flow of the water. The sand and fine particles would get trapped behind the riffles, and the rocking motion would agitate them. This agitation sorted the heavier and lighter sands, just as a stream would.

Soon too much sand would build up behind a given riffle and the water would wash the excess to the next riffle. This excess was mostly lighter material; the heavier sands were left behind. Whatever heavy sands – or gold, washed over the top of one riffle had another chance to be retained on the next riffle. Ultimately, the low-density waste sands would wash off the end of the sluice as the heavier black sands – and hopefully some gold, would become trapped behind the riffles.

After a hopper-load or two of gravel had been washed, or whatever the diggings required, the miner would save the sands caught behind the riffles – a *cleanup*, and the process repeated throughout the day. Two or three men were often at work with a rocker: one to operate the rocker(s), one to dig, and one to fetch buckets of gravel and water. Sometimes a short flume would supply water for the rocker(s). The combined effort of the miners and the division of labor increased the quantity of gravel 3-5 times over that which would be processed by each man if panning separately.

Throughout the day the miners would exchange places. Between these "shift changes" they might carefully pan the collected sands to see how much gold they had saved, and to use these results to direct their efforts.

In the early days of working the rich placers around Idaho City, Idaho, many miners would pass over claims that paid $8 a day. In 1864, seven men working a claim in the Boise basin mines recovered 35 *pounds* of gold in nine days.[18] The Harkleroder brothers washed $10,000 from a 200 by 60 feet portion of ground in Sparta, Oregon.[19] The Montana Bar placer, found in the Confederate Gulch mining district of Montana, is the richest ground ever reported for that state. Two acres produced about $1 to $1.5 million, and one pan was reported to have contained $1,400 in gold![20]

At Coloma, men could earn as much as $25-30 a day with a rocker, though $10-20 was typical.[21] Some miners did better than others. Daniel Woods, a forty-niner working the placers at Curtis Creek in January of 1851, wrote the following in his diary:

"This morning, notwithstanding the rain, we were again at our work. We *must* work. In sunshine and rain, in warm and cold, in sickness and health, successful or not successful, early and late, it is work, *work, WORK! Work or perish!* All around us, above and below, on mountain side and stream, the rain, falling fast upon them, are the miners at work – not for *gold*, but for *bread*. Lawyers, doctors, clergymen, farmers, soldiers, deserters, good and bad, from England, from America, from China, from the Islands, from every country but Russia and Japan – all, all at work at their cradles. From morning to night is heard the incessant rock, rock, rock! Over the whole mines, in streamlet, in creek, and in river, down torrent and through the valley, ever rushes on the muddy sediment from ten thousand busy rockers. Cheerful words are seldom heard, more seldom the boisterous shout and laugh which indicate success, and which, when heard, sink to a lower ebb the spirits of the unsuccessful. We have made 50 cents each." [22]

In the mining camps, gold dust and nuggets were the accepted currency – a pinch might buy a shot of *Ho Joe*, rotgut whiskey at best. Gold was valued at $20.67 an ounce. Did that mean that an ounce of gold dust was worth $20.67? No, it didn't.

State	Fine Gold	Fine Silver	Fine Base	Value per Ounce
California	884	112	4	$18.40
Colorado	820	176	4	$17.15
Dakota	927	73	0	$19.25
Georgia	923	73	4	$19.16
Idaho	781	213	6	$16.39
Montana	895	101	4	$18.62
Oregon	873	123	4	$18.19

Table 1   Placer Gold Fineness and Value

Figure 6 Oriental Saloon, Bisbee, Arizona ca 1900
Courtesy NARA

Gold is very rarely "pure" – it is almost always mixed with silver in varying proportions, *electrum* being the resulting alloy. The amount of gold and silver in an alloy are measured in parts per thousand – the "fineness" of the metal. For example, pure gold would be 1000 fine. A "gold" nugget of ¾ gold and ¼ silver would be gold

750 fine, and silver 250 fine. *Base metals* might also be present. Base metals are low-value and chemically active, such as copper, lead, and zinc. Table 1 illustrates the typical fineness of a fairly large sampling of placer gold from different states collected in the early 1880's.[23] Bannack, Montana had exceptionally pure placer gold, averaging 990 fine, and at times reaching 999 fine.[24] Placer gold found in the Summit Valley district – later to become Butte, Montana, had significant silver. This resulted in "gold" worth from $11-$14 per ounce – perhaps 500 to 650 fine gold.[25]

Underground, gold is sometimes found in a crystalline form in small pockets or chambers, like a geode, but that is rare. The mining term for the chamber is a *vug*. Miners working in the Cresson Mine, located between Victor and Cripple Creek, Colorado, came across a vug large enough for a man to stand in. It contained $1,200,000 of gold crystals![26] Some gold – the so-called *free milling gold*, found associated with quartz could be fairly pure. Quartz gold from the Ortiz shaft, located in the Old Placers district of New Mexico, was assayed in 1864 and found to be approximately gold 992 and silver 008 fine – very pure as natural gold goes.[27]

Figure 7   Sluice Mining ca 1875
Courtesy NARA

Sluices and Long Toms

In the quest to process more gravel, sometimes of a grade lower than that which could be economically worked by a pan or rocker, the *Long Tom* was developed. The long tom was essentially a lengthened rocker. Finer material being washed down its length fell through a perforated iron plate and into a single riffle box below. The top section – the long box, served the same purpose as the hopper on the cradle, and was about 10-12 feet long.[28] See figure 7.

Miners dug along its length and shoveled the gravel directly into the box. Small flumes provided continuous wash water. The miners quickly learned that a liberal sprinkling of quicksilver behind the riffles would catch more gold. The mercury would wet much of the gold flakes and dust that otherwise might be lost in the turbulent wash water. The *amalgam* that formed would be *retorted* to collect the gold, and the mercury vapor possibly condensed for reuse. The use of mercury in placer mining was effective and widespread. The mercury was also readily available – it was produced from mines on the Coast Range just south of San Francisco.

In the winter of 1850-51, miners placed a series of riffle boxes at the end of their long tom. This proved successful in saving more gold – and the *sluice* was *re*born in California. Reborn? Yes. Sluices that used blankets to trap gold – *blanket sluices*, were in use for hundreds of years. See figure 8.

Figure 8   Medieval Blanket Sluices
Source: Lazarus Ercker's *Treatise on Ores and Assaying*

The Widow, a placer mine located in the Prichard Creek area of the Coeur D'Alene, Idaho, was an active producer in 1884. From 3-8 men spent their days shoveling dirt into a sluice, and cleanups were made almost daily. Typical results were: for Saturday, $160, Tuesday $158, Wednesday $270, Thursday and Friday $450. This averaged about $24 per day per man. The prior fall the cleanups ranged from $200-$800 per day.[29]

The Myrtle Mining Company, located in the Trail Creek area of the Coeur D'Alene, was engaged in placer mining in 1885. The five owners, together with 5-6 employees, worked the claims with water supplied by a 13-mile long aqueduct. $52,797.90 was made during the year, including finding a nugget worth $165 in November – perhaps $20 per man per day before expenses. Their weekly cleanups are shown in chart 1.[30]

While these miners in Idaho may have done pretty well for themselves in the mid-80's, many of their fathers and uncles didn't have it so good back in California. In the early days of the rush the diggins were good and the Argonauts few. A man could make $10-20 a day. Of course, the cost of living was just as high; the merchants and saloons quickly absorbed most of his earnings. Very few miners actually "got rich." As more and more Argonauts arrived, the competition grew, the easily worked diggins were rapidly depleted, and the independent miner was slowly transformed into a day laborer working for large companies. See chart 2.[31]

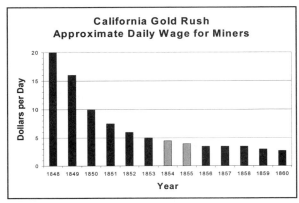

Chart 1

River Mining

The next logical step in the progression towards bigger mining ventures was to mine the entire river itself! Flumes and ditches – frequently miles in length, were used to divert entire watercourses, thus exposing the riverbed gravels for mining. Some of the diverted water was used to wash the gravel riverbed through sluices many hundreds of feet in length. The Golden Gate claim worked the Feather River in this fashion. See figure 9.

Needless to say, it was very expensive to engineer and construct the necessary dams, ditches, flumes, and sluices required for such an operation, especially on steep riverbanks and where ditches had to be blasted out of solid rock. Limiting the amount of timber and lumber used in the operation would substantially reduce costs too. One method of achieving this was to dispense with wooden sluices whenever possible, and to substitute the river's bedrock instead. A *bedrock sluice* was used to save the gold. It had riffles made of iron railroad rails securely bolted to the bedrock.[32]

Another method was to avoid diverting the entire river – divert only a portion of it instead. *Wing dams* were very effective in this regard. They were "L"-shaped; jut halfway into the river, and then made a right angle turn heading downstream for a considerable distance. In this fashion about half of the riverbed could be exposed for mining at a time. No expensive ditches would be required, and the water necessary for mining was readily available on the other side of the dam.[33] River miners had a season about five months long at best, when the water was low, which was sometimes disastrously affected by unanticipated showers late in the season.[34]

Figure 9
Golden Gate claim diversion flume on the Feather River, California ca 1875

Hydraulic Mining

In 1852, a Frenchman by the name of Chabot found that mining would be much easier if he used a flexible hose to divert water from a flume to his diggings. The following year, Edward E. Matteson was working in the same area. He decided to attach a nozzle to a hose, and use the jet of water to wash gravel from the hillside – that would certainly be a lot easier than digging it out by hand. *Hydraulic mining was born.*

The earliest versions used a rawhide hose and wooden nozzle. Canvas and iron, respectively, were then used. The canvas was the weak link, and was made as short as possible by replacing it with iron pipe. The small section of canvas was reinforced with iron rings, rope bindings, or netting, and was nicknamed *crinoline hose*.[36] By late 1853 hydraulic mining was widely used for working *auriferous* – gold-bearing, gravels.[37] See figure 10.

The pressure from the water supply was increased, as was the force developed by the jets of water issuing from these nozzles. The force quickly exceeded that which a man could withstand, so the nozzles were mounted to heavy tripods or skids, and were easily directed towards the embankments to be mined. These arrangements were referred to as *hydraulic monitors*, or simply as *monitors*.

Some monitors had nozzles of 6-9 inches in diameter, and operated under 500 feet of head pressure.[38] By 1871, hydraulic monitors were capable of discharging water at velocities up to 150 feet per second, attacking gravel banks 250 feet high, and consuming 4,220,000 cubic feet of water per day in the process.[39] In 1876, the Malakoff Diggins used eight monitors, each with an 8" nozzle – the miners that operated them were paid $2.50 per 12-hour shift.[40] Figure 11 depicts four monitors attacking a gravel bank in Nevada County, California.

The gravel embankments were washed through sluices to save the gold. The sluices were enormous versions of the long toms. The design of the sluices used for hydraulic mining was very similar to those used in the so-called *drift mining*, which will be described later; the following description[41] serves for both.

CALIFORNIA MINER'S SONG

I've picked and dug,
and packed and lugged,
And every honest scheme
I've tried on,
Till hunger made
me eat at last,
The mule I used to ride on.

With woolen shirt
and rubber boots,
in mud up to my knees,
And lice as big
as chili beans
fighting with the fleas.

Figure 10   Small-scale hydraulic mining
Rockerville, Dakota, 1889
Courtesy Library of Congress

Sluices used in placer and drift-mining operations could become very long. Within tunnels, they might range from as little as a few hundred feet to as much as 3600 feet (Van Emmons mine, Placer County, California.). Some were simply bedrock, but most were made of wood. Widths varied from about two to six feet, and the grade from about an inch to twelve inches per twelve feet. The riffles might be wooden blocks, basalt or some other tough rock, wood and rock combinations, or old rails. Outside of the tunnels, the flumes would continue on for a distance of from a few hundred feet to upwards of 4200 feet (Weed's Point mine, Yuba County, California). Widths varied from about a foot to six feet, grades from about two to ten inches per twelve feet.

The grade of the sluice would depend on both the nature of the gravel being mined and on the local topography. Finer, sandy gravels required less of a grade than coarser gravels containing cobbles and small boulders. The sluices were lined to the water level with two-inch planks to protect them from wear. See figure 12. *Drops* of a few feet were placed periodically – taking advantage of changes in topography whenever possible. The occasional drop helped to break apart loosely cemented material and clays, colloquially referred to as *cement*.[42] In some cases, the drops could be from 25 to 50 feet high.[43]

Grizzlies (parallel iron bars in a rectangular frame)[44] of diminishing aperture were placed along the sluice at intervals to gradually reduce the content to fine sands. As the finer material passed through and fell to the sluice below, the drop would assist in breaking up clayey gravels. Ultimately, the desired size of the material passing down the sluice would be no more than perhaps a few times the size of the largest particles of gold expected.

Figure 11
Moderate-scale hydraulic operations near
French Corral, Nevada County, California ca 1865
Courtesy Library of Congress

The hydraulickers lengthened their sluices to provide more opportunities to save the gold, this at considerable expense. Part of the expense was from the additional construction, but a significant portion was from having to maintain longer sluices that were being torn apart by the rocks and boulders traveling through them.[45]

Some gold was exceedingly difficult to collect due to the minute size of the particles. Snake River gold that could barely be collected had a value of 500 particles to the penny. The *flour gold* (the extra fine *yellow stuff*) easily contained over *seven million* particles per ounce. Though the gold was (and is) there, it was simply not possible or economical to recover it.[46]

Figure 12   Hydraulic Mining Sluice ca 1865
Courtesy Library of Congress

To save the very fine gold, a slow, comparatively gentle current is required – one that permits the finely divided gold particles a chance to settle. Very wide and flat sluices with a shallow grade were constructed next to or beneath the main sluice. These sluices were called *undercurrent sluices*, or simply an *undercurrent*.[47] Undercurrents were invented and developed in Nevada County, California.[48] Figure 13 shows an undercurrent used at the Malakoff Diggins, California.

The main flow would pass over a grizzly, and the finer materials and a portion of the water would fall through to the undercurrent. An auxiliary stream could replace any water lost. The larger gravel would continue being washed along the main sluice. The shallow and slower flow of the undercurrent would enhance the recovery of flour gold and small particles of amalgam. The sands would eventually reach the end of the undercurrent, and would be reintroduced into the main sluice.[49] Sometimes the entire area of the undercurrent – from 5,000 to 10,000 square feet, was covered with mercury-coated copper plates in an attempt to capture the finest particles of gold.[50]

Figure 13   Undercurrent Sluice
Malakoff Diggins, California ca 1875

At the beginning of the season – when water became available for hydraulic operations, as much as 1500 pounds of mercury might be introduced into the sluice, and then up to 1300 pounds would be added every 12 days or so to replace that which was lost. From a tenth to ⅓ pound of mercury was used per square foot of sluice box. Under the best conditions, 10% of the mercury was lost. Under normal circumstances, the loss might reach 30%.[51] Even with the extended sluices, undercurrents, and mercury used to provide every possible opportunity to save the gold, hydraulic mining could still lose upwards of ⅔ of the gold.[52] Part of the loss was from gravels that were cemented together – the drops failed to break them up, and the gold values were trapped in the cementing clays and minerals.

It wasn't until 1858 that the hydraulickers got the notion to run small drifts into the bank and loosen up the cemented gravel with a powder blast. Dutch Flat, California, was the first placer mining district to use dynamite for this purpose. This practice greatly enhanced the volume of material that could be worked where circumstances warranted it. At about this time it was realized that stamp mills could also be used very effectively on cemented gravel.[53] Large boulders were an annoyance to placer miners. If they could not be moved by some mechanical means, they would need to be blasted into smaller and more manageable pieces.[54] See figure 14.

Figure 14   Hydraulic Mine
Courtesy World Museum of Mining, Butte, Montana

In 1885, for 14 hydraulic mines operating in Del Norte and Siskiyou (8 mines), and in Stanislaus and Nevada (6 mines) Counties, California, the cost to mine a cubic yard was about four cents. For the latter two counties, the yield per cubic yard was about eight cents.[55] Hydraulic mining was very efficient, and could work gravels with very little gold value, but the environmental consequences of the method caught up with a vengeance. Many of the hydraulic mines were *huge*. The Malakoff Diggins is the largest hydraulic gold mine in the world. The pit created is 7000 feet long, 3000 feet wide, and 600 feet deep.[56]

The Dutch Flat district had at least 105 million cubic yards of gravel mined hydraulically, and at least 50 million mined from drift mining.[57] Enormous quantities of debris – mud, silt, gravel, and boulders, were choking the rivers, impeding navigation, and having a serious and detrimental effect on agriculture downstream from the mines. From 1853 to 1884, hydraulic mining operations in the Sierra Nevada released over 1.6 billion cubic yards of debris into the drainage system.[58] Between 1850 and 1914, and tributary to the Sacramento River alone, 23% of the debris (420 million cubic yards) was natural, whereas the remainder (1.4 billion cubic yards) was generated by mining. See table 2.[59]

The Sawyer Decision of 1884, handed down by Judge Lorenzo Sawyer against the North Bloomfield Mining Company (Malakoff), stopped hydraulic mining in the Sierra Nevada region, but not in the Klamath-Trinity Mountains.[60]

The Caminetti Act, passed by Congress in 1893, allowed hydraulic mining to continue provided all tailings were impounded in approved dams. These dams didn't necessarily work. A log-crib dam, jointly owned by five mines in Placer and Nevada counties, eventually breached and inundated the Bear River with debris.[61]

Source, 1849-1909	Cubic Yards (Millions)	Percentage Contribution
Hydraulic Mining	**1555**	**93.4**
Upper Feather River	100	6.0
Yuba River	684	41.1
Bear River	254	15.3
American River	257	15.4
Streams tributary to lateral basins of the Sacramento River	30	1.8
Mokelumne River to the Tuolumne River, inclusive	230	13.8
Non-hydraulic Placer Mining	**60**	**3.6**
Quartz Mining	**50**	**3.0**
Total	**1665**	

Table 2   Hydraulic Mining Debris

Dredging

Gold dredges are a clever combination of a sand dredge and gold saving equipment – a marriage of a boat and a sluice. Dredging is well suited for placer gravels that are relatively flat and not very deep.[62] The dredges crisscrossed shallow gradient river valleys and the wider parks. They could easily operate where there was very little available water, this being a side effect of their method of operation. See figure 15. They also created very little to no choking of nearby streams or rivers, unlike hydraulicking.

If a river was unavailable, a shallow pond was dug, perhaps twice the size of the dredge, and filled with water. The dredge was then assembled; a large, flat-bottomed hull, the gold saving equipment inside, an endless bucket line on the bow, and an aft-mounted tailings boom. Cables were strung from the dredge to the shore to assist in positioning the dredge within the pond. A large steel tube called a *spud*, pointed at the bottom and provided with lifting tackle at the top, was located on the aft end and was used to hold the dredge in place while pivoting.

Figure 15   Dredge at Jack Rabbit Spring
Moffat County, Colorado, 1912
Courtesy USGS

The buckets were started up, scooping gravel from in front of the dredge. See figure 16. The dredge would slowly pivot left to right and back again, chewing up the ground. The dirt was dumped at the end of the buckets' upward journey, on the endless chain to which they were fastened, ready to scrape out another bite. The gravel and dirt was then processed in a manner very similar to that used in sluicing – grizzlies to separate the larger rocks from the finer pebbles and sands, sluices, riffles, mercury amalgamation, and so forth.

The finer sands and silt would then discharge from the rear of the dredge. The rocks and boulders too big to fall through the grizzlies would discharge from the aft end of the dredge also, by traveling along the boom-mounted conveyor belt called the *stacker*. This coarse debris covered the finer stuff and formed a continuous and ever-growing sinuous pile.[63] See figure 17. As the dredge advanced forward, endlessly digging up gravel, it advanced its pond on which it floated. Likewise, the stuff coming out the aft end kept the pond's dimensions a roughly static size, slowly crawling over the landscape with the dredge. When the dredge reached an impassible barrier like a rock ledge or the limits of a claim, it swung a U- turn and headed back to chew up another strip of ground.

Dredging got its start in New Zealand in the 1880's. In the U.S. the Fielding L. Graves dredge, of an unsatisfactory design in 1894, was rebuilt, and in 1895 became the first successful dredge in the United States, working on Grasshopper Creek in Bannack Montana. It was powered by electricity, and had a capacity of 2000 yards of gravel per day.[64] Ben Stanley Revett, of the Colorado Gold Dredging Company, was the first to dredge for gold in Colorado. In 1896 a Risdon manufactured dredge was used on the Swan River, but failed due to shortcomings in the design; most notably, it could not reach deeply enough into the gravel without bucking, and the stacker was too short, which allowed gravel to slide back beneath the dredge. Two dredges built by the Bucyrus Company of Milwaukee and used that same year fared only slightly better.[65] See figure 18. By 1898, gold dredging began to catch on and spread rapidly.[66]

Figure 16   Dredge Buckets
Moffat County, Colorado, 1903
Courtesy USGS

By 1908, dredges were yielding 79% of the placer gold, and 35% of the overall gold in California. Chart 3 shows the first decade of gold production from dredges used in California.[67] Table 3 summarizes details of ten dredges operating in the Folsom and Oroville districts of California from 1912-1916.[68]

Figure 17   Wellington mine foreground, dredge tailings in French Creek. Breckenridge, 1926   Courtesy USGS

Precious Metal Mining and Milling Methods of the Frontier West   13

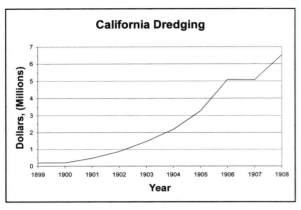

Chart 3

Figure 18
Colorado Gold Dredging Company's Bucyrus dredge.
Blue River, Breckenridge, Colorado 1909
Courtesy USGS

	Minimum	Average	Maximum	Costs, cents per cubic yard	Average	Percent
Bucket capacity, cubic feet	7.5	11.6	15	Labor	0.88	19.2
Number of buckets	60	77	86	Supplies	0.16	3.5
Digging motor, HP	150	275	400	Power	0.96	21.0
Total HP	301	713.5	1165	Water	0.08	1.7
Table area, square feet	1680	4527	7960	Repairs		
Average HH:MM worked per day	19:03	19:53	20:55	Labor	0.22	4.8
Average annual yield, cubic yards	1,449,000	2,182,700	3,181,000	Supplies	1.73	37.8
Average cubic yards per hour	190	303	427	General	0.55	12.0
Initial cost	$130,000	$231,500	$365,000	Total	4.58	100

Table 3   Dredge Statistics

Drift Mining

In some areas, ancient streams and rivers concentrated gold in valuable placer deposits, which were subsequently covered by layers of sediment or thick lava flows. The miners went to where the gold was – concentrated at or near the bedrock surface. This meant running *drifts* hundreds or thousands of feet into hillsides, and sinking *shafts* hundreds of feet deep; hence the name *California drift mining* or simply *drift mining* is applied to the underground mining of fossil placer deposits.

It very often paid handsomely: gravels near the surface may have been worth 2-10 cents per cubic yard, whereas the same volume of gravel near bedrock might yield from 50 cents to $15.[69]

The methods used were similar to hard-rock mining. One of the main differences was that drift mines usually followed a single river channel and mined a flat and shallow layer of compacted gravel. Hard-rock mining exploited ore deposits that were usually geometrically complex – veins of all dimensions going hither and yon, lenticular ore bodies, etc., and mostly in solid rock. But there were notable exceptions to that. More will be said about hardrock mining later.

Early drift mining in the Lincoln mining district of Montana produced nearly $7 million from a 7400-foot section of the gulch. The pay streak varied in width from 50 to 300 feet, and averaged over $375 per set, where a set was four feet wide and high by ten feet long.[70] Three late 1880's mines in Placer County, California – the

Hidden Treasure, Mayflower, and Paragon – illustrate representative sizes and capacities of drift mining operations. See table 4. Each made a tidy profit, even on gravel carrying less than $2 gold per ton.[71]

	Hidden Treasure	Mayflower	Paragon
Gravel character	loose	cemented	cemented
Avg. width breasted, feet	250	75	50
Depth of gravel breasted, feet	4-7	2-14	2-7
Length of channel worked, feet	7700	3900	5400
Length yielding pay, %	100	66	66
Avg. grade of channel, feet per mile	70	60	
Method of breaking ground	pick & cave	drill & blast	drill & blast
Avg. output, TPD	275	130	30
Miners & Timbermen	110	56	20
Millmen		6	2
Total Men	120	130	27
Avg. wages per day	$2.15	$2.75	$2.70
Tons per miner per day	3.20	2.95	1.87
Method of treating gravel	sluice	20-stamp	10-stamp
TPD milled per stamp		6.5	6.0
Avg. cost of Mining and Milling, per ton	$1.10	$3.25	$3.25
Avg. gross yield per ton	$1.75	$7.00	$10.00

Table 4   Drift Mining Statistics

California Placer Gold Résumé

The cost for handling a cubic yard of auriferous gravel, based on a miner earning $3 a day, is illustrated in table 5.[72] Rough estimates of the overall percentage contribution of all forms of placer mining to California's gold production are: 1848-50, 100%; 1851-60, 99%; 1861-70, 90%; and 1871-80, 70%.[73] California contributed 57% of the gold produced in the U.S. between the years 1845-1900. See chart 4.[74] Of the different mining methods used up through 1900, hydraulic mining in California out-produced all other forms of gold mining, including the well-established hardrock mining in the Mother Lode region.[75]

Method	Cubic yards per day per man	Cost per cubic yard
Pan	0.2	$15.00
Rocker	0.8	$3.75
Long Tom	4	$0.75
Hydraulic	30	$0.10
Dredging	242	$0.05

Table 5   Placer Mining Costs

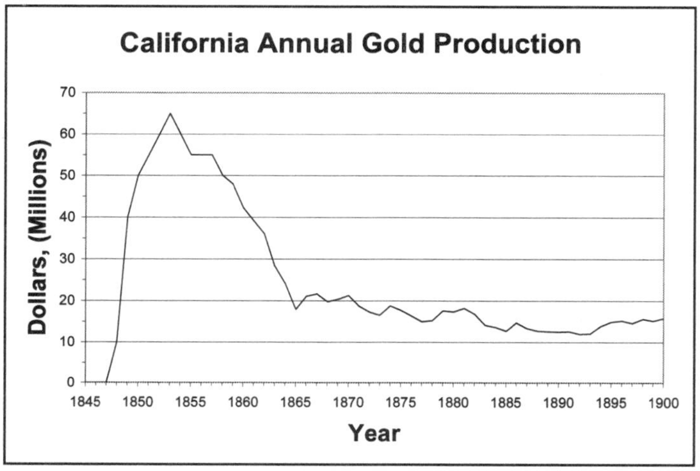

California Annual Gold Production

Chart 4

Figure 19   Panning Out ca 1865
Courtesy Library of Congress

Ditches and Flumes

Water is required for placer mining – long toms and sluices require a continuous flow. Hydraulic mines, as previously stated, required enormous quantities of water. Numerous reservoirs, ditches, and flumes were constructed – some at great expense, to supply the insatiable thirst of the placer mining operations. See figures 20 and 21.

The earliest waterworks company in California was formed in Nevada County, and had a mile and a half ditch constructed during 1850.[76] Water companies made substantial profits – at substantial startup construction expenses, by selling the water to the miners. The water was sold using a unit of measurement termed a *miners inch*, which varied from district to district. One definition is: the volume of water that will flow through a one-inch square aperture at a depth of six inches. This translates to about 2250 cubic feet of water per day.

Growth was exponential, barely capable of keeping pace with demand. By 1857 there were 4405 miles of canals, ditches, and flumes, costing $11,890,800, or $2700 per mile, In California.[77] By 1871 there were at least 4614 miles of ditches in use in California, with about 2.5 billion gallons of water used a day. Lengths ranged from a single ditch of 3 miles length in Inyo County, to 58 ditches averaging a little less than 17 miles each in El Dorado County,[78] the overall average length being 12 miles.[79]

The oldest ditches in Montana date from 1861, and those constructed in Idaho from 1863.[80] In 1868, the Big Ditch was constructed in Colfax County, New Mexico. This ditch, 41 miles in length and extending from Red River to Elizabethtown, first delivered water to Humbug Gulch on July 9, 1869. The ditch was built at a cost of $200,000 – nearly $5000 per mile.[81]

By 1870 an estimated 6000 miles of watercourses had been dug in the U.S. for mining and milling purposes, at an estimated cost of $15 million.[82] By 1880, the total length of ditches in the U.S. reached over 10,000 miles with a capacity of 7.56 billion gallons per day. The average cost per mile for construction was $2500. The ditches operated an average of 211 days a year.[83] Some areas experienced dry seasons that curtailed mining operations. The Homestake mills were sometimes shut down due to the water in the ditches freezing.[84]

Annual improvements cost about $40 per mile, or 1% of the original investment. An average of one person for every mile was required for maintenance of the ditches, working from ten to twelve hours a day. Ditch tenders were paid as little as

Figure 20   Hydraulic mining flume
Near Smartsville, Yuba County, California ca 1865
Courtesy Library of Congress

Figure 21   Trout Creek Flume
Helena, Montana 1872
Courtesy NARA

	Tenders	Builders	Cleaners
Arizona	3.00		
California	2.25	3.00	1.30
Colorado	2.75		
Dakota	3.25		
Georgia	1.00		
Idaho	4.00	4.00	2.63
Montana	3.50		
Oregon	2.17		

Table 6   Ditch Wages

50 cents a day at some locations in Georgia, and as much as $4.00 per day in the West. Chinese laborers received only about ½ to ⅔ what white men were paid for the same work, and generally only found employment as ditch cleaners. See table 6.[85] The quantity of water lost from evaporation varied greatly: in California, from 3-40%, Idaho 3-35%, and in Oregon from 2.5-60%.[86]

> "These ditches and flumes had to be watched constantly for breaks, so the ditch tender always lived over them and used a float that would slide a lot of tin cans from a shelf near his bed whenever a break occurred, and the noise would awaken him before a great deal of damage had been caused." [87]

Flumes were also used for timber and lumber operations. In 1874, a 27.5-mile flume – the longest in America at that time, was constructed along the headwaters of the Bear River in the northern flank of the Uinta Mountains of Utah. This flume, costing the Hilliard Flume and Lumber Company $2,000,000, required a crew of 700 men, 2,500,000 feet of lumber, 5,000,000 feet of supporting timbers, and a hundred tons of spikes and nails for its construction. A sawmill at the head end produced over 35,000 feet of lumber daily for consumption in the east. Cordwood was also floated down the flume to the Union Pacific railhead at Hilliard, where it was converted to charcoal for use in the Salt Lake valley smelters. During one 40-day period, 18,000 cords of wood were sent down the flume and stacked next to the railroad, the stack measuring 20 feet high by over one mile long.[88]

Notable Failures

Some ditches and flumes just didn't pay to be constructed, leading to financial disaster for the operators. At Indian Bar, California, hundreds of men labored for months and invested $3000, building a flume to divert a river; their return was only $41.70.[89]

The San Miguel Flume, also known as "The Hanging Flume," was another failure. Rich placers were discovered on Mesa Creek Flats, Colorado. A company was organized – the Montrose Placer Mining Company, for the purpose of hydraulic mining the placers. Col. N. P. Turner was selected to manage the operation. He prepared plans for the flume that would be required for the operation to be a success. It was of 23,640,000 gallons per day capacity, started in 1888, and completed in 1891. The flume was 4' deep, 5'4" wide, and 8 miles long, with 1.5 miles running along the San Miguel River (the intake) and 6.5 miles along the Dolores River. It required about 1.8 million board feet of lumber, and the final cost was $100,000.

What made this flume uniquely interesting is that much of it was built against a sandstone cliff. The flume was supported by iron brackets protruding from and mounted to the sandstone cliff, these being up to 100-150 feet above the river and 250-500 feet below the rim. A flat car on tracks with a counterbalanced crane supported the workers as they drilled the holes for and installed a few brackets, then the car was advanced. Occasionally the workmen were suspended from the rim as they installed brackets.

As it turned out, the project failed, partly due to the inability of the recovery system to capture the very fine gold. The Colonel, dejected by the financial ruin of the project, returned to Chicago where he committed suicide. The remains of much of the Hanging Flume can still be seen today – see figure 22.[90]

Figure 22   Hanging Flume, Dolores River, Colorado 2002   Author

The Miner's Ten Commandments

1   Thou shalt have no other claim but one.

2   Thou shalt not take unto thyself any false claims, nor shalt thou jump one.

3   Thou shalt not go prospecting again before thy claim gives out nor shalt thou take thy hard-earned dust to the gaming tables in vain for the more thou shalt put down the less thou will take up.

4   Thou shalt dig or pick only six days for on the seventh thou shalt washeth thy dirty clothes and darneth thy socks and choppeth the whole week's wood.

5   Thou shalt not think more of thy gold than thy father's blessings or thy mother's love.

6   Thou shalt not kill thy body by working in the rain nor by getting stewed or three sheets to the wind from drinking down whisky punches, rum toddies, or brandy slings.

7   Thou shalt not grow discouraged nor go home before thou strikes it rich lest in going home thou will work for fifty cents a day while thou might strike a lead and make fifty dollars a day by staying.

8   Thou shalt not steal a pick or shovel nor take thy neighbor's tools nor borrow those he cannot spare and return them broken nor remove his stakes to enlarge thy own claim.

9   Thou shalt not tell false tales about thy diggings in the hills nor salt thy claim to deceive thy neighbor.

10 Thou shalt not covet thy neighbor's wife nor trifle with the affections of his daughter but if thou truly love and covet each other thou shalt pop the question like a man. [91]

Endnotes

[1] ROBERTS1982 pages 5,7, LAPOINT1999 page 14, ASME.H084. It is claimed that Reed later got $1000 from the jeweler. In the first season of mining, a slave named Pete found a 28-pound nugget in the bottom of the creek. Before 1826, 84 pounds of gold nuggets had been found where any given piece was *at least* one pound. In April 1896 a nugget weighing almost 23 pounds was found on the property, buried 3.5 feet beneath the topsoil. ASME.H084.

[2] RICKARD1932 page 19 LAPOINT1999 page 14

[3] NITZE1996 page 17. Official records state that through November 1894, $11,754,369.60 in gold and $63,620.40 in silver – total of $11,817,990.00, was produced in NC. The report's authors estimate that as much as $24,000,000 may actually have been produced, much of it never officially reported.

ROTHWELL1896 page 243 NC, SC, GA, and AL produced a combined 52,819 ounces of gold in the four-year period 1893-1896. This accounted for about six-tenths of one percent of the gold produced in the US during this period.

[4] PETERSON1997

[5] WELLS2002 page 34

[6] AAA1978 page 23, CERES.123

[7] MONTANADEQ.129

[8] ABBE1985 page 61

[9] RHYOLITE. William F. Peck built his bottle house in Tonopah in 1902 [or 1903 – see *They lived in a glass house,* Vol. 12 No. 2 of *Central Nevada's Glorious Past*], possibly being the first of its kind. This structure was made from bottles and adobe, and the water used to make the mortar, if bought, would have cost $1.50 a barrel. Instead, recycled wash water was used. There were at least four bottle houses in Goldfield, Nevada. Calico, California sports a bottle house of unknown origin, mostly reconstructed. A structure in Tonopah was built from coal-oil cans. In Bodie the Boone Store's walls are clad with 5-gallon gaso-line cans that have been flattened after having the top and bottom removed.

[10] WOLLE1963 page 458

[11] FATOUT1969 pages 3,4,9,150

[12] PAUL1965 page 74

[13] Spriggs, Lamb, and Dillon are the three miners.

[14] The author, in his limited experience panning near Rico and Pitkin, Colorado, became quite proficient at recreational panning. The amount of magnetite recovered was remarkable. It is also worthwhile to note that the water in these mountain streams is *cold*. Those Argonauts that spent long day after day panning were a determined bunch.

[15] MONTANADEQ.101

[16] PAUL1965 page 52

[17] GAGR2001

[18] WELLS2002 pages 7, 11

[19] WOLLE1963 page 323

[20] MONTANADEQ.30

[21] PAUL1965 page 55

[22] PAUL1965 pages 87-88

[23] EMMONS1885 page 353

[24] MONTANADEQ.4

[25] WEED1912 page 18
[26] YOUNGO1970 page 149
[27] NORTHROP1975 page 64
[28] PAUL1965 page 62
[29] SMITHR1932 pages 79-80
[30] SMITHR1932 pages 87, 122-123
[31] PAUL1965 pages 120,349-350. 1854 and 1855 wages were not available, so they are estimated.
[32] SMITHR1932 page 83
[33] PAUL1965 page 128
[34] PAUL1965 page 125
[35] MAB.1882-7
[36] PAUL1965 pages 152-153, 156-157. Crinoline is a cloth made of horsehair and linen thread, used for stiffening fabrics. It is also the name given to a lady's hoop skirt.
[37] ARBITER1964 page 2
[38] HUNERLACH1999 page 181
[39] TAGGART1947 page 86
[40] MALAKOFF1993
[41] EMMONS1885 page 197
[42] PAUL1965 page 157
[43] TAGGART1947 page 87
[44] The author speculates that the name may have originated from the pronunciation of *bear* as *bar*, and that these screening devices were made of *bars*, hence *grizzly* was an appropriate name to use.
[45] PAUL1965 page 159
[46] WELLS2002 page 116
[47] PAUL1965 pages 152-153, 156-157
[48] PAUL1965 page 160
[49] PAUL1965 pages 152-153, 156-157
[50] HUNERLACH1999 page 182
[51] HUNERLACH1999 page 182
[52] TAGGART1947 page 87
[53] PAUL1965 page 158, AAA1978 page 50
[54] TAYLOR01989 page 124
[55] EMMONS1885 page 202
[56] AAA1978 page 55
[57] HUNERLACH1999 pages 179,185
[58] HUNERLACH1999 page 185
[59] GILBERT1917 page 46. Chart data from page 43.
[60] Hydraulic mining continued there until the 1950's.
[61] TAGGART1947 page 87, HUNERLACH1999 page 185, ALPERS2000
[62] PEELE1966 page 10-587
[63] That became one of the lasting legacies of dredge mining: the ground was inverted, with large boulders and rocks piled on top of the soil. Practically nothing grows in it. The piles of rock look pretty much the same today as they did nearly a century ago. Aerial photographs clearly illustrate the pivoting-advancing pattern used by the operators
[64] ROTHWELL1896 page 245. MONTANADEQ.4, BANNACK page 13, WOLLE1963 page 176. TURNBULL1962 page 247 gives October 7, 1891 as the first date in Montana, her source being the *Daily Independent*, Helena, Montana.
[65] TURNBULL1962 pages 241, 249-250. HENDERSON1926 page 12 gives a date of 1898, not 1896. TURNBULL1962 page 252: The Colorado Gold Dredging Company was formed in 1895.
[66] PEELE1966 page 10-587. A gold dredge was operated on the Rio Chama, near Abiquiu, New Mexico about 1900. ACKERLY1997
[67] USGS1909 page 316
[68] PEELE1966 page 10-589
[69] PAUL1965 pages 150-151
[70] MONTANADEQ.99
[71] PEELE1966 page 10-609
[72] TAGGART1947 page 87, PAUL1965 page 154
[73] PAUL1965 pages 145, 286-287
[74] 1848-58 1880 Census. 1859 average 1880 Census and PAUL1965 pages 345-346. 1860-62 1880 Census. 1863 avg 1880 Census and Paul. 1864-65 Paul. 1866-67 avg 1890 Census and Paul. 1868-74 avg 1880 Census and Paul. 1876 avg of 1875 (1880 Census) and 1877 (1890 Census) – no data could be found! 1878-89 1890 Census. 1890-1900 misc. USGS Mineral Annual publications.
[75] HUNERLACH1999 page 181
[76] PAUL1965 page 64
[77] PAUL1965 page 164
[78] RAYMOND1873 page 46
[79] EMMONS1885 page 205
[80] EMMONS1885 page 237
[81] NORTHROP1975 page 23, WELLSE1957 page 10, WOLLE1963 page 31. Wolle gives the length as 42 miles, and the cost as $280,000.
[82] SMITHD1993 page 14
[83] EMMONS1885 page 205
[84] FIELDER1970 pages 114-115
[85] EMMONS1885 page 237
[86] EMMONS1885 pages 220-222
[87] NILE1956
[88] BAILEY2002 pages 165-166
[89] FATOUT1969 page 10
[90] JESSEN1994 pages 115-118. Jessen states that the construction started in 1889, and that the capacity was 80 million GPD. A state historic marker at the overlook site on Hwy 141 states 1888, and 23,640,000 GPD. Panoramic photo taken on Y11 road.
[91] THOMPSON1968 pages 130-131

Hardrock Mining

| Figure 1 | Montana Mine, South Dakota 1889 | Courtesy Library of Congress |

Many miners became prospectors out of necessity – there were simply too many Argonauts for the available placer diggins, they didn't like the work, or the diggins were just too poor. Others enjoyed prospecting the remote hills and valleys on their own, away from the hustle and bustle of the booming mining camps, hoping to find that big strike that might bring untold wealth. They all understood one thing: the placer gold had to come from rock somewhere, and if they could just find the source, they could file a claim on the location, and hopefully – and at the very least, find a buyer for the claim.

Many of these *lode* claims were found using simple logic: pan for gold at intervals along a stream, and keep moving upstream until the colors suddenly disappear. When the colors vanish, the source of the gold has just been passed. Move back to the last location where colors were found, and then work uphill, methodically examining the soil and any outcrops until the auriferous source is found.

This required a keen eye for the types of rock that might be gold bearing, or were associated with gold bearing rocks. In many areas, quartz, rust-colored, or yellow-stained rocks were good indicators of possible valuable mineralization – *"iron rides a good horse."* Samples would be frequently taken, pulverized, and panned. Once the outcrop was located, additional samples would be tested, sometimes using a crude field assay, or brought into a nearby camp for a professional and thorough fire assay. More about assays later.

Wesley F. King describes prospectors' reactions when they made their discovery near Cooper Hill, Wyoming, in 1893:

> "We found Messrs. George and Tom Morgan, Wm. Whittingham and Victor Beaumier very much excited over the new find. Beaumier climbed a tree, sat down in the creek, and yelled 'lets do something.' Tom Morgan turned a back handspring and sat down on a cactus. Geo. Morgan began piling up the boulders believing them all rich ore."[1]

Luck: The Good, the Bad, and the Sneaky

There are countless tales of prospectors searching for a missing burro, only to find the animal standing motionless, glassy eyes transfixed on a glittering mass of mineralized riches. Other stories tell of the weary prospector resting on an outcrop, absent-mindedly chipping at the stone or hefting a piece of *float* rock broken from a larger mass, and much to his surprise discovering the lode. Even when the stories are not true, they still make for amusing tales.

Sometimes these tales may be true. On August 4, 1882, John Robinson, while out hunting, found a piece of valuable float on a hillside near Red Mountain, Colorado. The 12-foot deep shaft that quickly followed led to a lode that was to become the famous Yankee Girl Mine.[2]

Luck – *good*, *bad*, or *sneaky*, is an important part of mining history.

The Good

In 1885, at the Genessee mine at Red Mountain, Colorado, geologists made recommendations that led to deepening the main shaft from 15 to 175 feet. They also recommended sinking shafts and driving adits (defined later) all over the property. None produced anything but low-grade ore. A new mine manager decided to drive drifts north and south from the bottom of the main shaft, where "this was done not on professional advice but just to see what might be encountered." Fifteen feet to the north, a seven-foot wide galena ore body was found assaying 200 ounces of silver to the ton.[3]

As the placer gold gave out at Angels Camp, California, Bennager Rasberry changed the camp from placer to hardrock mining in a single shot – literally. While out hunting, the ramrod of his gun jammed, so he shot it into the ground. This revealed gold-bearing quartz, and within three days he was $10,000 richer, and the boom was on again.[4]

While arguing with A. E. Benoist about their prospecting expedition being a humbug, W. H. Kearney angrily swung his pick at a rock. The broken fragment was lined with silver, much to the two men's surprise. The location was immediately staked and recorded as the Old Dominion, which produced $500,000 in the first year alone.[5]

In October 1850 in Grass Valley, California, George Knight stubbed his toe on a chunk of gold bearing quartz. This incident led to the Gold Hill Mine, which produced $4 million between 1850-1857.[6]

The Bad

In 1879, Arizona prospector Tom Wilson sold out his share of the Homestake claim, near White Oaks, New Mexico, for $40 in gold washings, $2 in silver, and an old pistol. This claim later sold for $300,000.[7]

Shoshone Johnny discovered a promising lead, began working it, and then traded it to Bob Montgomery for a new pair of overalls. This prospect became a part of the Montgomery-Shoshone properties in Rhyolite, Nevada, which produced nearly $1.4 million between 1907-1911.[8]

Figure 2   Miner's Camp
San Juan Mountains 1875
Courtesy Library of Congress

Five miners staked the Boss Tweed claim, in Pony, Montana, in 1875. Tom Carmin traded his share for a wheelbarrow. This may not have been the best move for him as the mine later sold for $560,000.[9]

Two men, Heffner and McCann, established the Lexington group of claims in Butte in 1865, which they sold to Andrew J. Davis in the early 1870's, a horse reportedly being the purchase price. Davis invested in the mine, and profited from its ore production over a four-year period. He then sold the Lexington to French investors in August 1881 for $1,000,000 cash and $2,000,000 in stock.[10]

John Swickhart located the Quartette mine in Searchlight, Nevada about 1897. He traded the mine for "five dollars, a team of mules, and a plug of tobacco." This mine produced "many millions" by about 1915.[11]

The Sneaky

On August 4, 1906, a carload of Gold King concentrates ran away from Gladstone, picked up speed, and eventually derailed a half-mile later, spilling its contents. A group of prospectors working in the area quickly staked "placer claims" on the site of the spill. The train crew immediately arrived, righted and reloaded the derailed car, and sent the car on its way to the smelter in Durango. The "claims" quickly vanished.[12]

Edwin Bennett, author of *Boom Town Boy*, tells of miners on contract finding a hidden vein, and hiding it for later:

"A story is told of some miners who got a contract to drive a crosscut in one of the A. E. Reynolds properties. They had contracted to drive a crosscut into the hanging-wall a certain distance to where they would encounter another vein if the engineers' figures were correct. This they did and found the vein as predicted, but, about midway to their crosscut, they ran into another vein the engineers had not mentioned. They didn't mention it either. Saying they had run into some soft ground, they put in a bunch of drift sets and lagged off the vein so tightly none of the vein matter could sift through. At that time it was impossible to get a lease on any of the Reynolds properties, but in later years it was reported that the men who had driven the crosscut got a lease, on which they didn't do badly at all."[13]

Claims

Our prospector has found an outcrop that has every indication of having value. The first step would be to *claim* it. This amounts to establishing rock cairns – also called *monuments*, at the corners of the rectangular claim, blazing of trees, or effecting some other accepted designation of the boundaries. The claim, typically 300 by 100 feet, would be oriented in such a way as to encompass the maximum amount of the lode. This was difficult to determine, especially if the trend of the rock were not obvious, as in, say, a layer of tilted strata exposed at the surface and visible for hundreds of yards.

Next to his discovery point, or roughly in the center of the claim, he would build a larger monument. On a scrap of paper he would record his name, the date, the description of the claim, a bit of legal mumbo-jumbo, and any other pertinent information deemed necessary. The notice would be put in a tin can for protection, and placed under the topmost rock. In some localities, and until a proper survey could be made, a common reference point was used for establishing the locations of claims. A large boulder at the south end of Elkhorn, Montana served this purpose, with the letters "I.P." and a "+" chiseled into it, referring to the "+" as the "Initial Point."[14]

These actions gave him a legal mining claim to the location. He then needed to quickly record the claim with the official claims recorder at the nearest mining district. He generally had about 30 days to do so. If no district existed, one was created, and an officer was elected and sworn in to be the official claim recorder. Being the initial discoverer in a new district also entitled the prospector to a perquisite for "the right of discovery" – two claims could be made instead of one. To retain his claim, the miner would need to perform *assessment work* – about $100 worth of labor and development within the first 90 days, and then the same amount annually. Labor was valued at about $3 per day. Failing to do so meant the possible loss of his claim once the time expired – the claim could be *jumped*.

In 1866, the government created provisions for *patented* claims: no assessment work was required, but taxes needed to be paid. This cost a miner about $1000, proof of the existence of precious metals in economic quantities, a minimum payment for the acreage, professional surveys, recording, and the filing of 12 separate documents.[15]

Part of recording a claim was naming the claim or mine. Some of the names given were amusing. The Holy Terror was named as such after the wife of one of the owners asked that the mine be named after her.[16] See the box to the right.[17]

This process worked fairly well throughout the west, but sometimes opened the floodgates for incredible amounts of litigation. Lawsuits were fought over vague location markers and improper surveys, errors in the official recordings, the path the lode followed underground, and a host of other reasons. The lawsuits were calculated to pry the claim from one party and award it to another. A popular legal trick was to force a claim owner to buy an adjoining – and probably worthless, claim out of court, this to settle the dispute and get on with development and mining. The famous Comstock Lode got its start in 1859, and by the end of 1865 had produced about $54 million in bullion. During this time, litigation consumed one fifth of this amount![18]

When a rush started, anybody and everybody filed claims as quickly as possible, all in hopes of striking it rich, using the claim in a lawsuit against a neighboring, productive claim, or more likely selling (or reselling) a worthless claim for a substantial profit. Claims might be limited in size. This would give everybody a chance for a location. At Mokelumne Hill, California claims were limited to 16 square feet![19]

Amusing Mine Names
After Dinner & Perseverance
Badger Boy
Bobtailed Nag
Brush Heap
Buffalo Chip
Burnt Cabin
Club Sandwich
Cream City
Happy Camp
Hot Dog
Jay Eye See
Keep Cool
Lost Wheelbarrow
Lucky Blunder
Miser's Dream
Muc-a-muc
National Debt
Neglected
Obnoxious
Old Lout
Podunk
Port Wine
Root-Hog-or-Die
Selfrising
Spud Patch
Wake Up Jim
Wee Wee
Wild Hope
Wild Delirium
Wooly Horse

During the Meadow Lake, California rush in 1865, 741 company locations and 10,910 individual claims of 100 feet each were filed in the office of the Nevada County Recorder. These properties ultimately produced an estimated $200,000 over the years 1865-1924 – a whopping $18 per claim, on average.[20]

The rush to the Reese River mining district began in early 1863. By September of that year, 1300 "mining companies" were reported. By March of 1864, 2500 mining claims had been filed, yet through 1863 a trifling $16,109 worth of bullion had been produced.[21]

1897 Hindsdale County, Colorado records show 8144 lode claims, 126 mill sites, 100 placer claims, 302 patented lode claims, 20 patented placer claims, and 26 patented mill sites recorded. The recorders were kept mighty busy![22]

A very small sampling of the *many* rushes, big and small, gold and silver, follows:

- ♦ Nevada   1858   Comstock Lode discovered (Ophir and Little Gold Hill ore bodies).[23]
- ♦ Arizona   1858   First placer gold rush in Arizona to the Gila River[24]
- ♦ Colorado   1859   Jackson finds gold near present-day Idaho Springs.[25]
- ♦ Utah   1863   Utah's first rush, to Bingham Canyon[26]
- ♦ Nevada   1863   Reese River (Austin) Rush[27]
- ♦ Nevada   1864   Silver-lead ore discovered at Eureka.[28]
- ♦ California   1865   Meadow Lake gold rush begins.[29]
- ♦ Nevada   1869   Silver rush in White Pine.[30]
- ♦ Colorado   1871   Ute and Ulay veins discovered; Lake City district formed.[31]
- ♦ Dakota   1874   Gold discovered in the Black Hills (Homestake Mine).[32]
- ♦ Colorado   1880   Silver mining begins in Aspen.[33]
- ♦ Colorado   1881   The Red Mountain district formed.[34]
- ♦ Colorado   1891   Gold rush to Cripple Creek.[35]
- ♦ Alaska   1897   The Klondike -Yukon gold rush begins.[36]
- ♦ Nevada   1900   Tonopah discovered.[37]

More than a few rushes turned out to be a *humbug*. A prime example is that of the rush to South Pass, Wyoming. A special census, taken in 1869, showed 1517 persons in the area. Surely there were more fortune-seekers present at the peak of the rush in 1868. Between the summers of 1868 and 1869, it is estimated that only $155,000 was taken from both the placer and the lode mines. Wells, Fargo & Co. shipping records show $60,000 for 1870, and $36,000 for 1871. In 1881, the Hub Gold Mining Company renewed mining on the old Miner's Delight property. 443 tons of ore were milled early in 1882, producing a return of $4200 on an investment of $82,561 in development and machinery, and this does not include the cost of the mine! The Carissa Gold Mine – see figure 3, produced an estimated $120,000-$360,000 worth of gold over its lifetime, which spanned into the 1930's. No doubt many times more money was put into South Pass than was ever extracted.[38]

Figure 3   Carissa Mine, South Pass, Wyoming 2002   Author

Some boomtowns and the associated mining districts were nothing but frauds, designed to bilk greedy speculators of their hard-earned pesos. Assistant editor of the Laramie *Sentinel*, E. W. "Bill" Nye, wrote the following concerning Cummins City, a bogus Wyoming mining boomtown:

"Two months ago, I might say, the little village of Cummins City was nothing but a little caucus of prairie dogs, and a ward meeting of woodticks. Now look at it. Opera houses, orphan asylums, hurdy-gurdies, churches, barber shops, ice-cream saloons, dog fights, musical soirees, spruce gum, bowling alleys, salvation, and three card monte. Everything in fact that the heart of man could yearn for."[39]

Streets Paved with Gold!

A "gold rush" of sorts occurred in Coulterville, California, in 1899. After a fire, the rubble from an old stone and adobe building was used to fill potholes in the streets. The adobe began to dissolve with the first rain, exposing the cache of gold coins that had been hidden in the walls of the building. The main street was quickly reduced to quagmire as the citizens dutifully joined in on the "rush" for the coins.[40]

Mining

Now that the claim was filed, mining began. What to do with this hard rock, gold and silver locked away inside? Most of the Argonauts had placer mining experience at best. Very few had experience in deep mining – only a handful worked in hardrock mines back in Georgia or Carolina. The miners were ill equipped for the task, chipping away with picks and shovels, the mine resembling a crude pit excavated from the rock. Progress was slow; lessons were learned.

The miners with hard rock experience were the *Cousin Jacks* – Cornishmen, from Cornwall and Devon. There they had worked the tin and copper mines to great depths, and had developed the skills necessary to support a major industry and to refine deep mining engineering and techniques into a highly respected and professional trade. Cousin Jacks were in great demand in the primitive mines of the West. Deep mining began in Nevada County, California in 1850. The Cornishmen sunk shallow *shafts* until they struck *pay dirt*. These numerous, small excavations became known as *coyote holes*.[41]

Some of the early mines used primitive methods for hauling out the ore, and in moving between the various levels of the workings. Many of the miners were Mexican, and they used techniques (or lack of) from the silver mines in Mexico. The Mexican Mine, one of the early, big producers on the Comstock, used notched logs as ladders and rawhide buckets slung from the forehead for hauling ore.[42]

At the New Idria Mine in California, similar practices were in effect in 1861, as noted by William H. Brewer:

"The distribution of ore through the rock is very capricious, and where a thread of it can be found it is followed up, so the workings run in every conceivable direction, and being mostly mined by Chilean and Mexican miners, the work is more irregular by far than the burrows of animals. Sometimes we climbed down by rope, hand over hand, bracing the feet against the wall of rock, sometimes on *escaladors*, sticks merely notched. But the trip was interesting, and as they wanted our professional advice, we saw all, the two men devoting the day to us."[43]

Terminology

Before proceeding, it is helpful to know some of the terminology used to describe underground passageways. Here's a brief primer. Many of the terms used have multiple meanings. Other terms will be defined as they are encountered.

The primary passageway or entrance into the mine workings is a *shaft* if vertical, or an *adit* if horizontal. A *tunnel* is a primary, horizontal passageway that has access to the surface at *both ends*. The term tunnel is frequently used to describe adits, especially in coal mining. The point of entry is a *portal* if through an adit or tunnel, or a *collar* if from a shaft.

A *drift* is a near-horizontal secondary passageway that is connected to a shaft or an adit. Drifts usually follow the vein or ore body being mined. A *raise* is a vertical or inclined passageway driven at an upward angle, and a *winze* is the same except driven downwards. Passages used primarily for materials handling are *haulageways*. Compartments used strictly by miners are *manways*. A *crosscut* is a near-horizontal tertiary passageway connected to a drift, and is usually used to connect drifts and *stopes*, but also for exploration, ventilation, etc. A stope is the portion of the mine that is being worked for exploitation of ore. Stopes range from narrow man-size passageways following a vein in every possible direction, to enormous cavern-like excavations.

The *back* is the roof or top of an underground excavation. The place where one stands is called both the *bottom* and the *floor*. The sides are the *ribs*. Passageways are *driven* or *advanced*. The surface being advanced forward is the *face* or *heading*. *Sinking* advances shafts and winzes.

Many mines are worked at evenly spaced vertical intervals, or *levels*, which are often 100 feet apart. A *station* is where a level meets a shaft. All of the horizontal passageways are run at a slight incline of perhaps a 1° angle. This allows water to drain towards the nearest shaft so that it may be pumped from a central location, or to the nearest adit or tunnel to drain from the portal.

Hardrock mining works around a basic cycle of activities: drill, blast, load, and haul, each with its own set of tools and techniques.

Drilling

Drilling was performed by hand until the introduction of the steam- or compressed air-powered rock drill, and even then was used well into the 20th century. Machine drills are covered later. The miner held a steel drill, frequently called a *drill steel*, *drill*, or just *steel*, in one hand, and a hammer in the other, the hammer weighing about four pounds. The drill was chisel-like.[44] See figure 4. He would strike the drill with the hammer, then rotate the drill about a quarter turn, this to reposition the drill's cutting edge, and then strike it again. The miner swung his hammer perhaps 20-30 times a minute, for hours at a time – slow but steady progress. Because a single miner, a single Cousin Jack, drilled alone, this is referred to as *single-jacking*. See figure 8, page 29.

When a new drill hole was started, a short drill was used, called (you guessed it) a *starter*. After a few inches had been drilled the cutting edge became dull. A longer and very slightly smaller diameter drill was then used for the next few inches. Slowly the drill hole advanced as the number of dulled steels increased. The blacksmith at a mine was a *very* busy man, not only keeping drills tempered and sharpened, but also fabricating parts and repairing most anything made of metal. See figures 5 and 6.

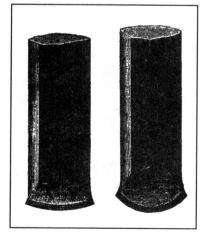

Figure 4   Drill Steel Cutting Edge
Source: Drinker, 1893

The cuttings from drilling could clog the drill hole, especially if the hole were at a downward angle. During drill changes, and as required, the hole was cleared of the debris using a long-handled and slender wooden or copper *miner's spoon*, or a *blow-pipe*. When the drill is aimed at an upward angle, it is *overhand*; downward is *underhand*; thus drilling upward is *overhand stoping*, and downward is *underhand stoping*. Gravity was used to advantage wherever possible. Driving a raise was preferred to sinking a winze.

Stulls – large, log-like pieces of wood used to support ribs, are frequently used in mines. They may be positioned horizontally or at an angle. To support the stull, step-like notches must be cut into the rock. These notches are called *hitches*, and the drill steel used to cut them is a *moil*.

Figure 5   Underground Blacksmith Shop   Author

Where the opportunity existed – namely, enough space, one miner would hold and turn the drill – the *shaker*, as a second miner struck it with an eight-pound, long-handled hammer. Drilling in this fashion is called *double-jacking*. The miners would take turns swinging the hammer. About twenty strokes per minute were typical for double-jacking.[45]

An experienced miner holding the steel while an inexperienced miner swings the hammer might decide it was time to trade places by saying "let me skin awhile."[46] It wasn't easy to position the drill steel for the miner swinging the hammer, and to turn it correctly, all the while keeping the steel centered in the advancing drill hole. If the drill weren't rotated correctly, a three-cornered hole that gets progressively worse – a *Dutchman*, would result. A novice improperly turning the drill steel while double-jacking caused this.[47] If the drill hole was not kept straight and aligned, the drill steel might *fitcher* – jam. Bennett tells of his friend Tom Fowle working his first shift underground, with his father, the two double-jacking:

> After a little while Tom's dad stopped striking, sat down and started to take off his shoes. "What are you doing, Dad?" Tom asked him. "Just taking off my shoes," was the reply. "What for?" Tom wanted to know. "Well, it's like this," his father said. "I don't mind swinging this hammer up and down while you are down there taking it easy, but I'll be damned if I'm going to follow the head of that drill all over the bottom of this shaft, dragging these heavy shoes."[48]

Figure 6   Bit Sharpening Hammer   Author

The overall rate of double-jack drilling exceeded that which the two miners combined could do alone. Just how fast did they drill? That is difficult to say. Many factors are involved, such as the hardness of the rock, sharpness of the drill, orientation of the miner in respect to the drill hole, and skill, strength, and motivation of the miner. A sampling of figures provides a rough sketch of the rates typical for hand drilling:

♦ In Berlin, Nevada, overhand stoping in a very hard quartz vein averaged 5 feet of holes and dulled nearly 34 drill steels, breaking 1.16 tons per miner.[49]

♦ At the Daly-Judge mine in Park City, Utah, single-jack miners averaged 12 feet of holes per shift in soft ores, 6 feet in quartzite.[50]

♦ In the San Juan Mountains of southwestern Colorado, two men could advance a heading of 5x7 feet about 6 inches a day.[51]

◆ At White Pine, Nevada, a 7x9 foot adit was driven 103 feet in 30 days using two 8-hour shifts, or a little less than two feet per shift per day.[52]

◆ A good team of double-jackers could drill eight two-foot deep holes in a *split-round* shift: two shifts to do one, complete round, where the upper ½ of the heading is drilled and shot by the first shift, and the remainder by the second shift.[53]

◆ Frank Crampton, author of *Deep Enough*, learned the art of drilling in Cripple Creek, Colorado. He and two other miners completed a 300-foot contract in six weeks. Working overlapping 12-hour shifts, an average of a little over a foot of advance per man per day was made.[54]

Figure 7   Drilling Contest   Author
Miner's Union Day, Columbia Gardens
Butte, Montana, ca 1900

Drilling contests were frequently held, the contestants drilling as fast and as hard as they could to attain the deepest drill hole in a fifteen-minute period. See figure 7. Rates nearly as high as three inches per minute might be achieved with a practiced, motivated, and well-rested team swinging the hammer 60 times per minute and not missing a stroke between drill or position changes.[55]

Figure 8   Miners single-jacking in the Logan Mine, Boulder County, Colorado
Courtesy Carnegie Branch Library for Local History, Boulder, Colorado

Blasting

A number of drill holes were made by a *lot* of laborious effort of the miners. There was no guesswork involved – skilled miners knew exactly how and where to drill the holes to minimize the labor involved and to maximize the amount of rock broken once blasted. After all, nobody wanted to swing a hammer more than was necessary.

The pattern of drill holes required to break the ground was as variable as the rock in which they were drilled. Figure 9 illustrates a pattern known as a *Michigan* or *Burnt-cut Round*.[56] This image shows the drill hole pattern exposed behind a "partition" of rock, where the miners would drill from the far side. This pattern would be suitable for a large, 8x8 foot heading, such as would be used for a major haulageway. The drifts and crosscuts found in most mines were generally smaller and required fewer drill holes, but the principles behind their placement and order of firing were similar. An "X" pattern was preferred for advancing drifts by machine drills in Park City, Utah mines.[57]

The miners placed sheet iron or *lagging* – lumber planks, in front of the face. This made the loading portion of the mining cycle a *lot* easier. Canvas sheets were also used.[58] The dulled drills and everything else that was loose or valuable – like a lunch pail, see figure 10, would be moved away from the face a fair distance.

Powder was then brought up to prepare for blasting. This was *black powder* loaded into paper tubes in the earlier days; later on pre-packaged stick *dynamite* was used. Details are covered later in *Explosives*. *Powder monkeys* are the men in charge of the explosives, which were stored in *powder houses* or *magazines* – small shacks or brick structures on the surface, and small, excavated and isolated rooms underground. See figure 11.

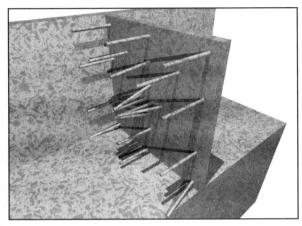

Figure 9   *Michigan* or *Burnt-cut Round* pattern   Author

All of the explosives used in mines were (are) dangerous, and on occasion went *ka-boom* at the wrong time. Accidents happened, property was destroyed, and men lost their lives. In 1891, at Red Mountain, Colorado, the Silver Ledge Mine shaft-house burned, and ignited 40 pounds of dynamite in the powder house. The resulting explosion destroyed most of the mine's surface structures.[59]

Even selling the explosive stuff was a risky business, as downtown Virginia City, Nevada found out:

> "On June 29, 1873, at 11 o'clock p. m., the McLaughlin & Root building on the corner of Taylor and B Streets, was blown to pieces by the explosion of 100 pounds of Hercules powder, 6 cases of nitro-glycerine, 100 pounds of giant powder, and 200 pounds of common powder, which had been stored in the bedroom of General J. L. Van Bokkelen. The General and nine others perished. It was supposed that the explosion was caused by a mischievous monkey that the General kept in his apartment. The General was an agent for explosives."[60]

Figure 10   Miner's Lunch Pail   Author

If dynamite were used, it would need to be warmed if the temperature of the sticks were at or less than 56° F, the freezing point of nitroglycerine. This was the case in many hardrock mines. Specially made dynamite warmers that used warm water as the heat source – see figures 12 and 13, were made for the job, but it wasn't unusual to see a miner walking along a passageway keeping sticks of dynamite warm underneath his arms. Many an explosion occurred from dynamite being thawed on stoves.

Fuses were cut to the correct lengths; longer pieces took correspondingly longer to burn. See figure 14. This allowed the miner to control the order in which the powder charges exploded. The drill holes were scooped free of loose bits of rock. Then the sticks of powder were inserted and very carefully *tamped* – pushed back, tightly into the drill holes. The sticks were sometimes cut lengthwise so that when carefully tamped they would be pressed up tightly to the sides of the drill hole. Tamping should *always* be performed with a wooden rod – never metal, or it might cost the miner his life. This "rule" was frequently violated.[61]

Figure 11   Powder Magazine, Victor, Colorado 2002
Courtesy Dan Wilson

During the driving of the Treasury Tunnel in the Red Mountain mining district, the hydraulic pressures encountered underground could be so great that the charges would be pushed from the drill holes. The miners put their blasting powder inside of metal gas pipes and then forced the pipes into the drill holes.[62]

The amount of powder used was kept to the minimum required to do the job. This not only saved money, but also lives. Overloaded holes shattered the surrounding rock, which made the workings dangerous and required additional, expensive timbering.[63]

The last stick to go into a given drill hole was slit on the side, and the pre-cut length of fuse inserted into it. For dynamite, a blasting cap was crimped onto the end of the fuse before inserting it into the end of the explosive stick. See figure 15. It was placed into the hole, and then the hole was firmly tamped with "*dirt.*"

Figure 12 ▲   Author
Dynamite Warmers
Figure 13 ▼   Author

When all of the holes had been loaded in this fashion, the face had dangling from it a bunch of fuses of different lengths – *rat-tails*. The miner would carefully inspect his work, double check that all loose items such as tools had been removed, and that no obstacles were along his path of egress from the face. He then prepared a special fuse used to ignite the charges. This *spitter* was a short length of fuse with a series of evenly spaced notches cut through the outer wrapping and into the powder core.

He was now ready to begin *spitting* – lighting, fuses, and would ensure that two candles were burning. He would light the spitter with the candle flame, and when he did, the jet of flame and hot gases spitting from the spitter would most likely extinguish the candle. The other candle allowed him to continue to see what he was doing. Now was not the time to fumble with matches to light a candle.

As the spitter burned towards a notch, he would hold the notch up against the end of the first fuse he wished to ignite. A flame would shoot out of the notch and readily ignite the fuse. He would then move the spitter to the next fuse and light it, and continue until all had been lit. The length of the spitter – the time it took to completely burn, provided the miner with a warning for when his safe time for spitting the round was up.[64]

He would then call out the traditional *"Fire in the hole!"* and then run like hell, right? Wrong! He would call out the warning, but then would get his candle and *slowly* walk to a place of known safety. The miner would be foolish to risk falling down near the shots, possibly being injured, or worse yet, being knocked unconscious and subjected to the concussions of the explosions, flying rock, and toxic fumes that would soon follow. At the very least, he didn't want his candle to be snuffed out when all hell was about to cut loose behind him.

Having retreated to a place of safety, he would listen to the dull thuds of the charges going off one by one. He counted them to determine if all went. Misfires are sometimes called *steamboats*.[65] If they didn't all go, the next shift would be warned of the very great danger of unexploded charges.[66]

In larger mines, a specified time was assigned for the firing of the rounds. Sometimes thoughtless miners started their rounds early, and in the process endangered other miners' lives. Bennett experienced this while working in the silver mines of Creede, Colorado:

"I had just spit seven or eight holes when the first of the Finlander's shots blew out my light. I lit it again in time for his next shot to put me in the dark again. By then I knew that was no place for me, and I started down in the dark. I had to go down a sixty degree slope, from stull to stull, and then across the same distance to a pillar that would protect me from my shots when they started to go. Before I started across, I lit a match and got the general picture of those three stulls ahead and started across. On the last stull and one jump from the pillar, the first of my shots went, peppering me with small stuff, but nothing big came my way, and before the next shot went, I was under the pillar. By that time shots were going all around, so I waited them out, lit up, and went down to the level with murder in my heart for one Finlander."[67]

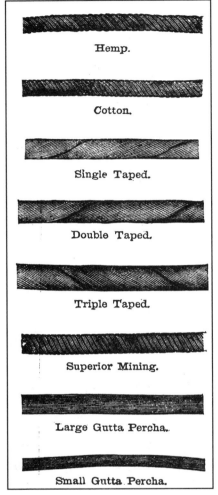

Figure 14   Fuses (life-size)
Source: Drinker, 1893

Blasting Sequence

Figures 16 through 20 illustrate the various sets of drill holes, and are described in the order in which they are fired. See figure 9 on page 30 for the entire drill hole pattern.[68] Each of these images has the appearance of a chunk of rock with a vertical "partition" in the center. On the far side of this "partition" the miners would work, drilling into the rock towards the viewer. About six inches of rock – the "partition," is left in the scene. The open area on the viewer's side of this "partition" is rock that has been "removed" from the scene so that the drill holes – which look like solid cylinders of rock a few feet long, may be clearly seen and described.

Figure 16 shows two holes drilled in the center of the heading. These are the *relievers*. They would not be filled with powder charges. The purpose of the reliever is to provide a space for the surrounding rock to expand into when the explosives shatter it. Most times only a single reliever was

Figure 15   Blasting Cap Tin   Author

needed. Larger headings, like that shown, required more relievers. All of the following illustrated drill holes were loaded with explosives that were fired – *shot*. Collectively, all of the holes are fired together as a *round*.

Next are the *cut* holes. These holes, usually numbering three or four, are drilled so that a converging cone or pyramid shape resulted. The reliever provides a place for the shattered rock to expand into, and a conic or wedge-shaped portion of the face would be blown out.

The *enlargers* follow, which accomplish just that, and they blow their rock into the space made by the cut shot. See figure 18. The enlargers are followed by *trimmers*, which create clean corners.

Most of the rock that was shattered up to this point was blown into the spaces created by the previous shots, the result being a big pile of broken rock at the face. The last shot – the *lifters*, as seen in figure 20, would create a clean break along the bottom and also lift the pile of rock up and deposit it a few feet back from the newly created face, on top of the sheet iron previously mentioned.

After the round had been fired there would be a choking cloud of rock dust and gases, generated by the explosives, hovering about the working face. Depending on the geometry of the workings and the effectiveness of the ventilation – natural or forced, time was allowed for the dust to settle and fresher air to circulate into the workings.

Loading

In the smallest mines, the miner might be responsible for loading up the broken rock, the pile of it being called *muck*. This might involve *mucking* – shoveling, the muck into a wheelbarrow – an *Irish Buggy*, or even laboriously carrying it in small buckets and up ladders and through tight passageways if the workings required it.

At larger mines, men were hired whose specific duty was to load muck. They are *muckers*, and the shovel they use is called a *muck stick*. The miner and mucker would head back towards the working face. The mucker would push an *ore car* back on the mine rails. The car might be loaded with a set of sharpened drill steels and other supplies.

At larger mines, an entry-level position – a *nipper*, was often offered to boys. Their job was to pick up dull drill steels and deliver sharpened ones to the miners, plus run errands, deliver messages, etc.

The miner and mucker would stop at least a few yards from the muck pile, however. The miner would grab a long, heavy iron bar, and begin inspecting the back and ribs for any rock loosened by the blasts. This is known as *barring down*. Gently tapping the bar against the rock would make a distinctive ringing sound if the rock were solid and securely held. Loose – and dangerous, rock would make a dull thud. Anything loose would be pried down if small enough.

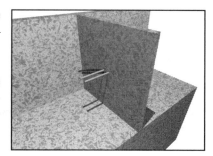

Figure 16   Relievers   Author

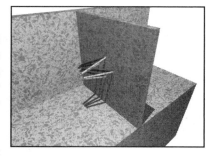

Figure 17   Cut Holes   Author

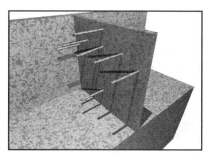

Figure 18   Enlargers   Author

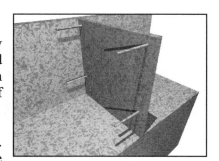

Figure 19 ▲   Trimmers   Author
Figure 20 ▼   Lifters   Author

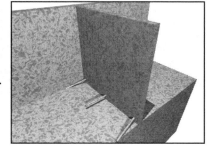

It is much better to intentionally bring loose rock down than to have it accidentally fall, injuring someone later. If a large area of the ground were unstable, support timbering would need to be installed. In small mines, the miner also did his own timbering; in larger mines skilled *timbermen* would perform the necessary work. Timbering, of which some was colossal, is covered in the next chapter.

If the previous shift indicated that there had been misfires, extreme caution was used in locating the unexploded charges. The charge might be in the muck, waiting to be exploded when struck by a pick or muck stick, or in the heading, waiting for a drill – especially a machine drill, to set it off.[69] *Many* miners lost their lives from unexploded charges.

If the previous round went well, there was muck – tons of the stuff, waiting for the mucker. His job was not an easy one. It is backbreaking work mucking rock into cars, and it took hours to complete the task. See figure 21. That is where the sheet iron (or lagging) helped so much – it provided a smooth surface from which to muck up the rock. It also allowed the mucker to push the car off of the rails and position it conveniently for loading, the sheet iron acting as a turning plate for the car's iron wheels.

Pieces of rock too large to shovel were lifted and thrown in the car. Pieces too large to lift were broken down with picks and heavy, long-handled hammers called *sledges* – this is known as *sledging* the ore.[70] On the rare occasions where a huge piece was present, a *paster* – also called *mud-capping* or *blockholing*,[71] was used to break the rock. Dynamite was placed on the surface of the rock, or into a very small drill hole made with hammer and steel, covered with mud, and then fired. This technique was also required for breaking rocks too big to fit into ore chutes.[72]

Figure 21   Muckers   Courtesy Mount Morgan Historical Museum, Inc

Drills And Mills

Hoisting ore to the surface is a costly operation, and once there, transporting it to be milled or shipped could also be very expensive. Every effort was made to minimize handling and re-handling the material. Some mines sorted the muck into classes: valuable ore, low-grade ore not valuable enough to mill at a profit, and worthless rock called *gangue*. The chunks of rock might be broken into smaller pieces to separate ore from gangue. Breaking rocks with light, long-handled hammers is known as *spalling*, and with light, short-handled hammers is *cobbing*.[73]

The sorted muck might be loaded into different cars, the contents identified with a tag. In some instances, the gangue or low-grade ore might be stacked along drifts or dumped in older workings, or used as fill for certain types of timbering.

While the mucker was at work, the miner started drilling the next round. When the mucker finished, he might help the miner and learn the art of drilling and setting up a round, or help *trackmen* extend mine track, *pipemen* install water, compressed air, and ventilation pipes, timbermen install timbers, etc.

Hauling

When the mucker filled a car, he would push – *tram*, it to the *station tender* for the level on which he worked, and fetch from him an empty car. The station tender was responsible for loading and unloading cars and supplies from cages – see *Hoisting*. In larger mines, men whose job is to push cars around and about are *trammers*. See figure 22. Or, he might tram the car to a nearby *orepass* and dump the muck into it. Mules were frequently used for tramming short trains of cars down long haulage drifts in the larger mines. Compressed air-powered trains and *electric mules* – small locomotives, were used for hauling trains of cars.

Orepasses were used in some of the larger underground mines. See figure 23. They act as a reservoir between the ore supply coming from the stopes and the demand for ore on the surface. Orepasses were large, vertical or near-vertical cavities excavated from the rock, or were built of timber in square sets (described later). There are openings at the top in which to dump the ore, and *chutes* with *gates* at the bottom from which to draw it out. See figure 24.

Figure 22   Trammers in the Gould & Curry Virginia City, Nevada ca 1865 Courtesy Library of Congress

Sometimes the ore would get stuck in the chute leading from the orepass to the gate. Clearing a clogged chute was a very hazardous assignment that miners simply didn't volunteer for. Frank Crampton accepted the job, and almost paid with his life. After inspecting ore wedged tight in a chute, he crawled out of the chute to prepare his charge:

> "I selected three of the longest bamboo poles I could find, lashed them together from end to end, strapped twenty sticks of sixty to the small end, put in two number six caps with twenty feet of fuse to each of them."

Figure 23   Cars dumping into an orepass Courtesy Mount Morgan Historical Museum, Inc.

He then crawled back up into the chute and positioned the charge, spit it, and carefully made his way towards the chute gate. Something told him that he had better move – and move fast. This he did.

Figure 24   Orepass chutes and gates   Author

> "Just as I made the opening of the chute a dribble of muck started to come down. Then larger pieces, and I was no more than clear of the chute-mouth, and in the drift, when the whole thing let go and came down."

Crampton barely managed to get away as the charges went off prematurely, the blasting cap having been struck by falling rock. The rock, collapsing chute timbers, and blown-apart debris took a few shifts to repair. Crampton was not fired…

> "… for the same thing had happened to the stiff I had replaced. There was a difference though: he had not got away in time."[74]

Hoisting

The man whose job it is to hoist is (you guessed this one too) a *hoistman*. Even in the smallest of workings, there comes a point where miners, tools, rock and water need to be hoisted out of a developing shaft, and miners, tools, and explosives need to be hoisted in. The simplest mechanism that performs this task adequately is the hand-cranked *windlass*. See figure 26. It has a working limit of depth of around 75-100 feet, and uses hemp rope of ¾ to one-inch diameter. Two men can hoist about 4 tons from 75 feet every 8 hours.[75]

Rarely used was the *whip* (not pictured), which was little more than a horse or man pulling on a rope that went over a pulley and down into the shaft. There was little braking ability other than the hands and heels of the operator. There was no mechanical advantage like that which is gained by winding the rope around a cylinder with long handles, as in a windlass, so the capacity was very limited.

As the workings got deeper, a more robust means of hoisting to greater depths was necessary. The horse-powered *whim* was well suited for this task. See figures 27 and 28. It worked to depths of about 50-300 feet, with wire rope being preferred to hemp. Two men and, naturally, a horse (or mule) are generally required on the surface. The tonnage hoisted in 8 hours varies with the depth from which it is raised: about five tons from 300 feet, ten tons from 200 feet, and about twenty tons from 100 feet.[76]

Figure 25   *Jim Crow*, used to bend mine rail   Author

Figure 26   Windlass, ca 1911   Courtesy USGS

A whim requires a fair amount of flat, level space in which the horse or mule would plod along in an endless circle. Sometimes this was even accomplished underground. In 1850, Barron and Company, owners of the New Almaden quicksilver mine (California), had a well-timbered tunnel driven over 800 feet into Mine Hill. At a point 769 feet from the mouth, a 38-foot diameter cavity was excavated, and a two-compartment shaft sunk. A mule-powered whim was installed in the cavity for hoisting.[77]

Shafts could quickly outgrow the capacity of whims and animal power. Large amounts of money were required for further development of the mine. This is where many mines transitioned from the collective efforts of perhaps a few to tens of men, to one of large companies, far-away capital investment and absentee owners, the issuing of stock, etc.

A costly steam engine would be installed for the motive power, and a large wooden *headframe*, or *gallows frame* as the structure was sometimes called, erected for supporting the cable and bucket or cage. At the top of the headframe is a *sheave wheel* – a large-diameter pulley, over which the cable passed. The large diameter is necessary to reduce bending strains on the cable. The shaft might also be expanded to accommodate two or three *compartments*, perhaps one or two for hoisting and one for pumping. The capacity of a fully developed steam hoist was limited only by the power of the engine, the strength of the cable, and the total load to be hoisted. The headframe became an icon for deep mining. See figures 29 and 30.

Figure 27   Horse Whim   Courtesy USGS

The man responsible for running the engine is the *engineer*. At very large installations *oilers* might assist the engineer. The engineer often operated the hoisting equipment, which was driven by the steam engine; thus "engineer" is frequently used to describe a hoistman. *Firemen* kept the steam boilers stoked with fuel. *Landers* loaded and unloaded the buckets and cages at the surface. *Topmen* performed various jobs on the surface. Sometimes they were crippled miners kept on the payroll.

At the beginning of the 20th Century, Tonopah, Nevada experienced the gamut of hoisting methods. At first whips and windlasses were used, followed by whims, and finally steam, gasoline, and electric-powered hoists.[78]

Figure 28   Horse Whim
Source: Behr, 1896

Figure 29   Inclined Headframe
Courtesy Mount Morgan Historical Museum, Inc.

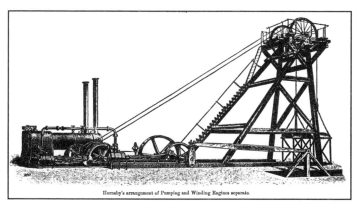

Figure 30   Hoisting and Pumping Engine and Headframe
Source: Lock, 1890

Rope and Cable

Round wire rope was used for hoisting as far back as 1834, having been produced by A. Albert for a mine in Germany. It wasn't widely used, however, until about 1880 when uniform grades of steel could be manufactured in suitable lengths.[79] In 1864, Andrew Smith Hallidie invented flat woven-wire rope. See figure 31.[80]

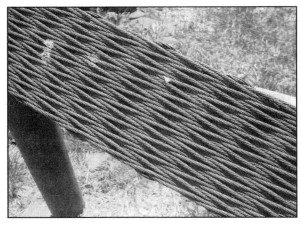

Figure 31   Flat woven-wire rope   Author

Flat wire rope, unlike round wire rope, has the distinct advantage of being readily mended on site by weaving or sewing in replacement sections.[81] See figure 32. Flat rope was wound on a reel – as the rope wrapped around the reel, the effective diameter of the reel rapidly changed. This gave a mechanical advantage to the hoisting engine, and a gradual acceleration as the cage was hoisted towards the surface.[82]

Comparisons between hemp, iron, and steel flat woven-wire rope are shown in charts 1 to 3.[83] In the 1880 Census, which includes details on 383 western deep mines, flat steel rope was used primarily on the Comstock, where 68% of the reporting mines used it, 10% used round cable, and 21% used hemp rope. The remaining deep western mines used flat rope 5%, round cable 43%, and hemp or manila rope 46% of the time.

The flat steel rope used on the Comstock were coated with tar to prevent rusting, and the cables used in the 1880's at Red Mountain, Colorado were thickly coated with grease. At Red Mountain the mine water carried such a high sulfuric acid content that anything made of iron rapidly corroded.[84]

Figure 32   Flat wire rope mending machine   Author
◄Chart 1 and Chart 2   ▼Chart 3

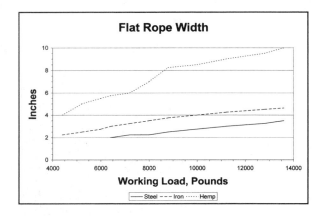

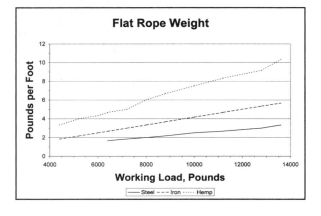

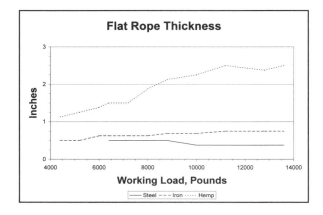

Buckets, Cages, and Skips

By 1880 *buckets* – also called *kibbles*, were used for hoisting about 66% of the time, except in Nevada, where *cages* or *skips* were used 69% of the time. See figures 33 and 34.[85]

Cages were mostly a single deck, and sometimes two decks, one above the other. The first three-deck cage used on the Comstock Lode was at the Consolidated Virginia, May 1874.[86]

Dan De Quille, noted Virginia City, Nevada newspaperman and author of *The Big Bonanza*, described a specialized hoisting system used on the inclined ore bodies at the Savage mine.

The vertical shaft intersected the Comstock Lode at about 1300 feet in depth, and from there the shaft followed the lode on an incline of about a 45° angle. The cable in the incline was supported by rollers, and ran beneath a sheave wheel at the junction of the incline and shaft.

The cars used for this purpose – called *giraffes*, had smaller wheels on the higher side and larger wheels on the lower side, leveling the car. They were outfitted with six seats – two on the front and two on either side.

The giraffe and incline required a powerful and novel hoisting arrangement. Two 200 HP engines were used. The hoisting reel was tapered, being 15 feet long, 22 feet in diameter on the large end, and 13 feet in diameter on the small end.

The weight to be hoisted – and accelerated, included not only the car and 5-ton load of ore (8 tons of ore if a second car was connected in tandem as a *back-action*), but also the weight of the cable. The cable was 4000 feet long and weighed 25,190 pounds. As the car was hoisted up and cable was wound around the reel the total weight to be hoisted diminished. The cable started winding on the smaller end of the reel. This provided a greater mechanical advantage to the engine for hoisting the entire load.

The cable, and its weight, slowly worked its way towards the larger end of the reel. This caused a steady decrease in the load to be hoisted and an increase in speed until the end of the incline was reached. At that point the giraffe was brought to a stop and the ore removed and transferred to cages in the vertical shaft.[87]

The Barbee & Walker Silver Mining Company of Silver Reef, Utah, hoisted a giraffe on a 400-foot incline with a 21 horsepower engine and a ⅞" steel rope.[88]

Figure 33   Miners on a Bucket
Monongahela Mine

Courtesy Carnegie Branch Library for Local History
Boulder, Colorado

Figure 34   Bullion Hoisting Works
Virginia City, Nevada ca 1865
Courtesy Library of Congress

Hoisting Safety

Some method of communication was required between the hoistman and the miners or station tenders. Using one's voice was only effective for a short distance, and then only if the hoistman was immediately next to the shaft. Rope bell cords were used to ring a bell next to the engineer. Different sequences were used to instruct the engineer to start, stop, hoist up or down, or position the bucket or cage in any desired position. See figure 35 for signals used in Colorado. On receiving a valid hoist signal, the engineer would move the cage as instructed. Dials on the larger hoists indicated the position of the cage within the shaft.

It was crucial that the engineer not perform any action unless instructed to do so. It was also crucial that the engineer not be distracted while on duty. Men's lives depended on this. Signs were posted on the hoisting platform stating something to the effect of:[89]

Figure 35   Bell Signals   Author

"NO PERSON IS ALLOWED ON THE PLATFORM, OR TO SPEAK TO THE ENGINEER WHILE ON DUTY."

In April 1868, electric wiring was installed at the Savage Mine for use in signaling the hoistman. When it was discovered that it wasn't completely reliable, it was replaced with bell cords.[90]

By 1880 79% of deep western mines signaled using a wire or rope bell cord to ring a bell or gong. Only 1% used a telephone or telegraph. Problems with insulation, acidic water, and batteries accounted for much of the resistance to adopting their use in mines.[91]

Where buckets were used the descent or ascent in the shaft could be rather precarious. The bucket had a tendency to spin and swing back and forth, and on occasion hit the walls of the shaft. The occupants held on tightly and stayed as close to the center of the bucket as possible during the ride. On occasion the cable would break, and the bucket would fall to the sump. Many miners were hurt or killed, either by falling with or from the bucket, or being hit by one as it fell.

Figure 36   Sawtooth Safety Dogs   Author

Figure 37   Cage Safety Spring Mechanism   Author

Timbers that ran the length of the shaft guided cages. Even so, a broken cable meant a quick fall to one's death hundreds or thousands of feet below. Accidents of this nature spurred the development of safety devices for cages. Not a lot could be done for buckets, though. According to the 1880 Census, cage safety devices were used in about nine out of ten installations.[92]

A popular method consisted of spring-loaded toothed eccentrics, also known as *saw-tooth safety dogs*,[93] designed to bite into the shaft's wooden guides if the rope broke. See figures 36 and 37. Under ordinary use, the weight of an empty cage was sufficient to keep the spring compressed and the dogs disengaged. In the event that the cable broke, the powerful spring would engage the mechanism, rotate the dogs so that they bite into the timber guides, and rapidly stop the runaway cage.[94] This was an effective system, though not entirely foolproof.

Overwinding was another cause of injury and loss of life. This is when the engineer fails to stop the cage as it reaches the platform and it is hoisted right into the sheave wheel. Overwinding safeties typically worked in one of two ways: the ascending cage would disengage a clutch on the hoisting engine, or it would trip a valve that would cut the supply of steam to the hoisting engine. The former had the distinct drawback that, if an overwind occurred, the cage would be disengaged from the hoist, and "if the safeties against falling are out of order, the *gravity* of the accident is likely to be increased…"[95] Giraffes were equipped with safeties much like cages in shafts.[96]

Another safety issue was the big, deep, open hole in the ground called the shaft. Men were known to fall into it on occasion. Mines on the Comstock developed latticework that covered the shaft compartment to prevent these accidents. The *bonnet* – the top, of the cage raised the lattice as it reached the surface.[97]

Illumination

Hardrock miners used candles for illumination. They were merely placed on any convenient surface. The Comstock miners are credited with developing the *miner's candlestick* – also called a *sconce*,[98] in the early 1860's. The first patent issued for a miner's candlestick was in 1872; the last in 1917.[99] The candlestick could be driven into any convenient timber or crack in the rocks, or hung by a small hook if the model was so provided. See figure 38. Bennett cautioned that "one could buy a good candlestick for a dollar, the same kind that are now [1960's] being made and rusted up to be sold to the tourist trade for prices up to five dollars each."[100] Buyers beware!

Figure 38   Miner's Candlestick   Author

Safety lamps, first introduced by Davy in 1815, were very popular in coalmines, but saw very limited use in hardrock mines.[101] "Lard" oil lamps – developed in Scotland about 1850, found occasional use in western mines. These little teapot-like lamps burned whatever was handy, such as bacon grease, oil such as cottonseed, kerosene, or crude, and produced a smoky flame. Later they were adapted for burning *Sunshine*, a mixture of 3% mineral oil and paraffin. Sunshine had the advantage of burning without smoking, but was hazardous to the miners because the paraffin fumes condensed in their lungs.[102] See figure 39. Carbide lamps found extensive use in mines after the turn of the century. The first patent was issued to F. E. Baldwin in 1900.[103]

Candles could be rather expensive. During the 1849 rush they sold for $3 each![104] During the boom at White Pine, Nevada in 1869, candles sold for 35 cents each. Miners made about $5 a day.[105] As mining camps matured and freight rates fell, candles became cheaper. Many mines provided

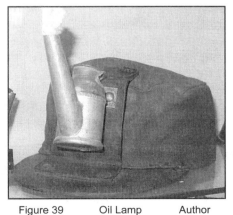

Figure 39   Oil Lamp   Author

candles for the miners. Others required the miners to provide their own, especially if they were working under contract. During off-hours, miners that boarded didn't worry about candles. The others needed candles or lanterns to light their homes. Some saved up the *snuffs* – the small pieces left at the end, for use at home.[106] A few found an unusual way of achieving this. Mike "Rabbit" Rabitz, a miner in Creede, customarily drilled in the dark, taking home the unused candles:

> "He would lay out his steel in the order in which he was going to need it, start a hole, and blow out his light. Drilling all the while in the dark, he would finish that hole and light up to start another."[107]

Figure 40   Author
Basket used for burning pitch
knots at hydraulic mines

Some operations required a staff dedicated to illumination. At the Sutro Tunnel in 1878, fourteen-year-old boys were kept busy working in the *torch room* – a small building near the portal that had candles, oil, and lamps. They were responsible for all of the illumination needs of the workforce. As mules exited the portal, the boys grabbed the lamp from the mule's collar, refilled it with oil, and on entering the portal the mule had a lighted lamp placed back in the collar.[108] Underground illumination could be improved simply and inexpensively by the use of whitewash on the walls.[109]

Hydraulic mines were operated day and night. Burning pitch on the ground provided the nighttime illumination. Iron baskets mounted to iron bars were then used to elevate the burning pitch, and provided the ability to quickly relocate the light as required. See figure 40. After this kerosene lamps with large reflectors were used. When electric power became available, electric lighting was used.[110]

Many miners resisted change, preferring to stay with the tried and true. In 1903, the Daly mines in Park City attempted to switch to using oil lamps. The miners staged a walkout, and nine days later, they returned back to work with their candlesticks in hand.[111] Candles were still in use at the Iowa-Tiger mine in 1912.[112] Figure 41 shows part of a shift of miners with their lunch pails, candles, candlesticks, and oil lamps.

Figure 41   Mine crew with lunch pails and illumination ca 1900
Courtesy World Museum of Mining, Butte, Montana

Figure 42   Author

Ventilation

Adequate ventilation of the underground workings is of paramount importance. Hardrock mines, unlike coalmines, generally did not produce significant amounts of poisonous gases. This was not always the case, however. Gases would seep from the rocks, and even in very small concentrations could prove deadly. In 1867, two miners working at the New Almaden mine died from suffocation when they ventured into workings filled with carbon dioxide.[114] Unknown gases that were probably associated with hydrothermal activity occasionally overcame Comstock miners.[115] Miners have their own terminology for the different poisonous gases.[116]

- ◆ afterdamp   gases from a fire, primarily nitrogen, carbon dioxide, and carbon monoxide.
- ◆ blackdamp   carbon dioxide, usually part of afterdamp.
- ◆ chokedamp   carbon dioxide.
- ◆ firedamp   methane.
- ◆ stinkdamp   hydrogen sulfide.
- ◆ whitedamp   carbon monoxide.

Add to this the noxious fumes from blasting, the ever-present and deadly rock dust, and the smells of rotting timbers and mule and miner offal. This foul air might be made worse – unbearable, by heat and humidity. One quickly concludes that ventilation is critical.

Natural ventilation was ineffective if the mine had a single opening at the surface; there was no path to develop circulation. Fans called *blowers* were required to force fresh air into the mine. The Roots brand blowers were very popular – see figure 43. Ventilation was far more effective once two or more openings existed. Additional shafts, drifts, crosscuts, adits, and tunnels were driven to enhance natural ventilation, and to improve mine access, ore removal, and drainage. Sometimes these passages were driven, at great expense, solely for providing ventilation.

Neighboring mines would frequently connect their workings to increase the volume of circulated air. Nearly all of the mines along the Comstock were connected in this way. Ventilation was improved dramatically, but so was the risk of enormous and uncontrollable fires. Everything has its price.

Where the outside air is drawn into the workings it is a *downcast*; and where the air exits to the outside it is an *upcast*. The natural convection might not be sufficient to properly ventilate the mine, and large blowers were used to assist the process. The Newhouse (Argo) Tunnel in Idaho Springs, Colorado, had the opposite problem. Air control doors were

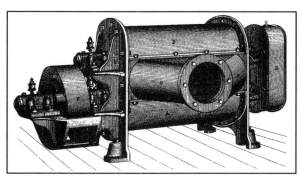

Figure 43   Roots Blower   Courtesy USGS

installed at the portal to diminish the flow because it was so great.[117] Sometimes the direction of the airflow would change from day to night, or from season-to-season, depending on changes in the relative air temperatures and densities.

Fresh air would not circulate into the new drifts and crosscuts where the miners actively worked, even with improved natural ventilation, unless other connections were made. Forced ventilation was still required in these areas, and was supplied by blowers and a system of pipes, and the compressed air used to operate machine drills. See figure 44.

Heat

Deep mines become hotter with depth, some to the point where it was intolerable. The Stewart mine in Butte, Montana, was one of the hottest in the district, with temperatures as high as 130° F in the deeper stopes.[118] See chart 4.[119]

The mines along the Comstock Lode were notorious for being extremely hot and humid. James Galloway, in his diary, wrote of working in the mines of Virginia City. On February 6, 1875, he wrote that he "went to work on the Con. Virginia at 3 p. m., wheeled waste, very hot, 8 hours for $4." Later he noted that he "worked on the south end on 8th floor, was fearfully hot, made me sick" and "terribly hot where I work" – a recurring theme in the deep mines of the Comstock.[120]

Figure 44   Ventilation Pipe   Courtesy USGS

The temperature increased with depth, to the point of being unbearable. See chart 5.[121] In the Imperial shaft, at a depth of 1700 feet, temperatures ranged from 130-140° F until ventilation was effected, reducing the temperature to 100°. In 1877, hot water of 157° was struck in the Savage mine.[122] In the Sutro Tunnel, near the Julia shaft, the temperature was nearly 109°. Near the Combination partition, the temperature was over 94° and the relative humidity was a sweltering 98.5%.[123]

In 1868, Roots blowers were installed at the Hale & Norcross, and the temperature fell from 100° to 90° within a few days. In the nearby Bullion mine,[124] a ventilation drift opened from the Imperial shaft was driven for a length of 1700 feet before any attempt was made to connect it with other workings. The temperature at the working face ranged from 130-140°. When a connection was made with another shaft "the temperature fell rapidly from 138° to 100 Fahr."[125]

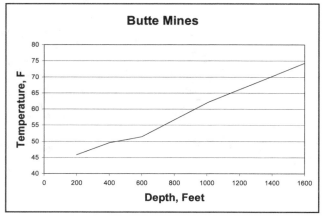

Chart 4   Temperature as a Function of Depth

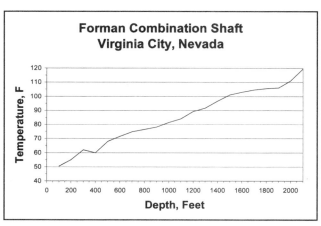

Chart 5   Temperature as a Function of Depth

Elliot Lord, author of *Comstock Mining and Miners*, wrote the following concerning the extreme heat at extreme depths, the need for large quantities of ice that were used in little shacks where the miners would frequently rest, and the greed that drove them on: [126]

"Here the men employed could not leave their work as often as the miners who guided the drills, but were forced to breathe this suffocating vapor till they often staggered forth from the station half blinded and bent by agonizing cramps. When the pain was so great that men began to rave or talk incoherently their companions would quickly take them up and carry them to the coolest place on the level..."

"In the hotter levels three gallons was a moderate allowance for one man during a shift of 8 hours; and 95 pounds of ice was the average daily consumption of every miner employed in the hottest workings of the California and Consolidated Virginia mines during the summer of 1878."

"Yet for the sake of high wages and the information which gamblers prize, men were willing to suffer this heat and continue the search for ore ... tempted by the silver of the Comstock mines, men will explore their depths until they drop dead at the stopes."

Changing Ore With Depth

Most hardrock mining concerns quickly find out that ore deposits change with depth, and often not in a favorable way. Surface deposits have had the benefit of time and natural weathering and erosion processes. These processes lead to the preferential concentration of values, and to the formation of easily worked or milled oxidized ores. The value of the minerals sometimes increases until the water table is reached; below the water table, precious metal values often diminish and sulfide minerals prevail. Perhaps one of the most interesting examples of the change of ore with depth is Butte, Montana. A sketch of Butte is included in the last chapter.

Smelter returns for the Guston mine, in the Red Mountain district of Colorado, are shown in chart 6. The ore transitioned rapidly from very high grade to very low grade. Even so, about 69,000 tons of ore was mined at a cost of a little over $1 million, and smelter returns amounted to about $2.5 million. A little over $1.1 million in dividends were paid during the first five of these years, but during the last few years of operation, when the smelter returns just about equaled the cost of mining, dividends ended. Operations ceased in 1897 [127]

The general trend of the argentiferous sulfide ores in the Red Mountain district, with increasing depth, was high-grade lead, then to mid-grade copper, and lastly to very low-grade iron. [128]

Delamar, Nevada, like so many other mining camps, saw declining gold values with depth.[129] See chart 7.

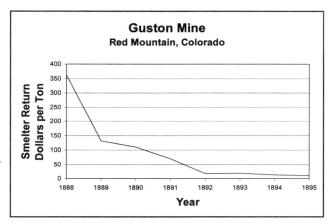

Chart 6   Guston Mine Smelter Returns

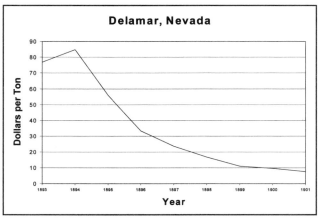

Chart 7   Delamar, Nevada Declining Values

Tunnels

Tunnels were driven through mountains for canals and railroads, in addition to mining. The first tunnel in the U.S. was the Auburn Tunnel, constructed between 1818 and 1821. It was located at Orwigsburg Landing, Pennsylvania and was part of the Schuylkill Navigation. It was originally 20 feet wide and 18 feet high (from the canal bottom) and 450 feet long. The tunnel was later converted to an open cut. The name of the engineer who located and built it is not known. See figure 45.[130]

The first railroad tunnel was the 900-foot Allegheny portage tunnel, built between 1831 and 1833. Oddly, it was later abandoned when railroads replaced canals – this tunnel served as a short railroad link for canal systems.[131]

The Hoosac Tunnel was the first U.S. tunnel to be bored using mechanical rock drills and nitroglycerine. It was started in 1855, and after numerous interruptions, was completed in 1876. It is 4.73 miles long.[132]

One of the primary functions of a mine tunnel was to drain water. In Park City, Utah, many of the mines and mills used the water flowing from drainage tunnels for other purposes: the Silver King mine and boarding house supplied all of their needs from the Henrietta tunnel, and in 1903, as additional water was needed, it was siphoned from the Alliance tunnel; water from the Daly-Judge drain and work tunnel supplied a portion of the Daly-Judge mill's needs.[133]

Tunnels also permit access to workings from lower elevations. This proved crucial for year round mining in many districts. Park City was subject to frequent and deep snowfalls that halted many mining operations located on the higher slopes. The working tunnel used by the Daly West, Daly, and Ontario mines was 2.5 miles long. It accommodated uninterrupted access to the mines and mills during the winter.[134]

Concerning driving a tunnel in the hopes of discovering new veins, Frederick Ransome noted – with sage words, that

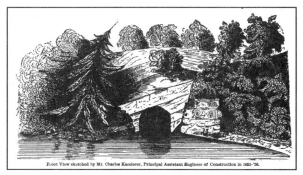

Figure 45   Auburn Tunnel
Source: Drinker, 1893

> "it may be pointed out that, in so far as the projectors of long tunnels count upon finding richer or more abundant ore than is indicated near the surface, they are playing a game of chance in which the probabilities are decidedly against them."[135]

The Revenue Tunnel

The Revenue Tunnel was begun in late 1888, designed to intersect the Virginius vein and surrounding mines in the Mount Sneffels mining district, near Ouray, Colorado. In January of 1893, the Virginius vein was intersected at a distance of 7435 feet. It was a carefully planned and executed venture with many objectives:

- ♦ The elimination of hoisting and pumping expenses.
- ♦ Consolidation of ore preparation, milling, and boarding facilities.
- ♦ Reduction of transportation expenses to Ouray.
- ♦ Year-round access to the mine workings.
- ♦ Greatly reduced need for hazardous winter travel in an area that is notorious for avalanches.[136]

♦ Spanish Mine, California, 1887. Over a 22-day period, 2796 tons of ore were mined at a cost of 37.5 cents per ton, of which 32.4 cents went for labor. The mill treated this ore for 23 cents per ton, where 12.3 cents went for labor. The total operating cost was 60.5 cents per ton. The ore yielded $1.16 per ton, leaving a profit of 56 cents per ton. The mine was open-cut, and Chinese laborers were employed at $1.40 a shift. This is perhaps the lowest mining cost ever.[162]

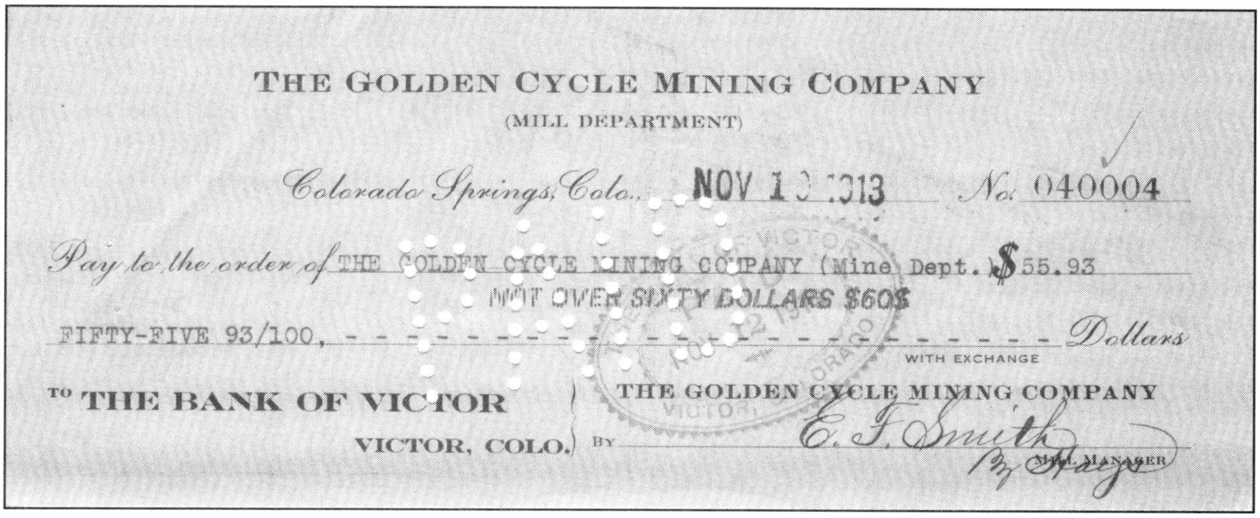

Figure 50   Cancelled Check   Author

Figure 51   Miners working on the 850-level, Mount Morgan
                             Courtesy Mount Morgan Historical Museum, Inc.

Endnotes

[1] DUNCAN1990 page 178

[2] SMITHP1994 page 35

[3] SMITHP1994 page 146

[4] AAA1978 page 26

[5] WOLLE1963 page 264

[6] CERES.297, AAA1978 page 52

[7] NORTHROP1975 page 24.

[8] WOLLE1963 page 354, COUCH1943 page 118

[9] MONTANADEQ.119

[10] MONTANADEQ.183

[11] WOLLE1963 pages 358-359

[12] SLOAN1975 pages 223, 236

[13] BENNETT1966 page 88

[14] USDA. Still visible in 2002

[15] JACKSONW1963 page 110

[16] WOLLE1963 page 444

[17] ACKERLY1997, CSA2001, DEQUILLE1959 page 81, DUNCAN1990 page 146, IDL2001, EMMONS1885 page 202, MONTANADEQ.132, MONTANADEQ.183, RANSOME1901 page 245, RAYMOND1873 pages 195, 401, SLOAN1975 page 21, TWAIN1980 page 166, WEED1912 page 20, WOLLE1977. A few are 20th Century names.

[18] SMITHG1998 page 61, BANCROFT1890 page 127 estimates $9 million.

[19] CERES.269

[20] FATOUT1969 pages 47-48, 145

[21] ABBE1985 pages 3,8,16

[22] MORSE2000 page 23

[23] WIER1957 page 291

[24] WOLLE1963 page 64

[25] MORSE2000 page 17

[26] WOLLE1963 page 369

[27] WOLLE1963 page 337. WIER1957 page 291 gives 1862 for when the Reese River district was formed

[28] WIER1957 page 292

[29] FATOUT1969 page 32

[30] JACKSONW1963 page 19

[31] MORSE2000 page 25

[32] GREGORYC1980 page 236

[33] ROHRBOUGH1986 page 56

[34] SMITHP1994 page 32

[35] GREGORYC1980 page 236

[36] GREGORYC1980 page 236

[37] WIER1957 page 294

[38] MURRAY1972 pages 14-17, 30-31. Total production for the entire state of Wyoming, from 1867-1955, is a paltry $1,925,863. Carissa gold production from a state information sign adjacent to the mine.

[39] DUNCAN1990 page 59

[40] AAA1978 page 15. The abandoned stone buildings clustered around the Vulture mine in Arizona were knocked down and run through a mill, averaging $20 per ton. WOLLE1963 page 68

[41] PAUL1965 page 147

[42] BANCROFT1890 page 112, SMITHG1998 page 83. SMITHG1998 Page 310: Produced about $1,500,000 from 1859-1865.

[43] FARQUHAR1966

[44] Hungarian miners introduced chisel bits in 1749. DRINKER1893 page 52. Prior to that they were little more than sharpened points.

[45] SMITHP1994 page 106

[46] WOLLE1977 page 80

[47] BENNETT1966 page 90

[48] BENNETT1966 page 90

[49] PEELE1966 page 10-126, in 1905, 8-hour shift.

[50] PEELE1966 page 10-126, in 1907.

[51] BIRD1986 page 19

[52] JACKSONW1963 page 192, in 1876.

[53] FETCHENHIER1999 page 21

[54] CRAMPTON1956 pages 25-26

[55] CRAMPTON1956 page 65

[56] Based on an illustration from PEELE1966 page 6-09.

[57] BOUTWELL1912 page 23

[58] RANSOME1901 page 156 - The Silver Lake mine.

[59] SMITHP1994 page 182

[60] SMITHG1998 page 246

[61] CRAMPTON1956 pages 24-25

[62] SLOAN1975 page 141

[63] CRAMPTON1956 page 24

[64] CRAMPTON1956 page 25, PEELE1966 page 6-14

[65] WEDERTZ1996 page 191

[66] PEELE1966 page 6-14

[67] BENNETT1966 page 210

[68] Based on an illustration from PEELE1966 pages 6-09, 6-14.

[69] PEELE1966 page 6-14

[70] PEELE1966 page 28-15

[71] TAGGART1954 page 4-92

[72] BENNETT1966 page 169

[73] PEELE1966 page 28-15

[74] CRAMPTON1956 page 70

[75] PEELE1966 page 12-57. Rate based on 3 minutes being allowed for filling, unloading, and lowering the bucket, and an "average man" performing about 2500 ft-lb work per minute.

[76] PEELE1966 page 12-58. These figures are subject to the degree of stubbornness of the horse or mule, however.

[77] JACKSOND2001, SCHNEIDER1992 page 22

[78] CARPENTER1953 page 5

[79] BRITANNICA1958, *Wire Rope*, page 675

[80] SMITHG1998 page 47. TRENNERT2001 page 9 gives 1856.

[81] VICTOR2000 page 1

[82] VICTOR2000 page 1

[83] EMMONS1885 page 135

[84] DEQUILLE1959 page 224, SMITHP1994 pages 147,178

[85] EMMONS1885 page 140

[86] SMITHG1998 page 159

[87] DEQUILLE1959 pages 121-122,236-237

[88] EMMONS1885 page 481

[89] DEQUILLE1959 page 224

[90] LORD1883 pages 366-367

[91] EMMONS1885 page 142

[92] EMMONS1885 page 140. The author pities those miners working in the other ten percent of the reporting mines.

[93] VICTOR2000 page 1

[94] EMMONS1885 page 140

[95] EMMONS1885 page 140. Author emphasis.

[96] DEQUILLE1959 page 237

[97] DEQUILLE1959 page 152

[98] VOYNICK1984 page 23

[99] MALLICOAT2000

[100] BENNETT1966 page 89

[101] GREGORYC1980 page 235

[102] MALLICOAT2000, DICICCIO1996 page 49

[103] MALLICOAT2000. Calcium carbide (CaC_2) was formed into pellets and placed in a small chamber in a metal lantern. When water (H_2O) was slowly dripped onto it, a chemical reaction occurred creating calcium oxide (CaO) and acetylene gas (C_2H_2), which was burned with air (O_2) to produce the illuminating flame.

[104] RAYMOND1873

[105] JACKSONW1963 page 117

[106] BENNETT1966 page 89

[107] BENNETT1966 page 89

[108] STEWART1962 page 156

[109] EMJ1930 page 105. This seems like a rather obvious thing to do. The only mine the author has visited where whitewash was observed being used is the Edgar Experimental Mine, Idaho Springs, where it was used in the shop.

[110] NILE1956

[111] THOMPSON1968 page 123

[112] SLOAN1975 page 288

[113] TAYLORJ1964 page 344

[114] SCHNEIDER1992 page 46

[115] DEQUILLE1959 pages 122-124

[116] USBM1996. *Damp* is probably derived from the German *dampf*, meaning a fog or vapor.

[117] SOWELL1976 page 60

[118] MONTANADEQ.183

[119] WEED1912 page 104

[120] GALLOWAY1947 page 15

[121] BANCROFT1890 pages 130-131, LORD1883 page 397

[122] BANCROFT1890 pages 130-131

[123] YOUNGG1909 pages 960, 961 1908

[124] The Bullion never produced a single dime's worth of ore, but did assess the stockholders some $3,872,000! It was situated on a completely barren portion of the lode between the Chollar-Potosí and the Exchequer. The Chollar-Potosí produced over $16 million in milled ore, but dividends exceeded assessments by a scant $142,423. The Exchequer produced a pitiful $52,000, no dividends, and $700,000 in assessments. SMITHG1998 page 310.

[125] LORD1883 pages 391-392,393

[126] LORD1883 pages 393,393-394, 397

[127] RANSOME1901 pages 221-222

[128] RANSOME1901 pages 219, 226, 249, 250 (includes the Zuñi)

[129] COUCH1943 page 84

[130] BRITANNICA1958, DRINKER1893 page 23

[131] BRITANNICA1958

[132] BRITANNICA1958, MCCORMACK1950 page 329

[133] BOUTWELL1912 page 22. In the mid-1990's, on a tour of the Ontario mine in Park City, the author noticed a sizable cistern alongside an access drift. The guide explained that it was used for underground purposes, and then mused that the company would probably produce a significant income by bottling it for sale - cashing in on

the bottled water craze of the time, as the water was very pure.

[134] BOUTWELL1912 page 24

[135] RANSOME1901 pages 250-251

[136] GREGORYD1996 pages 108,114

[137] SMITHG1998 pages 107-115

[138] DRINKER1893 pages 341-347, 375-377

[139] MCKINNEY1995 page 31, states that the compressors were installed in April. DRINKER1893 pages 375-377, and STEWART1962 page 121, state that the drills were first used in March. It is not clear if the dates are wrong by a month or so, or if steam was tried on the drills and abandoned when it was discovered that the heading became intolerably hot, and that effective air compressors were by then available.

[140] DRINKER1893 pages 375-377

[141] LORD1883 page 366, DRINKER1893 pages 375-377. Nov 1869-April 1870, 224 sq feet heading; May 1870-Mar 1874, 64; Apr 1874-Oct 1874, 112; and Nov 1874-End, 80.

[142] STEWART1962 page 149

[143] SMITHG1998 page 112, STEWART1962 page 156. MAB1879-8 gives $6,000,000.

[144] MAB1879-8

[145] DRINKER1893 pages 375-377

[146] From May 1875, to August 1878, 76,718 carloads of rock were removed from the tunnel, traveling an estimated 412,000 miles round-trip. The distances are calculated from the known heading starting and ending points for each month, the average of the two being used. Each car removed an average of 11.4 cubic feet of the advancing tunnel during this period. These actual production figures, combined with the estimated values, were then used to estimate those for the period November 1869 to April 1874 where only the progress and heading size are known.

[147] SOWELL1976 pages 53, 65, ARGO2000 page 1, PEELE1966 page 6-28. Sowell states that the tunnel was completed "in about 9 years," putting the completion at about 1903. Peele lists "1902-1909" in a table relating to the tunnel's costs. HENDERSON1926 page 12 states that the Newhouse Tunnel was started in September 1893 and was completed on November 17, 1910. The *Argo Tailings* "newspaper," available at the Argo Mill, states that the tunnel was completed in 1910. Add to this the start date painted on the tunnel's portal stating 1893, not 1894.

[148] SOWELL1976 page 57 states the former, PEELE1966 page 6-28 states the latter, but makes no mention of the length.

[149] SOWELL1976 pages 54-62. The Argo Mill, opened in 1913, was conveniently located at the tunnel's portal for this purpose. ARGO2000. HENDERSON1926 page 15 states that the Argo amalgamation-concentration-cyanidation mill was completed in 1912, but by 1913 amalgamation was discarded. The mill purchased some ores, and provided custom milling and concentrating services for others. The mill may be visited today. The water draining from the tunnel is being treated as part of a Super Fund-designated site. The author muses that the tunnel might provide a novel way for Denverites to travel to the casinos in Blackhawk and Central City.

[150] CPI2002

[151] RAYMOND1873 page 238

[152] GREGORYD1996 page 57

[153] GALLOWAY1947 page 37

[154] SMITHP1994 pages 39,42,91,154

[155] BANCROFT1890 page 111

[156] ARBITER1964 page 258

[157] FINLAY1909 page 347

[158] SMITHP1994 page 185

[159] CARPENTER1953 page 51

[160] FINLAY1909 pages 380-381

[161] FINLAY1909 page 347

[162] RICKARD1932 page 63. DAY1892 page 150 gives the following figures: In November of 1887, mining cost 31.4 cents and milling 20.8 cents, for a total of 52.2 cents per ton.

TIMBERING
PUMPING
EXPLOSIVES
MACHINE DRILLS

Figure 1   Gold Coin Mine near Anaconda, Montana 1905
Courtesy World Museum of Mining, Butte, Montana

Timbering

As the miners sunk shafts, advanced drifts, raises and crosscuts, and mined ore from the stopes, support of the surrounding rock was often necessary. Unsafe rock is generally referred to as *bad ground*. The different methods of timbering that were developed had as its primary goal the safety of the miner.[1]

Other benefits, and dangers, for the miners were often direct side effects of the various timbering strategies used. The reader should appreciate that *none* of the timbering schemes ever developed will support a mountain if it wants to move: a *zillion* tons of rock does what it likes, and no arrangement of match sticks is going to stop it!

In many mines, the ground is very solid, and timbering is only required to shore up the slabs and chunks of rock that are loose enough to fall, but can be safely held in place by the right timbering. Preventing the initial movement of rock goes a long way towards keeping it held in place.[2] Stopes 30 feet wide and 200 feet high, and requiring no timbering, were not uncommon in Cripple Creek.[3]

Timbering may be required because of natural fractures, or the weakening of these fractures by blasting, especially from overloaded drill holes. The passageways in a mine may traverse layers of different strata, where a portion may be inherently weak or prone to collapse. In extreme cases, like that encountered on the Comstock, layers of clay under tremendous pressure were squeezed from between the surrounding rock and into the drifts and crosscuts, completely blocking them in a matter of days. Ore bodies, especially those that are low-grade, are often very large in size. Mining the entire volume leaves a cavity that can no longer support the superincumbent earth, which begins to cave-in unless supported.[4]

Stulls – also called *props*, are used to keep the ribs of passageways and narrow stopes spaced apart. See figure 2. *Post and cap* timbering supports the back. See figure 3. Depending on how bad the ground is, post and cap timbering may be spaced at very close intervals to provide maximum support.

Cribbing is used underground to line shafts. A simple interlocking framing holds the timbers against the walls of the shaft. Cribbing is also used aboveground for creating level places and for holding back the ground. The simple notching of the logs is not unlike that used for log cabins. Gangue was frequently used as the fill. See figures 4 and 5.

Spiling

While driving a drift or adit through extremely bad ground, a technique known as *spiling* (or *forepoling*) is used. Drill

Figure 2   Stulls   Author

Figure 3   Post and Cap Timbering ca 1885
Courtesy Library of Congress and
Santa Clara County Parks & Recreation Department

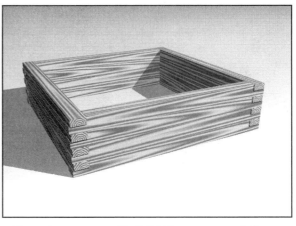

Figure 4   Shaft Cribbing   Author

steels are driven into the top of the unstable and advancing face at an angle slightly up from horizontal, and a couple feet of loose earth is dug out. This small advance is then immediately reinforced with closely spaced and heavy timber *sets*. Lagging is driven forward and beneath the steels, and supported by the sets. This is repeated over and over, slowly advancing the drift. The miner's exposure to the unstable ground is minimized this way.[5]

Figure 5   Cribbing of the A. G. and Minnie mines
Leadville, 1908   Courtesy USGS

Extremely bad ground was encountered while driving the Ontario drain tunnel in Park City, Utah:

> "The ordinary spiling and breast boards proved useless; advance could be made only with spiles of selected timber shod and capped with iron and driven home with compressed air, and to prevent the rock walls from starting on the spiling huge sacks of hay were packed behind it. It is stated that frequently 40 to 50 carloads of loose ground would escape through a crevice only as large as a man's hand."

This tunnel – nearly three miles long, was started in 1888 and completed in 1894. The cost was $400,000, or an average of $26 per foot. Parts of the bad ground cost $3500 per foot.[6]

Pig-Stying

In large stopes, a timbering method known as *pig-stying* was occasionally used. Low-quality logs unsuitable for general mine timbering were laid down next to each other to form a floor. A second floor was then laid down upon the first, but at a right angle. This was repeated until the volume requiring support was filled and the logs reached the back. It was inexpensive if the logs were cheap and readily available – no special carpentry was required, and no skills were needed in placing the logs.[7]

The Homestake mine in South Dakota used a variation of pig-stying in worked out stopes. A few alternating layers of old timbers, tightly placed, covered the floor, and then the remaining volume was filled from above with waste rock. This method was perfected in 1892.[8]

Square Sets

In 1860, development of the Comstock Lode was in full gear. The ore bodies were enormous – nothing like them had ever been encountered. The ore was composed of a very rich but friable broken quartz and clay. Even if timbers of a suitable length could be found, conventional post and cap timbering could not support the enormous weight of the superincumbent earth. The Ophir mine management called upon the services of Philip Deidesheimer to find a solution for their timbering problem. After a few weeks of careful study, he devised an innovative method of timbering called *square sets*.[9] It is interesting to note that Deidesheimer did not patent his idea, but instead shared it freely.

Shortly after its introduction it was universally adopted throughout the Comstock, and spread throughout the world. The square set is a simple and functional timbering scheme. It is well suited for any large underground working, no matter what the shape, and for most any size as will be seen.

Each set resembles the corner of a cube, and is composed of three timbers: a vertical *post*, and a horizontal *cap* and *girt*. A typical method of joining the three timbers is illustrated in figure 6, where the cap is to the left, the girt is to the right, and the post ascends from beneath. Close examination of these images reveals that the cap

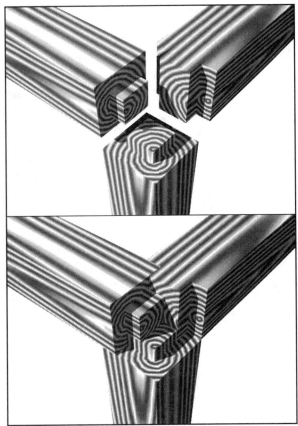

Figure 6   Square Set Joint   Author

gets three times greater support from the post than the girt does for this particular type of framing. It is the load-bearing member of the two. The orientation of a square set is arranged so that the girts are parallel with the long axis of the ore body or vein.[10]

Regular, rectangular structures are inherently unstable, much like a house of cards. Even so, cross bracing was only infrequently used in square sets. Perhaps less obvious in the illustration is how easily a square set might come apart and collapse. The timbers illustrated may be assumed to be typical in size, that is, about twelve inches square.

The protruding portion of the girt – the *tenon,* that rests on the post only needs to be pulled away three inches to fall free from one post, or six inches from both supporting posts. Likewise, the cap only needs to be pulled six inches to completely fall from one post, and a foot for both.

Square set timbering had to be held together very tightly to prevent a catastrophic collapse. Wedges were driven between set members and the surrounding rock for this reason.[11]

In May 1883, a large cave-in occurred in the aptly named Gopher mine, which had become part of the expanding Homestake properties. Harry M. Gregg, manager, wrote in a letter that,

"we come into an old Gopher chamber and a large mass of ore that was loose on acct of exposure to air fell and carried all the two upper floors with it on one end and all timbers to 4th floor on the other end. I think we have control of it now and hereafter I will see that the timbers are kept closer to the work."[12]

In 1883, stopes close to the surface and poorly supported collapsed, swallowing up one of the Homestake blacksmith shops. On September 25, 1910 the No. 3 Independence stope – 190 feet long, 45 feet wide, and from 10-100 feet high, caved in on the 300-level and broke through to the surface at 110 South Gold Street in Lead.[13]

Square sets permit the extension of the rectangular framework in three dimensions; thus virtually any size and shape ore body can be filled with the prismatic structure. Some of the stopes filled in this way were *huge.* The Santa Rita stope in the New Almaden mine was 400' long, 100' wide, and 40' high.[14]

The Comstock Lode consisted of a series of massive ore bodies spread out over a two-mile length of the lode. Some were *lenticular* – lens-shaped, and others sheet-like in overall shape. The ore bodies had a *dip* – an inclined orientation relative to the horizontal, of about 40-45°, and were sandwiched between valueless rocks known as *country rock.* When the lode is viewed from end to end, the country rock lying above the lode is the *hanging wall,* and that which the lode rests upon is the *footwall.* Large chunks of the hanging wall broke free and sank into the lode long ago. Miners called these worthless or low-grade bodies *horses,* and were forced to mine around them.[15] The discovery of a horse in the middle of a large ore body was disheartening. Fissures in the hanging wall sometimes contained very valuable mineralization.

The Crown Point-Belcher *bonanza* – prosperous workings or a rich ore body, located on the footwall, extended 600' vertically, 775' along the length of the lode, and was up to 120' wide! Figure 7 shows a perspective view of the stopes of this bonanza.[16]

Five horizontal levels, spaced at 100-foot vertical intervals, are shown, the first being 1000 feet underground. The checker pattern used for each level is a 25-foot square, with each complete checker containing 25 5x5' square sets. The levels cast shadows on the "floor" of the illustration, which has checkers that are 100 feet on a side. This gives an idea of the enormity of the ore body. Along the floor and up the "wall" is a bar that represents the boundary between the two mines, the Belcher being closer to the viewer. About 17 square sets, one atop another, would be required for one level to reach the next level above; thus, for each checker on a level, 425 sets are required to reach a checker on the next level.

At the 1200-level the ore body begins to separate, a ribbon of ore splitting off and following the boundary of the lode and the hanging wall. This sheet-like mass of ore grew thicker as it descended towards the 1400-level. Below this level both ore bodies suddenly contracted and vanished – *pinched out*. The workings transitioned from bonanza to *borrasca* – unproductive and worthless.

Discovery of the bonanza surely filled the hearts of the owners and stockholders with avarice. The unexpected and rapid pinching-out of the bonanza was no doubt dispiriting. Exploration continued to depths reaching over 3350 feet in the hopes of finding other great bonanzas, though little ore of significance was ever found below the 1650-level.[17]

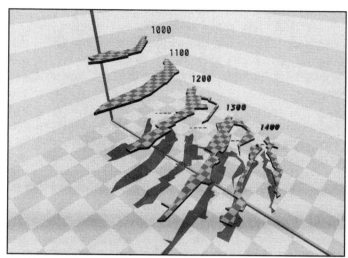

Figure 7   Crown Point-Belcher Bonanza Stopes   Author

The square sets filled this entire, immense volume; a tremendous quantity of timber was used. The tonnage mined from the Comstock mines was enormous – approximately 9.9 million tons through 1900.[18] Virtually all of the ore mined was replaced by square set timbering. See charts 1 and 2.[19]

The Consolidated Virginia buried about six million board feet of timber annually.[20] Through the productive life of the Comstock Lode, estimates range from 450-600 million board feet of timber and lumber were used in the mines.[21]

"Every ton of ore extracted from the Con. Virginia and California mines leaves a corresponding vacuum. That space is filled with solid 14- and 16-inch timbers, leaving only sufficient space between the huge bulkheads for the passage of men and cars. The cost of these timbers at the mines is $21 per thousand [board] feet, but even at these figures, it is much cheaper to fill with timber than to employ men to fill them with waste rock. – *Engineering and Mining Journal*"[22]

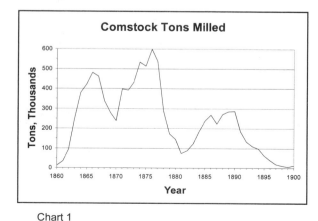

Chart 1

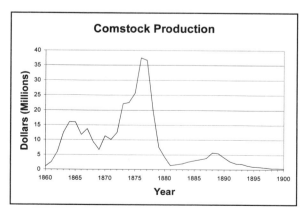

Chart 2

Ore Exploitation Using Square Sets

The Comstock Lode epitomized the exploitation of enormous ore bodies using square sets. Once an ore body had been discovered, and properly explored and ventilated by drifts and crosscuts from different levels, it was then prepared for exploitation. In square set stopes it was typical to run a raise to the level above to provide ventilation, ease in handling timbers (use gravity wherever possible), etc.

A *track-floor* or *sill floor* is opened on the level. This includes drifts and crosscuts on the new station level, where tracks are laid for ore and waste removal, and for bringing in supplies. Car tracks were laid in all of the crosscuts, and connected with the track of the main drift by means of a turntable.

The initial square set timbers are placed in these passageways. Ore is then removed laterally and from above the track ways and replaced by square sets; thus advancing in small set-sized excavations. Miners were only exposed to the rock being directly mined along the peripheral surfaces of the expanding framework. The sets moving upward are *raise sets*, the first to start a new row is a *lead set*, and those moving alongside existing sets are *side sets* and *corner sets*.

The tops and sides of this expanding timber framework are firmly wedged against the surrounding rock. This ensures the integrity of the framework, which can take on enormous proportions, and helps stabilize the surrounding cavernous stopes. As the sets are extended, heavy plank floors are laid down. Access stairs and ladders are installed, and hoists are periodically relocated as mining progresses.

Figure 8 Comstock miners double-jacking ca 1868
Courtesy NARA

After drilling and shooting the round, see figure 8, the ore is conveniently mucked from the plank floors – the *shoveling floor*. It is loaded into wheelbarrows and taken to the nearest orepass. Orepasses are installed at regular intervals by enclosing columns of sets with heavy lagging. The ore collected is then loaded into cars, brought to the station, and hoisted to the surface. See figure 9.

When only the sets are relied upon for support, it is an *open square set stope*. Lagging four (or more) adjacent sets and filling the resulting column with gangue or low-grade ore provided additional structural support. These columns of broken rock would follow the vertical progression of the stoping. This is a *filled square set stope*.[23]

If the level above has been worked in a similar fashion, then eventually the top of the stopes being worked will reach the level above, and the square set frameworks are then connected as if one. When this was planned, a special *sill set* was initially laid down to facilitate the ultimate joining of the sets from the level below.[24] Square set timbers, stacked and awaiting installation, may be seen in the upper right corner of figure 22, page 35.

Figure 9   Comstock trammers ca 1868
Courtesy NARA

Dimensions and Framing

The Comstock square sets used timbers from 12" to 16" square. Posts were about six feet high, caps and girts five feet in length. The resulting passageway was barely four feet wide by five feet high.[25]

The timber required for a square set of a given dimension will vary according to the size of the stope, number of ore chutes, ladders, and manways. A set of dimensions 5' (girt) by 5' (cap) by 7'2" (post), using 12" by 12" timbers, might require 263 board feet of timber.

For 16 variations using square timbers, sizes ranging from 6'2" to 8'3" high, and 4'9" to 7'5" wide and deep, the average number of board feet required per cubic foot of ore was 0.695, not including timber for floors, chutes, manways, lagging, etc. The maximum, 1.138 board feet per cubic foot, was for the Savage (Virginia City, NV), the minimum, 0.436, was for the Goldfield Consolidated (Goldfield, NV). For round timbers, the average for 8 mines was 0.519 board feet per cubic foot, this for sets with a range of dimensions similar to the aforementioned square timbers.[26]

- ◆ Rossland, British Columbia, 1903. 16" round timbers were framed by hand. A carpenter could prepare one set (one each of cap, post, and girt) in about 90 minutes, costing about 55 cents per set in labor.

- ◆ Homestake Mine, South Dakota, 1903. 12" by 12" timbers framed by hand required about 90 minutes per set, costing about 60-65 cents in labor per set.

- ◆ Ibex Mine, Leadville, Colorado, 1902. A carpenter could prepare, using a single-ended framer, one set in about 30 minutes, at a labor cost of about 18 cents per set.[27]

Board Feet Measure

A board foot is equivalent to a piece of wood one foot long by one foot wide by one inch thick, or 144 cubic inches. A length of lagging, say, six feet long by eight inches wide and two inches thick would be eight board feet. A timber 16" square and five feet long would be nearly 107 board feet.

Decay

Contemporary accounts indicate that some of the mines on the Comstock were *gutted* – hastily mined of only the richest ore for a quick profit. A common accusation about this practice was that it was intended solely to manipulate stock prices, which may certainly be true. There was at least one valid reason why the mining may have proceeded in this fashion, and it had to do with the environment in the mines. The combination of the humidity and elevated temperatures caused the timbers to rapidly decay, which was a significant problem in the Comstock mines. The faster the ore was removed, the less chance of rotten timbers causing caving, and also the reduction of expenses in replacing timbers.[28]

Fire

Disastrous fires broke out in the underground workings from time to time; square set timbering is a tinderbox just waiting for ignition. In April 1869 a fire broke out on the Comstock in the Yellow Jacket workings and spread to the Kentuck and Crown Point mines. 37 miners lost their lives in this disaster, the worst non-coal mine disaster through 1900.[29] Portions of the mine workings were sealed in an effort to smother the fires raging in the timber-filled stopes. In 1873 miners were finally able to re-enter the burned out section of the Kentuck mine. It was reported that in many places the rock was still too hot to touch, and that the timbers had turned to charcoal.[30] A fire that began in the stopes of the Con. Virginia in 1881 was only partially under control four years later.[31]

> Mine fires were not always caused by timber. In 1897, fires started in the carbonaceous shale of the Smuggler mine in Aspen, which were still burning in 1904.[32]

Collapse

The cavernous stopes of the Comstock supported tremendous weights. The square set timbers could take only so much compression before they gave way and the supported rock caved in. Decay and underground fires hastened collapse. Compressive forces on square sets could force 18" square posts into equal-sized sills to a depth of 3 inches. Twelve-inch thick caps were compressed down to five inches prior to caving.[33]

Several of the early stopes on the Comstock were very near the surface, and in June of 1867, one of them collapsed. Grant Smith, author of *The History of the Comstock Lode*, describes Roswell K. Colcord's experience:

> "He was then the superintendent of the Imperial-Empire shaft at Gold Hill, and he and a friend had walked over to Virginia City to attend the theater. On the way back they were joined by a young fellow who said he was a clerk in Wood & Goe's store and slept there. When they reached the intersection of "B" and "C" streets where the brick store had stood, they saw a great smoking cavern in which the store had disappeared. The young fellow was thunderstruck. When he could talk he said that he had been spending the evening in a hurdy-gurdy house, learning to dance. If that was sinful, he said, he had rather be a sinner than buried in that hole." [34]

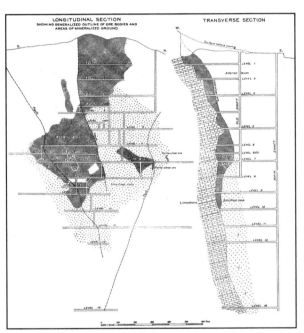

Figure 10   Horn Silver mine stopes
Courtesy USGS

♦ In 1886, timbers used to support a large chamber on the 1500-level at the New Almaden mine were compressed from 16" down to 6" by the weight of the back. In 1888 the ground collapsed and the timber and rich ore were lost.[35]

♦ On February 12, 1885, the Horn Silver Mine in Utah caved in. The massive collapse caved in the shaft down to the 700-level. Fortunately, the collapse occurred between shifts and nobody was hurt, though miners on the last cage out were caught at a point about 200 feet beneath the surface, where the collapsing shaft pinned their ascending cage. A rope dropped down from the collar rescued these miners, one by one. The cause of the accident was attributed to poor timbering in the stopes and to recent rain and snow weakening the ground. The stopes and most of the valuable ore still remaining above the 700-level were rendered inaccessible by the cave-in. See the dark shaded areas in figure 10. On April 5, 1885, yet another cave-in occurred, sealing off an important air passage and additional stopes.[36]

Reuse

It would be convenient to reuse some of the timber from square sets, especially when one considers the board feet used and the attendant cost. Reuse was dictated by the nature of the ground in which the sets were used. At the Comstock, the timber could not be reused. It was the only thing preventing collapse, and besides, the underground conditions rapidly rotted the wood, making it worthless in terms of reuse.

Sometimes square sets are used in wider veins to provide working platforms in overhand stopes. As the stope advances, the sets are disassembled and moved. This method was used at the New Idria mine in California, where the vein was over ten feet wide and dipped steeply.[37]

Open cut surface mining might expose square set timbering used in prior underground operations. If the mine were dry the timber could be salvaged. At Mount Morgan, Australia, square set timbers were salvaged and reused on lower levels and for retaining walls.[38] See figure 11.

Figure 11
Square Set timbering exposed by surface mining
Courtesy Mount Morgan Historical Museum, Inc.

Dewatering & Pumps

Few mines were fortunate enough to be dry. Many are *wet mines*, and are forced to deal with disposing of the natural groundwater that seeps – or pours, into the workings. Dewatering a mine can be very costly.

For surface mines or shallow pit-like excavations, a *water-elevator*, sometimes called a *Chinese Pump*, was used for small quantities of water. It consists of an endless belt or chain passing over two rollers, and was either hand-cranked or powered by an animal. Fastened to the belt are blocks of wood. The ascending side of the belt travels through an enclosed, rectangular wooden box, and the close-fitting blocks of wood trap and transport the water as they are pulled up and through the box.[39] Larger water-powered pumps were used at placer operations – see figure 12.

Mines situated where the local topography permits the driving of tunnels or adits could use these passageways to drain the workings. This was an expensive way of dealing with the problem of drainage, but it was very effective. Once the tunnel was driven, no machinery was required to drain the water that entered into it, though machinery might be required to pump it to the tunnel level. The tunnel also improved ventilation, and reduced ore handling if it doubled as a haulageway, so the cost was often more easily justified.

Drainage ditches were built into the floor of the tunnel to accommodate the flow of the water. The Sutro Tunnel drainage ditch was three feet square, and was lined with three-inch thick redwood planks to insulate the tunnel from the hot Comstock water.[40] In November of 1880, on the 3000 level of the New Yellow Jacket shaft, water of 170° was recorded.[41]

Figure 12   Pump used at Brown's Flat, Tuolumne Co.
ca 1866   Courtesy Library of Congress

Sometimes the water found practical uses. The Revenue Tunnel drained the Virginius mine through a box a foot deep and four feet wide, the track resting on top of it. The 60° water was used in the Revenue milling operations, which could even be run in the San Juan winters without worry of freezing water damaging the concentrating jigs or tables.[42]

Tunnel drainage also permitted old, flooded mines to be worked again. The Joker Tunnel, started in 1904 and completed in 1907, extended 4800 feet from Red Mountain Creek to the Genessee-Vanderbilt mine. It also had connections to the nearby Guston, Yankee Girl, and Robinson mines. When completed, water levels dropped from 400-900 feet in these mines, emptying through a two feet deep by four feet wide water drain in the tunnel's floor, and at a rate of 1200 gallons per minute.[43]

Mines with shafts could catch and divert water to tunnels for drainage. Cast iron *water rings* are sometimes installed at vertical intervals along the shaft to collect dripping water. *Splash boards* – small strips of wood set at an inclined angle, are also positioned to intercept and collect water dropping from or immediately adjacent to the shaft cribbing. The water is collected and transferred to a *cistern* – a holding tank, for pumping, or conducted to an adit or tunnel for draining.[44]

Figure 13
Hand Pump
Author

Perhaps the simplest method of dewatering underground mines was by using a small hand pump. Its capacity was sorely limited, however. See figure 13. Using a bucket hoisted by a windlass – like that used in a shallow well, was the next step up in capacity. It was sufficient for shallow shafts. The transition from man or animal-powered means to the use of machinery for dewatering a mine could be quite rapid. The Comstock got its start in 1859, and by 1860 the first steam hoisting and pumping machinery was installed at the Ophir. It consisted of a 15 HP (horsepower) engine.[45]

With increased hoisting power came increased dewatering capacities. Large *bailing tanks* were used in the deeper shafts. See figure 14. They were slowly lowered into the water that collected in the *sump* of the shaft. The small *clack valves* on the base opened, allowing the tank to fill. When the tank was hoisted, the weight of the water closed the valves. It was then emptied at the surface. The capacity of the tank was moderate, but the time spent hoisting it up and down the shaft reduced its overall effectiveness. In addition, the time spent hoisting tanks of water was time taken away from hoisting ore and miners. Costs went up and profits diminished, but the mine required dewatering to be worked. Steam and compressed air force pumps were also manufactured for mine dewatering. See figure 15.

The temperature and quality of the water also affected dewatering operations. In Lake City, Colorado, the tunnels at altitudes of 12,000 feet became blocked by permanent ice unless they were kept well drained.[46] The Polar Star mine located on Engineer Mountain north of Silverton, Colorado, when visited by Frederick Ransome, was rendered inaccessible due to the adit being blocked by ice.[47]

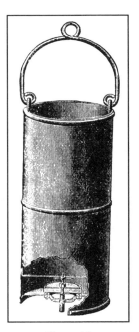

Figure 14
Bailing Tank
Source: Behr, 1896

The Yankee Girl's water carried a significant – and corrosive, amount of sulfuric acid and copper sulfate, derived from the exposure of the sulfide minerals to air and water. It quickly plated candlesticks and iron tools with copper. Continued exposure ultimately destroyed them. The pumps' inner linings had to be replaced monthly. Later, these pumps were replaced with bronze-lined versions, some costing upwards of $30,000. Iron pipes were replaced with wooden troughs.[48]

In 1910, the pump failed at the twelfth level of the Free Silver Shaft in Aspen, Colorado. Two divers from New York City were brought in to repair the pump. The divers were paid $100 a day from the moment they left New York. They repaired the pumps, and dewatering resumed. Two days later the pumps stopped, and the divers were brought back.

The pumps were again restarted. The mining company bought a diving suit, and the divers trained some of the miners in their use, so that they might deal with future pumping emergencies.[49]

Pennies From Water

The commercial value of dissolved copper was accidentally discovered in Butte in November of 1889 when the St. Lawrence mine had a fire. It subsequently flooded, and the mine water – containing 0.75% copper, was pumped through a Mr. Miller's yard. The copper salts precipitated onto scrap iron and tin cans in his yard. A year later, William Ledford leased the water draining from the St. Lawrence, precipitated the copper onto scrap iron in a 40-foot flume, and sold the precipitates to the Colorado and Parrot smelters. The industry grew, and by the early 20th century, 2,200,000 pounds of copper were produced annually from mine water.[50]

Figure 15   Double-acting Plunger Pump
Source: Behr, 1896

Pump Primer

Figure 16 illustrates three basic types of pumps: *force, suction,* and *double-action.* These are idealized pump mechanisms, and serve only to illustrate the general actions of the pumps.

The force, or *plunger,* pump (top) has the inlet beneath the cylinder, and the outlet on the lower right side of the cylinder. The inlet has an internally mounted clack valve, and the outlet an externally mounted clack valve. Vent holes are located on the top of the pump. To the right of the pump is an arrow, which indicates the direction that the piston is traveling. The piston of the force pump draws water into the cylinder on the upstroke, where the suction that is created opens the inlet valve and closes the outlet valve. On the *downstroke,* the water forces the inlet valve to close and pushes open the outlet valve, and is thereby forced from the pump.

The suction, also known as a *lift* or *sinking,* pump (center) has no valve on the outlet, seen on the upper right of the cylinder. Instead, it has valves on the top of, and passages through, the piston. The cylinder also has no vents. On the down-stroke, the inlet valve is shut and the valves on the piston are pushed open – the water is transferred from below to above the piston. On the *upstroke,* the suction created by the piston opens the inlet valve and draws in water, while the water resting above the piston keeps the piston valves shut, and is pumped out of the outlet.

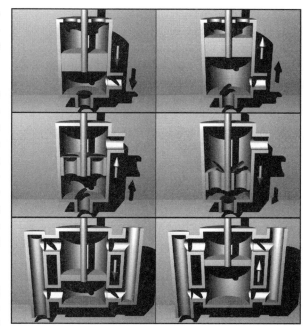

Figure 16   Force Pump (top)   Author
Suction Pump (center)
Double-action Pump (bottom)

The double-action pump (bottom) has an inlet manifold on the left side of the cylinder, and an outlet manifold on the right. Connections between the manifolds and the cylinder appear both above and below the piston, each with valves. On the down-stroke, the lower inlet valve is forced shut while the upper inlet valve is opened and water is drawn into the cylinder above the piston. At the same time, the lower outlet valve is forced open and the water is pumped out from below the piston, while the upper outlet valve is drawn shut from the suction. On the upstroke, the roles of the valves are all reversed. In this manner, water is pumped both on the *upstroke* and the *down-stroke* – hence double-action.

Cornish Pumps

Cornish Pumps, or perhaps more correctly, *Cornish Systems*, were the giants of 19th century pumping apparatus. The first use of such a system was by Captain Lean in 1801 at a mine in Cornwall.[51] The first Cornish System used in the West was at the Gold Hill Mine, Grass Valley, California in 1855.[52] Behr defines a *Cornish System* as:

> "… an arrangement whereby a rod simultaneously operates a series of pumps, all of which are plungers, except the lowest level, which is a lift pump. Each pump delivers the water to a tank, from which the next higher pump draws its supply."[53]

The above definition simply does not convey the size and scale of these devices. The Cornish System used at the New Almaden Buena Vista shaft had a flywheel 24 feet in diameter that weighed 25 tons. The pump rod was 1160 feet long, and made of 50-foot lengths of 10x10 inch timbers. See figure 17.

The influx of water in many mines, especially those operating far below the water table, could be enormous, as was the cost of installing and running the pumps required to dewater the workings. In 1882, the Contention Company of Tombstone, Arizona, installed a Cornish System using 12" pumps and capable of lifting 1,000,000 gallons per day, at a cost of about $150,000. The Grand Central installed a Cornish System using 14" pumps and 1,500,000 gallons per day capacity, at a cost of about $200,000. These two great pumping systems, combined with another series of direct-acting steam pumps of 500,000 gallons capacity already in place at the Grand Central, finally made headway against the severe water problem that was preventing further shaft sinking.[54]

Figure 17
New Almaden Mine's Buena Vista Shaft
Cornish System pumping engine ca 1885.
Note man sitting behind the flywheel for scale.

Courtesy Library of Congress and
Santa Clara County Parks & Recreation Department

Pumps

The pumps of Cornish Systems were located at intervals ranging from about 150 to 300 feet,[55] drawing water from *station tanks*, or cisterns. The cisterns could be made of concrete with a masonry dam where the pump station ground was solid. Where timbering of the pump station was required, wooden tanks were used instead. Care was taken to direct the flow of the water into the tank in a gentle manner, to reduce disturbing any sediment. Partitions were useful for that purpose. The pipe drawing water from the tank was located a few inches from the base of the tank – this would reduce drawing abrasive and fouling sediment into the pump. The output of each pump went to the next cistern stationed higher in the shaft, until the water either finally reached the surface, or reached a tunnel or adit from which it could be drained.

Large pumps – like that shown in figure 18, which has a 14"
piston and 10 foot stroke, were usually mounted on heavy
wooden beams spanning the shaft but resting on solid, excavated ground outside of the shaft timbering (*counterforts*).
The wood provided the strength to support the weight of the
pump, piping, and contained water, and also the flexibility to
absorb shocks caused by water-ram. Small pumps could have
their foundations attached directly to the shaft timbering,
spanning several sets. Very small pumps were provided with
lugs, and were mounted directly to the shaft timbers.[56]

The pump plunger rods were connected to the main, wooden
pump rod in a variety of ways. A typical method is illustrated
in figure 20, center.

Brass was the preferred metal for use in the pumps – it resists
acids better than iron does. Cast iron could still be used, and
protected to some extent by a thick coating of grease, if the
water temperature was not so high that the grease would
melt.

The *stuffing box* – mounted to the top of
the pump, provided a seal for the plunger.
It was stuffed with cotton or hemp saturated with tallow. For hot-water applications, the cotton was impregnated with
plumbago (graphite).[57]

Figure 18
14" pump used in Cornish Systems
Source: Hatch, 1895

Sinking-pump rods were clamped to the
main pump rod to facilitate relocating it
upon increasing the depth of the shaft. The sinking pumps located in the sump of the mine
shaft required frequent repairs due to the abrasive effects of sand drawn into the pump. See
figure 19.[58]

Pump Rods

The *pump rods* used in Cornish Systems were truly enormous. They were long sticks of timber fastened end to end by means of large iron strapping plates and bolts. A few examples
should make the variety of sizes of these pump rods – some immense, a little clearer:

Figure 19
Sinking Pumps

Source:
Behr, 1896

♦ The Ontario Mine in Park City, Utah used sections of wood for the pump rod that
   were 16" square and 70 feet long, transported on two rail cars with swivel frames.
   The sections were spliced together by four iron strapping plates, each 33' long, 10"
   wide, and 1" thick. The pump rod was 1060 feet long, and lifted 3,686,400 gallons
   per day from the 1000-level to the 600-level drain tunnel.[59]

♦ At the New Almaden mine, the rod used was 1160 feet long, the first 600 feet made
   of Oregon pine sections 50 feet long and 12" square, and the remainder 10" square.
   Each splice was made using four iron plates, each 20 feet long, 8" wide, and 1" thick,
   one for each side of the rod, bolted completely through the rod with 40 interlaced
   one-inch diameter bolts. See figure 20, right side of illustration.[60]

- The Santa Isabel shaft at the New Almaden mine used two pump rods, each 6 by 8 inches.[61]

- The North Star mine in Grass Valley, California had a pump rod weighing about 135,000 pounds – 35,000 pounds of which were the iron plates and bolts used to splice the timbers together.[62]

- The pump rod on the Combination shaft at Virginia City, Nevada was 3000 feet long and 15" square, the stroke at the surface being 7½ feet, with 6½ strokes per minute.[63]

Figure 20   Author
Left: Bumpers
Center: Pump plunger rod attachment
Right: Pump rod section splice

The maximum stroke of the pump rod is about ten feet. The elastic nature of the wood caused the rod to lengthen during the tension (upward) portion of the pumping cycle, and shorten – even buckle, during the compression (downward) portion of the cycle. Because of this elasticity, the pumps at the end of the rod would not get the action of a full stroke.[64]

The lateral motion of the pump rod was restricted to reduce the stresses and potential for buckling, thereby reducing the chance of breakage. *Guides* were installed at intervals of about 30 feet in the shaft, closely fitting the pump rod. Bolted to the guides, and clamped to the pump rod (using a frame of eye-bolts termed a *lamb's legs*), were strips of pine boards, designed to provide a close fit and take up the wear. Tallow was used as the lubricant.[65]

Wooden pump rods were fitted at the top with a brass box having long strapping plates. The box would be connected to the *beam* or *bob* by a *bob-pin*, and to the pump rod with bolts. Where the pump rod attached to the beam or bob, an arc was traced during operation. This resulted in a side-to-side deflection of the pump rod. An iron-plated guide called a *sweep-stay* was required near this attachment, and a considerable distance was required along the length of the pump rod to distribute this flexing motion.[66]

Bumpers were installed in the shaft – preferably above each pump, to catch the rod if it broke. Attached to the pump rod were blocks of wood positioned so that in case the rod broke, it could not fall more than the length of a stroke before being caught on a bumper. Alternating stacks of wood planks might be placed on top of the bumpers – the crushing of the stack would help to cushion the rod as it came to rest.

Bumpers were positioned so that if the pump rod broke, there would still be an extra margin of safe distance preventing the pump plungers from striking the lower parts of the pump. This not only protected the pump rod, but also the expensive pump hardware. See figure 20, left side of illustration.[67]

Ironwork of the pump rods was prone to corrosion. One method of preventing this was to first remove all rust using an acid, coating the iron with warm oil, and then painting it with red lead. Wood was planed and painted wherever possible. To prevent rotting, the ends of sections of pump rods were painted heavily prior to splicing.[68]

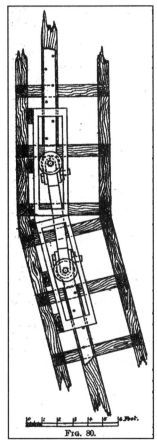

FIG. 80.

Figure 21
Pump rod angle change
Source: Behr, 1896

Directional Changes

Small changes in the angle of the pump rod could be accomplished by attaching rollers to the end of each rod, the rollers running inside a metal frame. The ends of the two rods were then coupled by a link that pivoted on link pins. See figure 21.[69]

Large changes in direction – including 90-degree turns, could be accomplished by using *angle bobs*. See figure 22. Clever arrangements of angle bobs would allow two pump rods to operate simultaneously and in opposite directions; thus a self-balancing system. See figure 22, "Fig. 77." in the center. This method was used at the Champion mine (Bodie, California, 400' depth), the Alta mine (Comstock, 2150'), and at the Santa Isabel shaft (New Almaden, 2000').[70]

Balance Bobs

The great length and weight of the pump rod plus the pressure of the column of water on the pumps would cause a great amount of tension in the pump rod on the up-stroke. On the down-stroke, the rod would be compressed from the resistance of the pump plungers. *Balance bobs* – counterbalances, reduced these stresses somewhat.[71]

Balance bobs were placed at vertical intervals as required to counterbalance the weight of that portion of the pump rod, typically spaced about 200–400 feet apart. The *bob stations* were fairly large in size. The ones used at the Buena Vista shaft of the New Almaden mine were 30 feet long, 12 feet wide, and 18 feet high. See figure 23.[72]

Balance bobs used small sections of rail to simplify fine-tuning of the counter-weight, which sometimes weighed upwards of 30 tons. Balance bobs were made of a wooden frame, and cast iron tension rods, *nosepiece* and *bishop-head*. The nosepiece was forked to fit around the pump rod, and connected by link to the pump rod's center to reduce bending strains on the pump rod.[73]

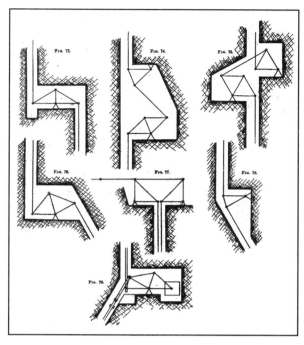

Figure 22 ▲
Figure 23 ▼

Directional Changes
Balance Bobs
Source: Behr, 1896

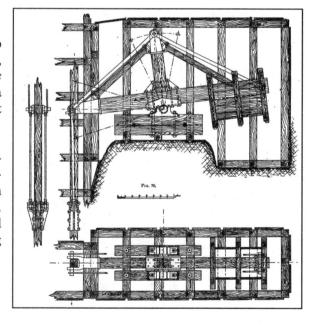

Operation

In practice, the pump rod weighed slightly more than the combined weight of the water and the balance bobs' counterweight; thus its descent by gravity would pump water up the pipes on the down- stroke, then the force of a steam engine would raise the pump rod on the upstroke. This cycle was typically repeated about 4–6 times per minute. Due to the weight of the pump rod, which must be balanced, and the engine pushing but not pulling, there was little value in using double-action pumps.[74]

The engines used on Cornish Systems might range from twenty to 144 inches in diameter of the cylinder, and nine to twelve feet stroke of the piston. See figures 24 and 25. Figure 25 shows a Davie engine, similar to that which was used on the Comstock at the Gould & Curry and Hale & Norcross mines.[75]

In 1874, the New Almaden Cora Blanca shaft hoist and dual pump rods were powered by a crusher plant steam engine located 500 feet away. A continuous cable run along tower-mounted rollers transferred the power to the pump and hoisting equipment.[76]

Figure 24   Cornish Beam Engine ca 1838   Author

Steam engines were not the only sources of power. The Sutro Tunnel made plans to use water drained from higher levels in the mine to power a water wheel stationed at the tunnel level. The water would drain through the tunnel after having been used in this capacity. The water wheel would power both a Cornish System located at a lower level in the shaft, and also hoists. The pumps thus powered at the lower levels would dewater the mine to the tunnel level, powered by the water drained from the higher levels – intelligent and cost effective use of what is normally a nuisance.[77]

Daily inspections and periodic maintenance were necessary to keep Cornish Systems operating smoothly. Special bell signals were used to instruct the engineer to start, stop, speed-up, slow-down, or position the pump rod in any desired spot for maintenance or repair.[78]

Jimmie Schneider, author of *Quicksilver, The Complete History of Santa Clara County's New Almaden Mine*, describes the motion of the pump:

"The action of this tremendous machine was a delight to watch, for though it was a ponderous engine it operated for years with the grace of a delicate watch and without any repairs."[79]

Figure 25   Davie Cornish Pumping Engine   Source: Behr, 1896

The monotonous, clock-like rhythm of the Cornish System was occasionally shattered by a catastrophic failure. In 1880, hot water was encountered at the 3080-level of the Comstock's New Yellow Jacket shaft, and caused such a rapid flood that it jerked the pump rod, which in turn caused the engine's cast iron flywheel to fly apart. Pumping did not resume for six months.[80]

Just give it a Whack!

There is a popular tale concerning the Cornish pump at the Ontario Mine in Park City, Utah. Nobody knew why the pump stopped or how to start it again. The mine owners were in a panic – the situation was desperate. A Scottish engineer was quickly summoned – he had experience with Cornish pumps.

He climbed on top of the flywheel, considered the situation carefully, and with one deft blow of his hammer on the great flywheel started the pump running again. The owners and managers were delighted, and asked the Scotsman his fee. He stated that it was $1000. The management was outraged, and demanded an itemized bill. To this the Scot replied,

"For hitting the wheel with a hammer, 50 cents; for knowing *where* to hit the wheel, $999.50!"[81]

The following facts and figures provide a sketch of the locations and sizes of some of the many Cornish System installations in the west:

♦ The last Cornish pump to be installed on the Comstock was at the Union shaft in 1879. It had one flywheel, 40 feet in diameter and weighing 110 tons. The engine weighed over 73 tons. 33 cords of wood were consumed daily. The pump rod was 16" square and 2500 feet long. Balance bobs were placed at 400-foot intervals. Scrap iron was used for counterbalancing. The capacity was 2,000,000 gallons per day.[82]

♦ In the Mother Lode-Bodie districts, at least 15 Cornish Systems were operating, with an average depth of over 600 feet, pumping an average of about 12,500 gallons per hour. Some reached 1300 feet in depth. Most were operated 24 hours per day, and powered either by water or steam engines, where the engines averaged about 60 HP.[83]

♦ The Champion mine, in the Rochester mining district of Montana, utilized a Cornish pump for draining a 90-foot deep inclined shaft.[84]

♦ For the mines reporting in the 1880 Census, 23 in Nevada – of which 18 were on the Comstock, used Cornish Systems, with averages of: pump rod length about 2000 feet, a capacity of 24,000 gallons per hour, and a 300 HP engine. Of 24 mines reporting for Arizona, California, Colorado, and Montana, the average system used had a pump rod of about 650 feet, a capacity of nearly 12,000 gallons per hour, and an engine of 60 HP, though four installations used water power of an unspecified HP, and six also powered hoists with the engines.[85]

Man Engines

The pump rods used in Cornish Systems sometimes pulled double-duty as a *man engine*. Man engines were first introduced in Germany in 1833. They were rapidly adopted in mines throughout Europe.[86] For a single pump rod, small steps and handles were attached at intervals along the rod, and in the pump rod compartment platforms – *sollars*,[87] were affixed to the shaft's cribbing, the vertical distances between both steps and sollars equaling the stroke length of the pump rod. The miner would stand on a sollar, and as the rod reached the end of its stroke, he would move to the step attached to the pump rod. He would ride to the end of the stroke, and move back onto the sollar. He would then wait for the pump rod to return to the other half of its cycle, and repeat this process until he reached his destination. Where two counterbalanced pump rods worked together in a single shaft – as seen in figure 22, "Fig. 77." in the center, the miner stepped back and forth between platforms attached to both pump rods. This is known as a *double-reciprocating man engine.*[88]

Climbing into or out of a 1970-foot deep shaft, like that of the Samson silver mine in Germany, took 90 minutes to climb down, and 150 minutes to climb out when using ladders. Painfully aware of the climb facing him at the end of his shift, the miner would conserve his strength and work at perhaps only ⅔ his potential underground. The man engine, when introduced in the Samson, reduced the time to 45 minutes for each trip, required no more effort than stepping from a platform, and added 150 minutes a day to the time spent mining.[89] See figure 26.[90]

The introduction of the man engine in one mine in Cornwall, where 250 miners ascended and descended a 900-foot shaft, reduced the expense of egress by 80%.[91] Data for the period 1873-1879, in Cornwall, demonstrated that man-engines were slightly safer to use than ladders. The death rate was 0.14 deaths per 1000 for miners using man-engines versus 0.21 for those that did not.[92] Miners in Bodie were reported to have "walked the pumprod" as much as 1400 feet.[93]

Figure 26

Samson mine Man Engine ca 1901
Courtesy Thomas Krassmann
Grubenarchäologische Gesellschaft

Regarding the experiences of a "well-known Comstock engineer," who had visited a few European mines, a reporter had the following to say about man engines:

"In most of the German mines, the men are compelled to walk up and down to the scene of their labors, either by an incline or by using long parallel stilts which move up and down alternately about 6 feet at a time. The mode of ascending and descending on these is to step from one to the other, as each ascends or descends, where a misstep would be certain death. His remark that in the Comstock the men went up and down to and from the lowest levels in two minutes, was received with polite incredulity. He refers to the mining tools employed in the same uncomplimentary terms, and asserts that an average day's work on the Comstock would seem incredible to the miners of continental Europe."[94]

Explosives

Explosives are used for shattering the rock that the miners drilled. Until Alfred Nobel patented nitroglycerine in 1865,[95] *black powder* was exclusively used. See figure 27, and also figure 1 on page 21 – the miner on the right is sitting on a black powder can. Black powder, a mixture of saltpeter, charcoal, and sulfur, has obscure origins dating back over 1000 years. It is used, to this day, for the pyrotechnic arts and for military purposes. It is manufactured in a granular form, and for mining applications was loaded into pasteboard tubes. Upon confined ignition, the powder burns[96] in a wink of the eye – *explodes*, and a large volume of hot gases are produced. It is the sudden formation and expansion of these gases, in the confined volume of the drill hole, which produces the shattering effect. As fast as it seems to happen, a black powder explosion is relatively slow as far as explosives are measured. Because of this, the shattering effect was rather *soft*, larger chunks of rock often being produced.

Figure 27   Black Powder Tins
Courtesy Scott Brady

Ascanio Sobrero invented *nitroglycerine*,[97] an oily liquid that is very sensitive to heat and shock, sometimes exploding[98] even "if one looked cross-eyed at it."[99] He refused to have anything to do with such a powerful and unstable compound. Nobel (and his family) felt otherwise, and patented its application in explosives. It proved to be far more powerful than black powder, and was also far more dangerous to handle.

Nobel and others found ways of taming nitroglycerine by mixing it with other active and inert substances, and loading the mixture into cartridges. Many variations of what is generically called *dynamite* were developed. Nitroglycerine is many times more powerful than black powder, and the resulting shattering of the rock is *hard* and very thorough. Extra care was necessary to prevent overloading the charges.

Miners rejected the new explosives at first. This was due partly to resisting anything new, and partly from the dangerous reputation that nitroglycerine-based explosives had. Dynamite had undesirable aging properties. The nitroglycerine would migrate through the paper tube and leak onto the surroundings. This made for potentially dangerous situations. See figure 28.

The explosives were made safer, and field tests demonstrated their superiority in many mining situations. The development of newer explosives occurred simultaneously with the introduction and improvement of machine drills, covered next. The new explosives slowly replaced the old.

Figure 28   Nitroglycerine Leaking from Dynamite

Courtesy Ron Hopkins
Fire, Arson, and Explosion Investigation Program
Eastern Kentucky University

From Nobel's patent of nitroglycerine on October 24, 1865 through the end of 1880, 111 original patents for explosives were granted in the US.[100] Highlights of the development and use of explosives follow.

1613   Drilling and blasting first used in Germany, possibly originating in Hungary.[101]

1670   Blasting introduced to England by German miners.[102]

1689   Pasteboard cartridges introduced.[103]

Explosives first used in mining in Cornwall.[104]

1830   Moses Shaw of New York patents the use of electricity for initiating an explosive charge.[105]

1831   William Bickford invents *safety fuse* in Cornwall.[106] Prior to Bickford's safety fuse, explosives were ignited by filling a tube, made from wood, rubber, paper, reeds, goose-quills, or straws, with a fine powder or powder-paste.[107] See figure 14, page 32, for a variety of fuses.

1845   Christian Friedrich Schönbein invents *nitrocotton* (nitrocellulose).[108]

1846   Ascanio Sobrero invents *nitroglycerine*.[109]

1865 Alfred Nobel patents the mercury fulminate *blasting cap*.[110] Blasting caps are small metal cylinders, generally copper, that contain a compound that is easily detonated by fire, which in turn provides the shock required to initiate detonation in explosives such as dynamite.

Nobel patents nitroglycerine.[111]

1866 Nitroglycerin used successfully at the Hoosac Tunnel, Massachusetts.[112]

Figure 29   Aetna 40% Strength Dynamite   Author

1867 C. J. Ohlsson and J. H. Norrbin of Sweden patent an explosive called *ammoniakrut*, which incorporated ammonium nitrate in its formulation.[113]

Giant Powder Company incorporated in California, August 13[114]

1868 Nobel patents (US) nitroglycerine-kieselguhr *dynamite* – "Dynamite #1."[115] See table 2. The kieselguhr was used to adsorb the nitroglycerine, a paste resulting. The strength of the explosive was diminished, however: the 25% kieselguhr was essentially inert, making no contribution to the explosive process. It did make the product far safer and readily packaged in stick form.

On the Comstock, black powder was the only explosive used until 1868, when *Giant Powder* (commercially manufactured dynamite) was tested at the Gould & Curry. Tamping wasn't used, and the results proved unsatisfactory. Favorable reports were made about the new explosive after a few months of additional experience and testing.[116] Table 1 illustrates the growth of the U.S. dynamite industry.[117]

Year	Pounds	Value
1880		$622,671
1890	30,626,738	$4,253,032
1900	85,846,456	$8,247,223

Table 1   US Dynamite Production

1869 Shaffner patents *Porifera Nitroleum*; ⅔ nitroglycerine and ⅓ ground sponge, cotton fiber, or sawdust impregnated with a sodium nitrate solution.[118]

1873 T. S. Beach patents *Rend-rock*.[119] See table 2.

Egbert Judson patents Dynamite #2.[120] See table 2.

Judson, who formed the Giant Powder Company (makers of dynamite by license from Nobel), also invented *Judson Powder* for gravel mining.[121] See table 2.

Figure 30   Apache 30% Strength Dynamite   Author

1874 J. W. Willard patents *Hercules Powder*.[122] See table 2.

1876 Nobel patents *gelatin dynamite*.[123]

Judson XX powder patented.[124]

1881 Silas R. Divine patents *Rackarock*.[125] See below.

1882 French engineer Paul Vieille discovers that Schönbein's trinitrocellulose could be colloided with alcohol and ether, and then extruded through a pasta machine. A practical *smokeless powder* could be manufactured.[126]

1885 R.S. Penniman creates the first *ammonia dynamite* to become popularly used.[127]

Figure 31   Hercules 40% Strength Dynamite   Author

There were many different formulations for black powder and dynamite. Each had advantages and disadvantages. "A" black powder is better suited for damp climates, whereas "B" powder costs less than "A" powder. Straight dynamite is not recommended where ventilation is poor. Straight gelatin is good for wet work and where ventilation is poor.[128]

Nitroglycerine-based explosives, especially the earlier versions, could cause racking *powder headaches,* even from handling the stuff before it was blasted.[129]

Table 2 summarizes the ingredients and formulations that make up these and a handful of other explosives used in the 19th century.[130]

Figure 32   Kimber dynamite packing machine, ca 1899   Author

Ingredient	Dynamite 1	Dynamite 2	Hercules 1	Hercules 2	Black A	Black B	Giant	Atlas Powder	Judson	Mica	Dualine	Tonite	Rend-rock	Rack-arock
Nitroglycerine	75	40	75.00	40.00			36	75	40	52	80		40	
Nitrocellulose											20	52.5		
Potassium Nitrate			2.10	31.00	75		48						40	
Sodium Nitrate		40				72		2	40					
Barium Nitrate												47.5		
Potassium Chlorate			1.05	3.34										77.7
Sulfur		6			10	12	8		6					
Sugar			1.00	15.66										
Rosin		6					8		6					
Charcoal					15	16								
Wood Fiber								21					13	
Wax													7	
Magnesium Carbonate			20.85	10.00					2					
Kieselguhr	25	8							8					
Mica										48				
Nitrobenzene														22.3

Table 2   Compositions of Explosives

Rackarock

On June 28, 1881, Silas R. Divine, acting on behalf of the Rend Rock Powder Corporation, was awarded patents # 243,432 and # 243,433.[131] These patents were for a novel explosive, later to be known as *Rackarock*. This two-component explosive – a solid and a liquid, were shipped to the consumer in separate packages. The solid was "a stable compound" and "by nature non-explosive." The liquid was a "well-known substance" and a "refuse of the hydrocarbon class."[132]

When ready to be used, the cartridges containing the powder are briefly saturated by the liquid – either by pouring the fluid over them, or by immersion in a basket. See figure 33. A mechanical mixture resulted.

The liquid was "not subject to freezing at ordinary temperatures" and the resulting explosive was "therefore not liable to freeze, as nitro-glycerine is, in the coldest weather." The liquid component was not miscible in water, lending itself to use in wet drill-holes.

A powerful cap and fuse, or electric exploder, were then inserted, and the explosive was ready for use. It was claimed that Rackarock was as powerful as No. 1 Dynamite. The fumes were also less harmful than dynamite.[133]

Figure 33   Preparing Rackarock
Source: Manufacturer and Builder

It is interesting to note the similarities between Rackarock and the modern mining explosive *ANFO*. ANFO – **Ammonium Nitrate/Fuel Oil**, is also composed of a solid oxidizer and liquid fuel, in this case about 94% ammonium nitrate and 6% fuel oil.

Machine Drills & Compressors

The introduction of machine rock drills, first powered by steam and later by compressed air, revolutionized hardrock mining. Drilling rates were many times greater than with hand drilling. Greater tonnages of ore were mined at an overall lower cost per ton, but at high installation expenses for the necessary hardware. There were still many advantages to hand drilling, however. No expensive machine drills and compressors were required. For the miner there was greater flexibility in placing holes in the face. This translates to the use of lighter charges per hole, less injury to mine timbers, less over-breakage of rock, and greater ease in setting of the timbers. Lighter charges and reduced timbering translated to lower costs for the mine owner – a very important consideration for the operators of the smaller mines.[134]

The early steam-powered drills were cumbersome affairs, prone to frequent breakdowns. The steam boilers were inconveniently located outside of the mine, and iron pipes were used to conduct the steam to the heading, the steam losing a lot of its power in transit. Flexible hoses were unreliable, leaking and bursting with annoying regularity. As the heading advanced, the system would need to be shut down and allowed to cool. The pipes and fittings were then relocated at significant expense. The miners suffered at the headings, where the steam exhausting from the drills did nothing to improve ventilation, and only made the workings intolerable. The development of air compressors suitable for the task obviated the problems inherent with steam. Compressed air could be transmitted almost any distance with little loss of power. Aside from a fine mist of lubricating oils, the air exhausting from the drills materially aided ventilation and helped to cool the headings.[135]

Acceptance of the new technology proceeded slowly but steadily. Many miners feared they would be out of a job, replaced by a machine. This was not true. It generally took at least two men just to set up and operate the early drills. The blacksmith was still kept as busy as ever. The drill bits used still required sharpening, and the machines required repairs – anything punching at rock a few hundred times per minute is bound to shake itself apart.

What the miners needed to fear were the clouds of dust produced by these noisy, buzzing machines.[136] The long-term effect of breathing rock dust leads to a debilitating disease known as silicosis. Silicosis, and other mining hazards, is covered in the appendix.

110 patents were granted to American inventors for drills and drill carriages between 1850 and 1875.[137] Highlights in the development and use of machine drills are outlined below.

1838 Brothers Isaac. M. and J. A. Singer experimented with a drop-drill (vertical only) on the Illinois and Michigan canal, and patented the machine in 1839. This drill is considered to be the first of its type to be successful. Singer later gained fame with another vertical reciprocating device. From 1852 to 1876, 80 patents were issued for drop-drill type devices.[138]

1849 J. J. Couch of Philadelphia obtained the first patent for a steam-powered percussion rock drill that did not rely on gravity. The design used a hollow piston through which the drill rod passed. The piston threw the drill rod forward like a lance. On rebounding from the rock it was caught by grippers on the piston, to be thrown forward again. Joseph Fowle assisted in building the drill. The drill was mounted on a frame on top of a boiler, which was mounted to a four-wheeled carriage. The whole assembly weighed thousands of pounds. See figure 34.[139]

Figure 34   Couch Machine Drill, 1849
Source: Drinker. 1893

Fowle files a caveat for a rock drill, where the steam acts directly upon the drill, and the drill rod is attached to the piston.[140] See figure 35.

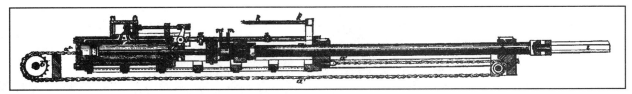

Figure 35   Fowle Machine Drill, 1849   Source: Drinker, 1893

1850   The first mechanical rock drill is used in the Mont Cenis Tunnel (Alps), France.[141]

Fowle's drill was operated by compressed air.[142]

1851   Fowle obtained a patent for an improved steam-powered rock drill that had the drill rod attached to the piston. The piston-drill rod assembly rotated by means of a ratchet and pawl mechanism. His idea of having the cutting tool as an extension of the piston persisted into the 20th century.[143]

Fowle comments on his invention:

> "My first idea of ever driving a rock-drill by direct action came about in this way: I was sitting in my office one day, after my business had failed, and happening to take up an old steam cylinder, I unconsciously put it in my mouth and blew the rod in and out, using it to drive in some tacks with which a few circulars were fastened to the wall. That was my first idea on the subject."[144]

Figure 36   Hoosac Tunnel
Source: Drinker, 1893

The Hoosac Tunnel, Massachusetts became the first U.S. tunnel to be bored using mechanical drills.[145] See figure 36.

1861   The first successful transmission of compressed air for drilling was at the Mont Cenis Tunnel.[146]

1863   Professor Rodolphe Leschot patented a *diamond drill* in Paris, France. *Borts* – black diamonds unsuitable for use in jewelry, are used, which cost about $6-$7 per carat in the 1870's.[147] Diamond drills use annular drill bits that produce a cylindrical core of rock inside the drill. See figure 37. The core is periodically withdrawn during drilling. These drills are very useful for exploratory work.

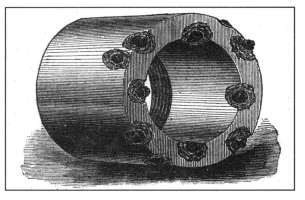

Figure 37   Annular Diamond Drill Bit
Source: Manufacturer and Builder

1865   Fowle sold his patent to Charles Burleigh, who improved the design.[148]

1866   Brooks, Gates, and Burleigh patented a drill that proved moderately successful at the Hoosac Tunnel. See figure 38. These drills consisted of 80 parts, weighed 240 pounds, produced 200 strokes per minute, and cost $400. 40 were used for about a four-month period. There were about 250 breakdowns a month on average. Of the 1084 total repairs, feed springs accounted for nearly half at 517.[149]

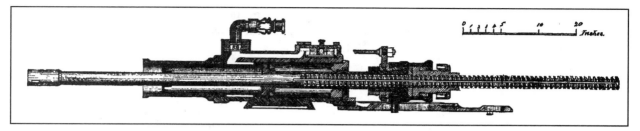

Figure 38   Brooks, Gates, and Burleigh Machine Drill ca 1866   Source: Drinker, 1893

The new patented Burleigh drill was first used in the Hoosac Tunnel. Although successful, 372 pounds made for a clumsy drill.[150] See figure 39. Note the exposed tappet and how it reciprocates the valve.

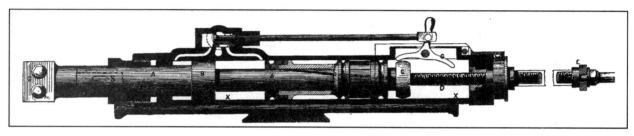

Figure 39   Burleigh Machine Drill, 1866   Source: Drinker, 1893

L. P. Jenks and G. A. Gardner patent a drill mounted on a column, where the column amounts to a threaded rod for raising and lowering the drill.[151]

The first air compressor used for powering rock drills in the U.S. was used at the Hoosac Tunnel. See figure 40. It was a four-cylinder arrangement powered by a 120 HP turbine-wheel. Operated at 70 RPM, it delivered 148 cubic feet of air per minute at 42 PSI. Thomas Doane was responsible for most of the design elements used in this compressor, and in the installation and subsequent modifications. This included a water-spray cooling system that reduced the compressed air temperature over 300°.[152]

Also used at the Hoosac Tunnel was a Burleigh compressor designed in 1866. See figure 41. This compressor has the distinction of being the first to gain general acceptance and use in the U.S.[153]

Thomas Doane developed a horizontal, two-cylinder compressor, and Burleigh developed a vertical, two-cylinder compressor, both of which became prototypes for future developments.[154]

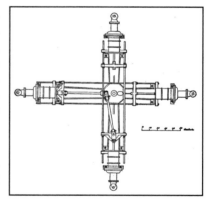

Figure 40
First compressor used for powering rock drills in the U.S.
Source: Drinker, 1893

Table 3 outlines a "Man-Machine Comparison." These figures are for work performed at the Hoosac Tunnel for a 105 square foot heading, per foot of advance, and using black powder.[155] Hand drilling required over three times as much labor as machine drilling to break the same amount of rock. On the other hand, the blacksmith was much happier with the machine drills, for he sharpened only one-sixth as many drills.

1868 Burleigh redesigned his drill, bought the Fowle patent on which his design infringed, and organized the Burleigh Rock Drill Company.[156]

1869 Burleigh drills were used in Silver Plume, Colorado in the Burleigh Tunnel.[157] This was the first use of a machine drill for driving a mine adit in the US.[158]

Severance & Holt patent a diamond drill. It was an improved version of Leschot's drill.[159]

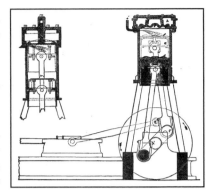

Figure 41 Burleigh compressor
Source: Drinker, 1893

1870 Rock drills are introduced into California. At this time, the Burleigh drill had not made it to California, but the Blatchley drill[160] and a carriage-mounted Severance & Holt diamond drill were in use. Steam power was tried, but the temperatures at the working face became unbearable. Compressed air, while effective, required costly compressors and was not used.

The Severance diamond drill, used at Telegraph Hill in San Francisco,[161] could run a tunnel at twice the rate of hand drilling and at only ⅔ the cost. Water was utilized to power the drill. This was accomplished by attaching a small *hurdy-gurdy wheel* – a water wheel, to the back of the drill's carriage. A two-drill rig could be powered by a 300-foot head of water delivered at a rate of 10-15 miner's inches (about 110-170 gallons per minute at 130 PSI). Where water was in short supply, a steam-powered water pump could be used to power the drills, the used water being returned to the pump.

	Hand	Machine
Man-days of labor	13.7	5.1
Drills dulled	280.9	48.8
Inches of holes	668	843
Number of holes	24.5	27.3
Pounds of powder	16.4	33.0
Feet of fuse	75.4	114.6
Pounds of candles	6.5	12.8
Cubic yards of rock removed	3.8	4.8

Table 3   Hoosac Tunnel Man-Machine Comparison

Sutro witnessed a demonstration of this setup and at once placed an order for the Sutro tunnel.[162]

1871 Simon Ingersoll patents a steam-powered rock drill with automatic feed and a supporting tripod. See figure 42. The tripod was the first convenient method of supporting the drill and permitted drilling at any angle. Tripods were widely used for 40 years.[163]

Ingersoll purchased the Fowle-Burleigh patents and merged with the Burleigh Rock Drill Company, forming the Ingersoll Rock Drill Company.[164]

The Ingersoll rock drills were considered at that time to be the best. All critical parts were enclosed, and the drill rod was rotated by a rifle-bar and advanced by a feed screw. Henry C. Sergeant, a partner in Sergeant & Cullingsworth Company,[165] introduced the "Eclipse" valve to the drill. As the piston moved back and forth, it uncovered passages that permitted compressed air to effect the change in direction of the piston. This greatly simplified the design and improved the drill immensely. This drill became known as the "Ingersoll Eclipse."[166]

Figure 42   Ingersoll Tripod Rock Drill
Source: Manufacturer and Builder

Drills And Mills

The Copper Falls Co, Michigan, used Burleigh rock drills powered by compressed air. About 40-45 feet could be drilled per shift. An improved compressor increased this figure to 55 feet. On an average 11-hour shift, an hour and a half was required to move the drill carriage, two hours to set up the drill, about four and a half hours were spent drilling, and a half hour was required to change drill steels a total of eleven times. The drilling was through troublesome copper deposits. Comparisons of machine and hand drilling revealed that the former cost $0.84 per ton and the latter $1.04. The machine drilling costs include the fuel for the compressor and the attending engineer's wages.[167]

1872   The exposed tappet on the Burleigh drill was enclosed within the drill to prevent breakage.[168]

Diamond drills were used for exploratory work in White Pine, Nevada.[169]

It was estimated by F. Shanly & Co., who had a contract on the Hoosac tunnel, that the Burleigh drills reduced costs by 33% and the time required to drill a given distance 50%, as compared to hand drilling.[170]

Albert C. and J. R. Rand start the Rand & Waring Drill and Compressor Company. They began manufacturing a tappet-valve drill that was an improvement on the Fowle-Burleigh design.[171]

Rock drills were used on the Comstock at the Yellow Jacket.[172]

Adolph Sutro purchased 12 diamond drills for $1000 each.[173]

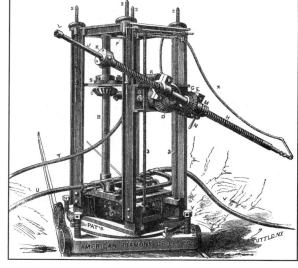

Figure 43   American Diamond Drill
Source: Manufacturer and Builder

The diamond drill found novel use in shaft sinking in Pennsylvania. This is referred to as the *long-hole* method. A series of vertical holes were drilled to a depth of 300 feet, at a rate of 34 feet per day. Convex drill bits with perforations were used instead of annular bits. Water was pumped through the drill rod to carry out the cuttings and to cool the bit. Afterwards the drills were removed and the holes filled with sand. The top four feet of sand was then removed using a sand pump, the bottom foot packed with clay, and the top three feet loaded and fired with Giant powder. This cycle was repeated every four feet, the shaft advancing at a rate of 25 feet per week. The sides and corners of the shaft were remarkably smooth.[174] See figure 44.

Figure 44   Long-hole shaft sinking
Source: Drinker, 1893

It is interesting to note the use of water in diamond drilling in 1872. This technique would not be applied to other forms of machine drills until much later.

1873   Professor De Volsom Wood patents a drill that uses a shock-less valve. See figure 45. It does not use an automatic feed; the inventor "maintains that there is nothing saved in its use, except in rare cases, and that the cost of keeping it in repair is a great objection to its practical use." A variety of sizes were manufactured, ranging in weight from 84 to 114 pounds.[175]

D. Minthorn patents dies for forming drill bits.[176]

A Burleigh and two Ingersoll drills, run on compressed air, were successfully installed in the New Almaden mine.[177]

1874 Burleigh compressed-air drills were used on the Sutro Tunnel for the first time.[178] J. B. Pitchford and Arthur De Wint Foote installed the air compressors that were used.[179]

The Consolidated Virginia begins using machine drills.[180]

A trial between Ingersoll, Rand, and Waring rock drills showed moderate variations between the different makes. Overall, the Rand drilled the fastest (1.8 inches per minute), followed by the Ingersoll (1.65) and the Waring (1.2). The Ingersoll required the least time for repairs.[181]

1875 Burleigh patented his drill that was modified in 1872.[182]

William Buckley – with great foresight, was issued a patent for a threaded, detachable drill bit, designed to use hard inserts. It is interesting to note that it wasn't until 1919 – 45 years later, that Arthur L. Hawkesworth, of Butte, Montana, patented the first detachable rock-drill bit that was extensively used. It wasn't until the early 1930's that tungsten-carbide inserts were first used in detachable drill bits in Germany – more than a half-century after Buckley's patent![183]

Figure 45   Wood Machine Drill
Source: Manufacturer and Builder

E. S. Winchester patents the use of rubber cushions placed inside the heads of the cylinder. When a drill penetrates a cavity in the rock, the piston may move to its extreme limit, striking the cylinder cover and damaging the unit. Drills are designed to have sufficient length of the cylinder to prevent this, or an elastic buffer to absorb the impact.[184]

1876 An Allison-Bannan No. 2 diamond drill rig – including a movable boiler of 16 HP and 1000 feet of 2" drill rods, cost $3872.40. It was capable of boring through hard conglomerate and shale at an average rate of nearly two feet per hour, costing $2.22 per foot, of this $1.15 was for labor and $0.67 for diamonds. Each bit used five 18-carat borts, and could drill about a ¼ mile before requiring replacement. The borts, when purchased in quantity, cost about $10 per carat weight.[185] See figure 46.

1877 Diamond drills could be purchased for about $750-$850.[186]

The results of drill trials appear in table 4. The 1877 trials were conducted in Sweden, all at 55 PSI, wet boring, and through hard syenite. Rates from the Sutro Tunnel are included for comparison.[187]

Figure 46
Allison-Bannan Diamond Drill
Source: Drinker, 1893

1879 The Rand & Waring Drill and Compressor Company changed to the Rand Drill Company, and the first Rand air compressor was introduced.[188]

1880 Hill devised and received a patent for a method of using compressed air that was ordinarily wasted. When the air being compressed reached a preset pressure, any additional air would escape through a valve, and would then be admitted to the steam line feeding the compressor's engine; thus displacing steam. This would have a governing effect on the engine, and economy would be gained by steam not being wasted in over-compressing the air.[189]

Sweden, 1877	Feet per Hour	
	Syenite	
Schram	16.5	
Rand	13.5	
Ingersoll	9.6	
Burleigh	5.7	
Sutro Tunnel, ca 1880	Andesite	Porphyry
Ingersoll	4.4	13.5
Burleigh	3.8	6.9

Table 4   Drill Trials 1877 and 1880

Table 5 lists the weights of five different Bryer Rock Drills, patented in 1878 and 1880. Table 6 lists the details for a number of Clayton duplex compressors. Note the installed weights. See figure 47.[190]

The 1880 Census reveals that of 65 reporting mines using 257 rock drills, 250 were percussion drills and seven were diamond drills. More than half were used on the Comstock. 30 Nevada mines used 195 of the drills. Six of the seven diamond drills reported were used in Nevada, mainly for exploring for hazardous flows of water in advance of mineral exploitation.[191]

No.	Hole Dia. (in.)	Drill Weight	Tripod	Column
1	3.5-4.0	400		
2	3.0-3.5	300		
3	2.5-3.0	175	135	200
4	2.0-2.5	105	110	150
5	1.5-2.0	65	85	150

Table 5   Bryer Drill Weights

1883 First mention of machine drills in use at the Homestake in South Dakota.[192]

Diamond drills used at the Hope mine in Philipsburg, Montana – possibly the first use in Montana.[193]

1884 The New Almaden mines were using nine Ingersoll drills.[194]

Sergeant patented a *hammer* drill, but it was unsuccessful because it did not clear the drill hole of cuttings. *Hammer drills* have the piston and drill rod separate, the former striking the latter in a hammering action. *Piston drills* have the piston and drill rod connected as one unit – a punching action results.[195]

Size	Cylinder Diameter		Length of Stroke	RPM	Cubic Feet per Minute	Weight	Number of Drills
	Steam	Air					
1	8	8	12	130	165	3000	2
2	9	9	13	125	180	5000	3
2.5	10	10	13	115	206	7000	4
3.5	12	12	13	115	300	10000	6
4	14	14	15	110	450	15000	8
5	16	16	15	95	625	17000	10
6	16	16	20	95	837	20000	14
7	18	18	24	85	1128	25000	20
8	20	22	24	75	1600	35000	
9	22	24	30	75	2600	45000	

Table 6   Clayton Duplex Compressor Specifications

1885 Sergeant leaves the Ingersoll Rock Drill Company and forms the Sergeant Drill Company. His latest drill operated a valve by a ring attached to the piston. This became known as the "Sergeant Auxiliary-Valve Drill," which he conceived while silver mining in Colorado.[196]

Ingersoll rock drills were used on 19 of 23 large tunnels.[197]

Lieutenant Derby, resident engineer at the Hell's Gate project, devised an interesting modification to the percussion rock drills being used. Rather than use a solid drill, he used a hollow one. A copper screw ring was attached at the end, and to this a crown bit with a serrated edge was attached. Water was pumped through the hollow drill steel, cooling the cutting bit and flushing out the workings. The former drills advanced 16 feet in an eight-hour shift; the modified drills advanced 25 feet. Repairs on the modifications were the only objections. The Rand Drill Company obtained a controlling interest in the patents.[198]

M. Traverdon successfully applies electricity to power a diamond drill. The borts were electroplated with copper and then soldered into the drill's bit.[199]

1887 Lucius J. Phelps of New York invents an electric rock drill.[200]

1888 Ingersoll and Sergeant merge to form the Ingersoll-Sergeant Rock Drill Company.[201]

1890 A diamond drill, powered by an internal combustion engine, was introduced at the New Almaden mine. The cost of drilling was $5 per foot, the same to drive drifts, so diamond drilling was abandoned.[202]

Figure 47   Clayton Duplex Compressor
Source: Drinker, 1893

The Mollie Gibson mine in Aspen used diamond drills that drilled a ⅞" core at a rate of 60 feet per day.[203]

C. H. Shaw of Denver designed a rock drill for overhead drilling. It was called a *stoper*. The drill was supported and positioned by a *pneumatic airleg*, which was also used to feed the drill into the rock. It used a hammer mechanism – the drill rod was separate from and hit by the reciprocating piston. A distinct advantage of the stoper was that drill cuttings easily fell from the vertical drill hole. Shaw failed to patent his design. Shaw should be given credit for what turned out to be two features still found in modern drills: airleg feed and the hammering action. This stoper was the first, successful hammer drill. It failed to gain acceptance, however, because the drill was used dry and consequently created a huge amount of dust; the miners nicknamed it the *"widow-maker."*[204]

D. S. Waugh of Denver improved upon and patented several features of Shaw's stoper.[205]

1891 The Edison General Electric Company introduced an electric percussion drill. Testing at the Last Chance mine in Wardner, Idaho was positive. Two air-powered drills, operating for 24 hours, required five cords of wood for the boilers, whereas two electric drills required only 1.5 cords.[206]

1892 The Edison General Electric Company introduced an electric diamond drill.[207]

1894 Addison C. Rand announced a surface-cooled, compound (multiple stage) compressor.[208]

J. George Leyner began experimenting with drills that used hollow drill steels, made by boring the hole like a rifle barrel, and welding the drill bit to the end. The Newhouse Tunnel in Idaho Springs, Colorado was used between about 1894-1898 to test many of his experimental designs.[209]

Figure 48   Miners on the 850-level
Courtesy Mount Morgan Historical Museum, Inc.

Drills And Mills

1895 First mention of diamond drills at the Homestake, South Dakota.[210]

1897 Leyner obtains patents for hollow drill steels. Compressed air is blown through the drill to flush out the drill cuttings. Leyner is credited with being the first to make a practical hammer drill that could drill at any angle. He sold 75 drills; the miners refused to use them due to the amount of rock dust blown into the workings. Leyner took them back, and almost went bankrupt redesigning them.[211]

1898 Jackson patents a hand-powered drill in May. See figure 49.

1899 The Silver Lake mine's "progressive management" began using Siemens and Halske electric drills.[212]

1900 Leyner introduces the *wet pneumatic drill*.[213] This *major* innovation passed both air and water through the drill steel. Other improvements were added, including automatic lubrication, reduced weight, and the ability to deliver upwards of 1800 blows a minute instead of 300-400.

Figure 49   Jackson Hand-powered Drill   Author

The dust problem was virtually resolved, the water helped cool the drill bit and prolong its life, and the mud that it created acted as a slurry abrasive that enhanced the drilling.[214] The reduced weight made possible a drill that one man could handle. The modified drills were clearly superior to other types of drills. They were referred to as a "water-Leyner" and sometimes as a "liner." Leyner obtained a patent for this, which was described as "the greatest single feature ever contributed to the advancement of rock-drill design."[215]

1904 The Daly-West in Park City, Utah installs air-powered rock drills.[216]

The Joker Tunnel averaged a little less than two feet a day when it was first started. After the introduction of machine drills, the progress averaged about ten feet per day.[217]

1905 Ingersoll-Sergeant merged with Rand Drill to form Ingersoll-Rand.[218]

The Iler Rock Drill Company incorporates June 5.[219]

C. H. Shaw Pneumatic Tool Company's small Hammer Drill costs $80 each.[220]

Leyner obtained a patent for a tapered, press-on type drill bit.[221]

At the Old Hundred Mine in Silverton, Colorado, miners using state-of-the-art pneumatic air drills could advance four feet per shift in relatively soft andesite and latite. Eight drill holes were required. 14 holes were required for the "regular vein mate-

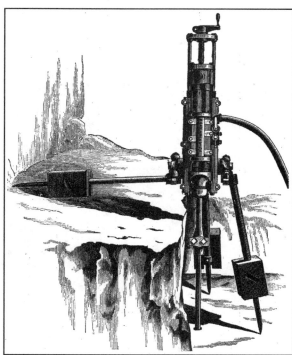

Figure 50   Rand Machine Drill
Source: Manufacturer and Builder

rial", and up to 17 were required for hard, white quartz. Up to 3.5 shifts were required for the harder ground – 2 for drilling and 1.5 for mucking. The management then decided to use the old hand-steel mining method for stoping instead of using machine drills.[222]

250 machine drills in use at the Homestake, South Dakota. [223]

1906   Iler introduces a 30-pound pneumatic rock drill, capable of drilling two four-foot holes into granite in 20 ½ minutes.[224]

1911   The Iler Rock Drill Company becomes the Denver Rock Drill Company on May 8.[225]

1912   The Ingersoll-Rand Company bought Leyner's patents.[226]

Machine drills are used for exploration and dead work, but single-jacking was still used for breaking ore in most of the Park City, Utah mines. [227]

1914   When Leyner's patents expired, every drill manufacturer quickly adopted his design.[228]

1927   The Denver Rock Drill Company merged with the Gardner Compressor Company, forming the Gardner-Denver Company.[229]

Figure 51   Diamond drilling in the Cable mine near Anaconda, Montana, ca 1906
Courtesy World Museum of Mining, Butte, Montana

Drills And Mills

Endnotes

[1] In many mines, the primary goal seems to have been keeping the workings open for exploitation. Safety for the miners appears secondary. Crampton experienced this firsthand, and was even warned about the mine he went to work in: "Down there men are cheaper than timber." CRAMPTON1956 page 81.

[2] Modern mines frequently make use of inexpensive but very effective chain-link fencing, or perforated steel *band-aids*, both held up securely by rock bolts.

[3] LINDGREN1906 page 135

[4] A very effective method of mining, *block-caving*, utilizes this effect to great advantage. A very interesting account of this method – and a fascinating history about a remarkable mine and the men and corporations that developed it, may be found in Stephen M. Voynick's *Climax, The History of Colorado's Climax Molybdenum Mine* 1996, Mountain Press Publishing Company, Missoula MT.

[5] FETCHENHIER1999 page 58

[6] BOUTWELL1912 page 25

[7] BOYLE2001. Used in Australia, as the timber required was plentiful and very cheap.

[8] TFIELDER1970 page 143

[9] DEQUILLE1959 page 90

[10] For this style of framing, and assuming 12-inch square timbers with a three-inch tenon, the cap has 54 square inches of support per post whereas the girt has but 18 square inches. PEELE1966 pages 10-215-218 illustrates 26 subtle variations on square set timbering, particularly at the joint.

[11] In 1912, the Tonopah Belmont Development Company, in an attempt to reduce costs, introduced *triangle sets* instead of square sets at the Tonopah-Belmont mine (Tonopah, NV). Its use was eventually discontinued. This was called the *Moore System*, and was a modification of the square set: the plane of the caps used triangular frames rather than rectangular. The plane of the girts continued to use rectangular sets. PEELE1966 page 10-231, CARPENTER1953 page 81.

[12] FIELDER1970 pages 118, 143

[13] FIELDER1970 pages 119, 207

[14] SCHNEIDER1992 page 48

[15] DEQUILLE1959 page 375

[16] SMITHG1998 pages 137,140. The computer graphic illustration is patterned off of the plan-view stope map on page 140. The numbers of square sets mentioned in the text are estimates, and are based on the typical set size used on the Comstock.

[17] SMITHG1998 page 209

[18] Approximately 4.46 million cubic yards, if one assumes that a ton of quartz is a cube 2.3 feet on a side, and that the 9.9 million tons credited to the Comstock through 1900 was all mined, which it was not. The tailings milled – that diminish this figure, may be assumed to represent the deadwork performed underground, where waste was used to fill worked out stopes. This works out to perhaps 800,000 sets in volume, assuming a set was a 6x5x5 cube.

[19] Data for this chart from COUCH1943 pages 133-134. The small tonnage for the Flowery district was subtracted from that of the Storey County figures where provided. For the years 1873, 1877-78, and 1882 where the gross yield – but not the tonnage, was known, the tonnage was estimated using the tonnage and gross yields from the other years.

[20] DEQUILLE1959 page 174

[21] SMITHG1998 page 247

[22] SMITHG1998 page 249

[23] Some of the low-grade ore fill used in the stopes of the Comstock in the "old days" was eventually mined and milled in the 20th century. SMITHG1998 pages 291,293.

[24] DEQUILLE1959 pages 232,234-235, PEELE1966 page 10-198

[25] BANCROFT1890 page 113, DEQUILLE1959 page 234, SMITHG1998 page 249

[26] PEELE1966 pages 10-224,10-225

[27] PEELE1966 page 10-225

[28] BANCROFT1890 pages 139-140

[29] SMITH1998 pages 122-123, USDL1998

[30] RAYMOND1873 page 144

[31] SMITHG1998 page 193

[32] HENDERSON1926 pages 12, 14

[33] TWAIN1980 pages 285,286

[34] SMITHG1998 pages 89-90

[35] SCHNEIDER1992 page 95

[36] UTAH2003, BUTLER1913 page 164. BAILEY2002 page 138 gives February 11 for the first caving.

[37] PEELE1966 page 10-198

[38] BOYLE2001

[39] BEHR1896 page 177

[40] STEWART1962 page 148

[41] SMITHG1998 page 245

[42] GREGORYD1996 pages 115, 142

[43] SLOAN1975 pages 157,203-204, 222, SMITHP1994 page 194. Sometimes spelled Genesee.

[44] PEELE1966 page 7-13

[45] DEQUILLE1959 page 89

[46] MORSE2000 page 13

[47] RANSOME1901 pages 187-188

[48] RANSOME1901 page 220, SMITHP1994 pages 147,178

[49] ROHRBOUGH1986 page 229, WOLLE1977 page 185

[50] MONTANADEQ.183. Butte sees the Berkeley Pit as both a tourist attraction and as a serious environmental problem. About 1 *billion* tons of copper ore were removed from the pit between 1955-1982. The pit contains about 30 billion gallons of acidic water with a pH of about 2.5. The hypolimnion – the deep water that starts about 40 feet below the surface, averages about 190 mg/L copper. This is roughly equivalent to 47 million pounds of dissolved copper… a potential resource waiting to be recovered.

[51] BEHR1896 page 43

[52] MCQUISTON1986 page19

[53] BEHR1896 page 43

[54] SHILLINGBERG1999 page 338

[55] PHILLIPS1873 page 378

[56] BEHR1896 pages 76,77

[57] BEHR1896 pages 72,73

[58] BEHR1896 pages 45,60

[59] BEHR1896 page 47, BOUTWELL1912 page 25. The weights of some of the pumping system components were staggering: pump body and straps, 40 tons; main beam, 72 tons; cylinders, 45 tons; pillow-block bearing, 35 tons; flywheel, 70 tons. THOMPSON1968 pages 38-39. The great Ontario Cornish pump, installed in 1882, was finally dismantled in September 1902. THOMPSON1968 page 176

[60] EGENHOFF1967b page 95. Behr states that the so-called Oregon Pine is Douglas Fir. BEHR1896 page 46.

[61] EGENHOFF1967b page 97

[62] EGENHOFF1967a page 67

[63] BEHR1896 page 45

[64] BEHR1896 pages 44,45,59

[65] BEHR1896 pages 54,55, SMITHG1998 page 281

[66] BEHR1896 pages 52,56,57

[67] BEHR1896 pages 53,54

[68] BEHR1896 page 51

[69] EGENHOFF1967a pages 66, 68

[70] EGENHOFF1967a pages 61,68, EGENHOFF1967b pages 91, 92, 97

[71] BEHR1896 page 59

[72] EGENHOFF1967b page 95, SMITHG1998 page 279

[73] BEHR1896 page 57

[74] EGENHOFF1967a pages 66-68, PHILLIPS1873 page 378, BEHR1896 page 44

[75] PHILLIPS1873 page 377

[76] EGENHOFF1967b pages 91, 92, 97, SCHNEIDER1992 page 59

[77] EGENHOFF1967a page 62

[78] PHILLIPS1873 page 380

[79] SCHNEIDER1992 pages 90-91

[80] SMITHG1998 page 245

[81] RINGHOLZ1972 page 20. THOMPSON1968 pages 39-40 gives $100, $99.50 and 50 cents for the *whack-the-flywheel* yarn.

[82] SMITHG1998 pages 278-280

[83] EGENHOFF1967a page 61

[84] MONTANADEQ.122

[85] EMMONS1885 pages 147-151

[86] EGENHOFF1967a page 68

[87] MCCOMBE2003

[88] EGENHOFF1967a pages 68-69

[89] ASME.H118

[90] Samson man engine image courtesy of Thomas Krassmann of Grubenarchäologische Gesellschaft - http://untertage.com/fahr/tkfahre.htm. This man engine used wire rope rather than wooden pump rods. It is still operation today.

[91] CORNWALL1968 page 161

[92] MCCOMBE2003

[93] EGENHOFF1967a page 69

[94] MAB.1880-10

[95] DRINKER1893 page 99

[96] Deflagrates: The combustion is extremely rapid; produces a flame; the gas pressure is relatively uniform throughout the unburned, combusting, and combusted regions.

[97] BRITANNICA1958, EKU2001

[98] Detonates: The chemical reactions take place at an extremely high velocity, high enough for a detonation wave to form. The unreacted zone ahead of the wave is at

ambient conditions; the reaction zone is at extremely high pressures and temperatures, with more-or-less incomplete combustion-like chemical reactions taking place; the reacted zone is at a lower pressure and temperature, where secondary combustion-like reactions take place. The pressure distribution is wavelike, with a very pronounced peak, and proceeds at velocities of several thousand meters per second.

[99] YOUNGO1972 page 212

[100] DRINKER1893 pages 99-107

[101] DRINKER1893 pages 50-51. Or possibly 1627.

[102] DRINKER1893 page 51

[103] DRINKER1893 page 51

[104] GREGORYC1980 pages 235

[105] DRINKER1893 page 40

[106] BRITANNICA1958, EKU2001, GREGORYC1980 page 235

[107] DRINKER1893 page 109

[108] BRITANNICA1958, EKU2001. Nitrocellulose found wide and varied applications in explosives, smokeless powder being one of great importance. It found application in other industries: celluloid films, billiard balls, lacquer, and other items were manufactured from this polymer.

[109] BRITANNICA1958, EKU2001

[110] BRITANNICA1958, EKU2001

[111] DRINKER1893 page 99. The author has seen 1866 and 1867 referenced as well.

[112] DRINKER1893 page 55

[113] DRINKER1893 page 55

[114] HAYNES1954 page 366

[115] DRINKER1893 page 55. Kieselguhr, or diatomite, is composed of about 90% silica. EUREKA2001

[116] LORD1883 page 366, SMITHG1998 pages 245,246

[117] HAYNES1954 p 367

[118] HAYNES1954 page 367. Patent # 93,753

[119] DRINKER1893 page 101, HAYNES1954 page 367. Patent # 138,841.

[120] DRINKER1893 pages 55, 71

[121] BAILEY2002 page 31

[122] DRINKER1893 page 103

[123] DRINKER1893 page 103

[124] ACKERLY1997

[125] DRINKER1893 pages 61-62,107. DAVIS1984 page 354.

[126] HAYNES1954 page 368

[127] DRINKER1893 page 103

[128] PEELE1966 pages 4- 5-7

[129] Presumably from unreacted nitroglycerine atomized with the other fumes. According to the Merck Index, nitroglycerine "produces [a] headache on tasting." It also states "on explosion harmless gasses are produced." Perhaps the authors failed to interview any miners. "Toxic effects may occur by ingestion, inhalation of dust or absorption through intact skin." This may account for powder headaches from handling. Therapeutically, nitroglycerine is an antianginal and vasodilator. VOYNICK1984 page 33 mentions these effects as being responsible for the headaches.

[130] BRITANNICA1958, PEELE1966 pages 4-07,4-08. Judson Powder, Patent # 139,468: HAYNES1954 page 367. Rack-a-rock, Dualine, Giant Powder, Mica Powder, Tonite, Atlas Powder: MAB1894-3. Giant Powder used either potassium or sodium nitrate, and either rosin or charcoal. DAVIS1984 page 354 gives 80/20 for Rackarock.

[131] DRINKER1893 pages 61-62,107

[132] DRINKER1893, page 107, lists the ingredients as a "Solid ingredient, such as chlorate of potash [potassium chlorate]" in the proportions "3 – 4-1/6 parts solid ingredient to 1 part of liquid ingredient," where the liquid was "nitro-benzole" [nitrobenzene].

[133] MAB.1887-12, MAB.1888-2

[134] PEELE1966 7-6

[135] YOUNGO1972 pages 204-205. The air was heated by compression, which caused many engineering and design problems for the developers of compressors. The hot, compressed air quickly cooled to near ambient temperatures in transit to the headings. As the air expanded in the drill – performing work, it cooled. Robert Lenon, technical writer for Young's *Western Mining*, mentions in a footnote on page 205 that "many a miner was killed by the partial combustion of oil of unsuitable quality; now and then the high compression of oil fumes would make an explosive mixture and blow up the compressor itself."

[136] If you've never heard a drill running underground, you owe it to yourself to do so. They are *loud*.

[137] SANDSTROM1963 page 291

[138] DRINKER1893 page 189

[139] SANDSTROM1963 pages 288, 289, MCCORMACK1950 page 328

[140] DRINKER1893 page 203

[141] GREGORYC1980 page 236

[142] DRINKER1893 page 207. Possibly 1851.

[143] DRINKER1893 pages 204-207, MCCORMACK1950 page 328, SANDSTROM1963 pages 288,289

[144] DRINKER1893 pages 204-207

[145] BRITANNICA1958 states 1851-1875. MCCORMACK1950 page 329 states 1855 was the start.

[146] MCCORMACK1950 page 329

[147] DRINKER1893 page 272, MAB.1871-11

[148] SANDSTROM1963 pages 289-291

[149] DRINKER1893 pages 55,202-203

[150] DRINKER1893 pages 208,209

[151] DRINKER1893 page 261

[152] DRINKER1893 pages 145-146. Possibly 1867.

[153] MCCORMACK1950 page 329

[154] SANDSTROM1963 page 302

[155] DRINKER1893 page 323. Figures rounded.

[156] MCCORMACK1950 page 329

[157] SMITHG1998 page 246. VOYNICK1984 page 34 states Silver Plume, Colorado, June 1870.

[158] HENDERSON1926 page 10

[159] DRINKER1893 page 272

[160] Possibly patented 1870. DRINKER1893 page 263. A percussion drill producing 300-600 blows per minute, with automatic feed. 22" long, 76 pounds, and required ½-1 horsepower to operate.

[161] SMITHG1998 page 246

[162] RAYMOND1873 pages 41-44

[163] INGERSOLL2001, MCCORMACK1950 page 329

[164] SANDSTROM1963 page 291

[165] MCCORMACK1950 page 330

[166] SANDSTROM1963 page 292

[167] RAYMOND1873 pages 489-490

[168] DRINKER1893 page 208,209

[169] JACKSONW1963 page 184

[170] RAYMOND1873 page 488

[171] INGERSOLL2001, MCCORMACK1950 page 330

[172] SMITHG1998 page 47, STEWART1962 page 121

[173] STEWART1962 page 111

[174] DRINKER1893 pages 222, 224, RAYMOND1873 pages 42-43

[175] DRINKER1893 page 264, MAB.1874-7

[176] DRINKER1893 page 265

[177] SCHNEIDER1992 page 57

[178] STEWART1962 page 121. April 25.

[179] MCKINNEY1995 page 31

[180] SMITHG1998 page 153

[181] MAB.1874-6

[182] DRINKER1893 page 266

[183] MCCORMACK1950 page 336

[184] DRINKER1893 pages 265,215

[185] DRINKER1893 pages 228-231

[186] DRINKER1893 page 228

[187] DRINKER1893 pages 254, 348 ca 1880 Sutro Tunnel.

[188] INGERSOLL2001

[189] DRINKER1893 page 160

[190] DRINKER1893 page 183 (compressor), 235,270,271,273 (drills)

[191] EMMONS1885 page 151

[192] FIELDER1970 pages 115-116

[193] NEU1996 page 12

[194] LAPOINT1999 page 535

[195] MCCORMACK1950 page 331

[196] INGERSOLL2001, MCCORMACK1950 page 330

[197] MAB.1885-5a

[198] MAB.1885-10

[199] MAB.1885-5b

[200] MAB1887-8

[201] INGERSOLL2001. MCCORMACK1950 page 330 lists the year as 1886.

[202] SCHNEIDER1992 page 101

[203] ROHRBOUGH1986 page 184

[204] SANDSTROM1963 pages 293,294, MCCORMACK1950 page 331. Possibly before 1890.

[205] MCCORMACK1950 page 331. SANDSTROM1963 page 294 states that Waugh obtains patents for the stoper in 1900 and begins manufacturing them.

[206] MAB1891-8. Lists the location as *Wardie* Idaho.

[207] MAB1892-9

[208] SANDSTROM1963 page 303

[209] MCCORMACK1950 page 332, HENDERSON1926 page 12

[210] FIELDER1970 page 158. On page 232, Fiedler writes "Another forward step was the beginning of diamond drilling in that year of 1916…" It is difficult to imagine that diamond drills were on site over 20 years before they were used.

[211] SANDSTROM1963 page 294, MCCORMACK1950 page 331,332, GREGORYC1980 page 236 states 1900.

[212] RANSOME1901 pages 40, 156. HENDERSON1926 pages 13, 214 gives 1900, and that they are the first use of such drills in Colorado.

[213] GREGORYC1980 page 236

[214] VOYNICK1984 page 79

[215] MCCORMACK1950 page 332 (quote)

[216] THOMPSON1968 page 123

[217] SLOAN1975 page 203

[218] INGERSOLL2001

[219] LEWIS2003, from a letter sent to Mr. Lewis in 1977 from the Gardner-Denver Company.

[220] LEWIS2003, copy of a letter sent from Shaw to Mr. L. G. Carlton, President of the Findlay Consolidated Mining Company in Cripple Creek, Colorado..

[221] MCCORMACK1950 page 336

[222] FETCHENHIER1999 pages 45,48

[223] FIELDER1970 page 181

[224] LEWIS2003, from a September 15, 1906 ad in the *Mining and Scientific Press*.

[225] LEWIS2003, from a letter sent to Mr. Lewis in 1977 from the Gardner-Denver Company.

[226] MCCORMACK1950 page 323

[227] BOUTWELL1912 page 23

[228] MCCORMACK1950 page 323

[229] LEWIS2003, from a letter sent to Mr. Lewis in 1977 from the Gardner-Denver Company.

TRANSPORTATION POWER AND FUEL ASSAYS

Figure 1   Union Pacific No. 119, Promontory, Utah 1996   Author

The miners have drilled and blasted the rock, and the muckers have loaded it into the cars. The trammers (and mules), station tenders, and topmen have brought tons of muck to the surface in cars. The ore was then trammed from the mine portal to nearby *ore bins*.[1] These bins act as surface reservoirs between mine supply and mill demand.

If the mine was large enough to justify constructing an on-site *mill* – an ore concentration or reduction works, then the bins were part of the mill structure. Otherwise ore bins were erected near the mine entrance for transportation of the ore as required. Tracks generally led from the mine's surface works to the ore bins. See figure 2. The size of the bins varied greatly depending on the tonnage produced by the mine. Figure 3 shows a small ore chute in Eureka, Nevada. Figure 4 shows the huge ore house and bins used by the Commodore mine at Creede, Colorado.[2]

Transportation systems were required to move ore to the mills and samplers, the products of the mills to reduction and refining works, and centers of commerce, to bring needed supplies, timber, and fuel to the mines and mills, and ultimately to move the employees to and from work. A variety of methods, many of which were very novel and innovative, helped integrate the metals industries and transportation.

Transportation

Ships, trains, stagecoaches, wagons, animals, and walking were about the only forms of transportation up until the 20th century.

Ships were a vital link between the East and the West, and between the States and the smelters in Swansea, Wales. Ships were also used on watercourses throughout the West. Navigation was occasionally impeded due to the weather. For example, during the frosty month of January 1889, mines in the vicinity of Burke, Idaho were compelled to halt operations due to ice in Coeur d'Alene Lake impeding barge navigation.[3]

Railroads became a crucial mode of transportation, interconnecting major cities and mining, agricultural, ranching and distribution centers throughout the West. The development of the railroad in the West lagged behind the East, however. Its arrival – greatly welcomed, generally meant prosperity or renewed activity in the nearby areas.

The most heavily used form of transportation was the beast of burden. Horses, mules, donkeys, and even camels were used for most transportation needs, both local and cross-country, throughout the expanding frontier West.

Figure 2   Tramming ore to an ore bin, 1903
Courtesy USGS

Figure 3   Ore chute, Eureka, Nevada 1871
Courtesy NARA

Figure 4   Commodore ore bins   Author
Creede, Colorado 1999

Ultimately, miners and millmen walked at least partway to work, sometimes in extreme desert heat, other times waist-deep in snow. Miners employed by the Moose Mining Company certainly had their work cut out, before they even got to work. The Moose Mine, located at 13,700 feet near the summit of Mount Bross in the Mosquito Range of Colorado, was nearly a half-mile higher in elevation than the company-owned boarding house in Quartzville. Every day the miners would hike the two miles to the mine, and by the time they arrived after 10 A.M., they were exhausted from the effort. The strenuous work of mining "in the clouds" then ensued at the dizzying altitude. Nearby was the Present Help mine, located at 14,157 feet, the highest producing mine in Colorado.[4]

Drills And Mills

Four-footed Friends: Mules, Burros, and Horses

Mules were the most frequently used animals for freighting purposes. They are trained as pack animals when they are four or five, and perform in this capacity admirably until they are retired at about 18-20 years of age.[5] These rugged animals carry or pull more tonnage for greater distances with less rest than either of their horse or donkey parents.[6] Carefully loaded mules can carry 300-350 pounds, and cover 20-25 miles a day. Mules quickly recover after a night's rest and are ready to continue packing the next day.[7] In the arid southwest a breed of small Spanish mule weighing about 600 pounds was preferred over horses and regular mules. They were strong, endured heat better, and required less water and feed.[8]

Theodore H. Savory comments about this remarkable beast of burden:

> "The mule has more than its share of admirable qualities. It is courageous and intelligent, hard of hide, sure of foot, sound of constitution and able to resist changes in climate and withstand thirst and hunger better than the horse."[9]

Horses and burros were also extensively used for transportation. Burros are donkeys bred especially for packing. The males are *Jacks*, and the females *Jennies*. See figure 5.

Figure 5   Jenny and foal   Author
Oatman, Arizona 2002

There were certain horses that could not be used – the aptly named *balkers*, *biters*, *kickers*, and *run-aways*. Every attempt was made to sell the creature to an unsuspecting buyer.[10]

Those horses that did make the grade proved to be very useful and quick to learn. A muleskinner's horse – leading a pack train of mules, instinctively knew when to advance forward as each mule was unloaded. In the San Juan Mountains, miners could rent a horse to go back to the mine after time off in the nearest town. Once there, they would tie the horse's reins to the pommel, and the horse would find his way back to the stable.[11]

Many of the trails leading to the mines could be quite dangerous, especially in the winter. The sure-footed burro or mule was used in these rugged areas. Figure 6 depicts such a route in the San Juan Mountains. Burros were not tied together in a string, but rather were herded by the skinner and his dog.[12]

Muriel Wolle, in *The Bonanza Trail*, relates a rather amusing – and tall, tale about an unusual event that a freighter in Mineral City, Washington experienced:

Figure 6
Cunningham Gulch Trail
San Juan Mountains
Colorado 1875

Courtesy NARA

> "On the trail to one of these camps a packer was leading a horse loaded with several boxes of dynamite, when the pack slipped and the frightened animal bucked it loose, scattering sticks of explosives all over the ground. The mules, which made up the rest of the train, stopped when they came to the sticks and began eating them greedily. The remaining miles to the camp were without mishap, but the bug-eyed packer kept well to the rear of his pack-string. He did not dare hit any of the animals all summer for fear of a delayed explosion."[13]

Prunes

Prunes was a well-loved and respected burro that worked in the Fairplay-Alma mining districts of Colorado. The last mine Prunes worked at was the Hock Hocking mine in Mosquito Gulch. After Prunes retired from the mining life, he was left free to roam around Fairplay, where the townsfolk frequently fed him his favorite meal: flapjacks fried in grease.

In 1930, old Prunes was trapped in a barn during a blizzard. When he was found days later, he was too old and had become too weak, and the miners decided that the humane thing to do was to put him down. A memorial was built in town, where Prunes was ultimately laid to rest. See figure 7. The next year, his most recent owner and companion, Rupe Sherwood, died at age 82. His ashes were buried behind Prunes, at his request.[14]

Figure 7   Memorial to Prunes   Author
Fairplay, Colorado 2002

Harriet Fish Backus, author of *Tomboy Bride*, heard about Prunes on her way from the Tomboy mine, near Telluride, to Leadville, Colorado. A forty-burro pack train, led by Prunes, carried molybdenum ore to the waiting train at Climax, Colorado.

"Prunes was then fifty years old. Fifteen years later, at the age of sixty-five, he was laid to rest at the cross-roads of the main street of Fairplay. All the stores and places of business were closed during the services befitting a faithful, hard-working little creature whose life had been spent assisting his human friends."[15]

Burros – see figure 8, are very well behaved and well liked by all who encounter them. That is, with the exception of the reason why they were given the moniker *Rocky Mountain Canaries*:

"Everybody liked the burros except for one thing. At the crack of dawn, summer or winter, the Jacks brayed to the Jennies and the Jennies brayed back. Talk about noise pollution."[16]

Figure 8   Burro   Author
Cripple Creek, Colorado 2000

Weights and Distances

A sketch of wagonload or pack weights, distances traveled, and the numbers of draft animals pressed into service at a variety of mining districts follows, providing a good idea of the work that these four footed friends performed for the teamsters and miners.

♦ As far back as 1660, mules transported salt from the Estancia salt lakes in New Mexico 700 miles to the silver mines of southern Chihuahua, Mexico.[17]

♦ In 1804, copper, mined at Santa Rita, New Mexico was transported by mule to Chihuahua (over 350 miles) and Mexico City (over 1100 miles) for coinage.[18]

- 10-mule teams frequently pulled 10-15 tons over the Sierra Nevada Mountains. During an eight-week period of 1862, 2772 teams composed of a total of 14,652 horses and mules pulled 19,386,200 pounds of freight over the mountains on their way to Virginia City.[19] Each animal pulled about 1325 pounds over this steep grade. Assuming that sixteen hours per day were spent driving the teams, a stationary observer would greet a new team every twenty minutes.

- In New Mexico in 1868, copper ore transported 1000 miles to Indianola, Texas, contained gold in quantities sufficient to defray transportation expenses.[20]

- In 1869 at White Pine, Nevada a team of 12 mules hauled 21,000 pounds, or 1750 pounds per mule. By mid-summer ore was transported from Hamilton (White Pine) to the mills by 400-500 pack animals.[21]

- About 600 teams were freighting in Leadville at the beginning of the 1878 boom.[22]

- At the Smuggler mine in Aspen, jacks carried about 200 pounds apiece over rugged terrain.[23]

- In 1882, the Yankee Girl mine kept 75-mule trains busy all winter shipping ore to Silverton, Colorado where it was then sent to St. Louis for smelting.[24]

- 200 teams were hauling lead-silver ore from the mines at Magdalena to the smelter at Socorro, New Mexico in 1883.[25]

- John Ashenfelter, a freighter in the Ouray, Colorado area, provided his services to the Mount Sneffels mining district. At one time he had 32 six-horse or mule teams, over one hundred pack burros and mules, and fifty saddle horses for the miners to ride to the mines.[26]

- Daily pack mule trains of over 125 animals, each carrying 230 pounds of ore down a steep trail from the Sunnyside Mine, kept a 15 TPD mill at Eureka, Colorado running.[27]

Figure 9   Burros loaded with ore
Courtesy NARA

- In Tonopah, Nevada 20-22 horses pulled 20-ton wagons on the Sodaville-Tonopah route. One ton of freight was allotted to each horse, plus one ton of feed for the team for the two-day journey. There were 150 horses and mules in late 1901, and by 1905 there were an estimated 2000 animals.[28]

- The mining and smelting works at Cerro Gordo, California required an extensive transportation network. The Cerro Gordo Freighting Company kept eighty teams of 14 mules, each pulling 3 wagons, in constant motion. Each team moved from station to station between Cerro Gordo and Los Angeles, the round trip taking nearly 4 weeks to complete.[29]

The large numbers of animals used in the various mining districts translated into economic opportunities for teamsters, muleskinners, stable owners, blacksmiths, tack shops, ranchers, and farmers. The cost of feeding the animals, especially during a rush, could be prohibitively high.

Feed prices during the 1869 White Pine rush varied greatly between the rapidly developing mining district and the nearest established stage line in Elko, Nevada. For the former, hay cost $450 per ton, and for the latter, about $30. Barley cost nearly 30 cents a pound in White Pine, but less than nine cents in Elko.[30] Considering that a horse might consume 18 pounds of barley and 20 pounds of hay per day, the cost to the horse's owner would be less than $2 in Elko and over $9 in White Pine. In Nevada in 1864 mules cost about $500 each.[31] In Pioche, Nevada in 1871 a horse cost $235, and a harness $64.[32]

Transportation charges were highly variable. Many factors influenced the rates, including the tonnage and size to be shipped, the cost and availability of feed and water, the distance to be traveled, the season and weather, the quality and safety of the route, competition from other freighters or railroads, tolls, and demand for the service to name but a few. A sampling of rates follows.

- During the winter of 1868-9 in White Pine, freight charges were 20 cents per pound ($400 per ton). By mid-summer rates dropped to 7 cents per pound ($140 per ton). By 1876 the rate for freight shipped to or from Treasure Hill & Eureka cost $20 per ton. During the winter of '76, a local freighter hired 30 men at a cost of $2000 to clear the snow-bound road between the mine and the mill so that he might stay in business.[33]

- In 1880 jack freight charges were four cents per pound ($80 per ton) from Aspen to Leadville.[34] Winter freight rates ran $40-$60 per ton in Aspen during the mid 1880's. In winter, freight was moved from wagon to sleigh and back to wagon again.[35]

- In Red Mountain, mines like the Hudson decided to stockpile ore in the winter and only ship in the summer. The Hudson saved up to $7 per ton in shipping this way. By late November 1883 the road between Ouray and the Yankee Girl mine, at Red Mountain, was completed. Stockpiled ore was then shipped – 50 sacks per sled. Otto Mears, the builder of this toll road,[36] received $5 for each team and wagon, and $1 for each pack animal – very high rates. Freight shipped from Montrose to Ouray was about $15 per ton, but only $7.50 per ton for the return trip if the freighters carried ore.[37]

- In 1888, freight rates for concentrates shipped from the Coeur d'Alene mining district were about $6 per ton, traveling first by narrow gauge railroad to Coeur d'Alene Lake, and then by boat to Coeur d'Alene City. An additional rate then applied to transport the ore to a smelting center: $8 per ton to Helena; $10.40 to Portland; $17 to Omaha; and $18 to Denver.[38]

- The Idaho Company had their 12-stamp mill freighted from St. Joseph, Missouri to Rocky Bar, Idaho at the cost of 30 cents per pound – a total of $8,400. The Pittsburgh and Idaho Gold and Silver Mining Company had their 80 horsepower, 40-stamp mill brought to Rocky Bar from Wallula, Oregon – on 45 "mammoth wagons", at a cost of $40,000.[39]

Snow Job

During the winter of 1864-65 in Auburn, Oregon – when the trails were three feet deep with snow, the Auburn Canal Company asked freighter John Wilson what his rate was for hauling lumber. He replied that it was $2.50 per thousand board feet. The canal company thought this too high, and left.

A few days later – and after another snowfall, they approached him again. This time his price was $5.00. Upset, the agent left, only to ask again a few days later. $7.50.

On the fourth visit – and after still more snow, the rate of $9.00 was agreed upon.[40]

Ore Wagons

Most supplies were freighted in horse or mule-drawn wagons. Wagons were called *prairie schooners*. With the exception of the very smallest of wagons, the animals were paired together. See figure 10. If two pairs were used, those in front are the *leaders*, and they tracked the road. Those on the tongue are the *wheelers*, and it was their job to provide braking on descents. The leaders were smaller, usually between about 1100-1300 pounds, and the wheelers were larger at 1400-1600 pounds.[41] On large wagons the wheelers were often oxen. If three pairs were used, those in the middle are the *swings* or *swingers*. Collectively the pairs are a *team*, and driven by a *teamster*.[42]

Figure 10   Small Wagon, 1912
Courtesy USGS

Many ore wagons, or *rigs*, hauled about eight tons. The big rigs weighed about 3000 pounds empty.[43] In Nevada in 1864, rigs could cost upwards of $1600.[44] The freight wagons used in Tonopah had rear wheels seven feet in diameter with 12" rims.[45] The axles of a wagon are called *hounds*. The expression "your dogs are growling" or "barking" originated from the sound the axles made when requiring grease.[46] When two wagons are pulled in tandem, the second is called the *back action*.[47] Ore was often pulled by up to 20-mule teams when there was more than one back action. See figure 11.

Figure 11   20 Mule Teams
Pinal County, Arizona 1897
Courtesy NARA

A *runaway* was the teamster's worst fear. Bennett tells of a runaway experienced by a teamster working a steep portion of West Willow Creek just outside of Creede, Colorado:

"It was sometime in the winter of 1893-94 that Bill Crook's roughlock broke. Now a roughlock isn't much to look at but it is a very important part of a muleskinner's equipment, specially [sic] so in the winter when the roads are icy. For the information of those who do not know, it is a long piece of heavy chain that is wrapped around the wheel of a wagon or the runner of a sled in such a way that it is between the wheel or runner and the ground, exerting a deterrent effect on the vehicle's inclination to obey the law of gravity and go like hell downhill over the spots where ordinary braking won't work.

Crooks had just rounded the last switchback when the wagon jumped, his wheelers 'hit the britchen,' and Bill knew he was in for a ride. Before the wheelers could start to run, Bill had their lines shortened and gave the leaders some slack. Holding the wheelers tight to do what they could to slow the wagon, Bill poured the silk[48] to the leaders to make them keep the lead bars out of the way of the jumping, sliding wheelers; once a wheel horse got a foot into the lead-bars it would be all over. With his wheelers jumping and sliding and his leaders trying to run away from the stinging lash, Bill rode her out. His path was erratic, sometimes perilously close to the outside edge where some of the outfit was sure to be killed if they went over; but, when he hit the bottom land at the forks with the Weaver road, where he could swing out into soft snow on top of a rocky base, he was still right side up with every horse on his feet. One of the heelers had lost a shoe and the worn down foot was bleeding and his leaders were welted up some, but a few days rest put the whole outfit back on the road as good as new."[49]

Ruts, rocks, holes, and deep sand was normal for the roads. On occasion, if the driver of an ore wagon got stuck, to get out he might use dollar-a-pound ore to fill the hole.[50] Freighters were known for their short tempers and profanity. In White Pine during the '69 rush, two ore wagons had their wheels lock in town, and one driver resorted to throwing a piece of chloride ore at the other driver, who then retaliated by pistol-whipping the former![51]

Figure 12   Feeding the teams on the Placerville route, ca 1865

Courtesy Library of Congress

The treatment of the animals could range from very good – as the occasional miner protested, to very poor. The legendary stubborn behavior of mules may not be entirely blamed on the animal, however. "Mules acquire the unattractive traits of stubbornness and ill temper only when they have been badly brought up."[53]

The behavior of men is not so easily explained away, and can very often be downright cruel. Backus, in the early 20th century, made frequent trips between the Tomboy mine and Telluride, Colorado. Muleskinners were passed on the narrow trail. On more than one occasion she witnessed their frustration with the mules:

"But stubborn as mules are, my anger leaped to white heat whenever I saw how an obstinate or helpless mule was sometimes mistreated. Then came the measure of the skinner's temper, brutality, and his command of profanity. At first he might coax, then he swore."

"When strong language brought no response from the mule, often stuck deep in the snow, the skinner kicked him with his heavy boots or lashed him brutally with a strap. The mule might lunge feebly, or settle down again calmly, perversely. Then the enraged skinner resorted to the iron shovel – banging it on the animal's head."[54]

Figure 13   Loading a small ore wagon
Courtesy NARA

Muriel Sibell Wolle, author of *Timberline Tailings*, received many letters from people that grew up in the mining camps of Colorado. Clifford W. Kingsley wrote her in 1950, sharing his recollections of working on the Rawley Tunnel in Bonanza, Colorado, and in particular about a hot-headed muleskinner by the name of Dutch Doyle.

Dutch tried using a carbide lantern on a mule that was used for tramming. The mule apparently did not like the lamp, knocked it off at the first opportunity, and came to a halt. Then the trouble began:

"When he tried to start the mule, nothing doing. I heard him and when I looked up he picked up a starter… and hit the mule a smack between the eyes. Down went the mule, but when he came to he was ready to go, off the end of an 80-foot dump. The mule hit first, and then the cars. They had to get a fellow on horseback to go up in the pass in 4 feet of snow to bring him back – a few places on his hocks were skinned. Three of the 5 cars went to the blacksmith shop."[55]

These incidents are surely the exceptions to the norm. Overall, the animals were treated well, if for no other reason than they were indispensable and very expensive to replace. As will be seen, even minor mistreatment of the mules could lead to one's immediate dismissal at some mines.

Underground Horses and Mules

In the larger mines, mules and horses were used underground for tramming. Some of the mines kept the animals on the surface if there was easy access from a tunnel or adit. On mines with a shaft or steep incline as the only point of entry, the animals were carefully slung and hoisted to the level on which they worked. The mules were kept in underground stables when they were not working. See figure 14. Many spent their entire working lives underground before being brought back to the surface and retired. The exception was when they were injured, sick, or during labor strikes.[56] By the turn of the century, many mules working in Leadville mines had "twenty-year seniority."[57]

Mules, especially the smaller Spanish ones, were preferred to horses in pulling cars in mines. Whenever something touched a horse's ears, it would rear its head up and hit the rock. Mules do not like their ears touched and would instead drop their head, avoiding injury.[58]

Horses were used underground in some of the Park City, Utah mines, where the height of the drifts permitted their use. The miners referred to them as "hay burners." Cats were brought into the mines to "mouse" the hay in the stables. At night, they slept on the horses' backs for warmth.[59]

Contrary to popular belief, the mules and horses working underground did not go blind. When the time came to hoist them to the surface they were blindfolded so that their eyes could slowly readjust to daylight.[60]

The mules were well cared for. "If a driver lost a mule through carelessness or negligence or abused a mule, he was fired immediately and told to get off the premises *quickly* – before the inside foreman lost his temper."[61] Some miners complained that the mining companies cared more for the mules than for the miners.[62] 'Cuter' was a favorite horse at the Commodore mine in Creede. One muleskinner "hit the horse on the rump with the flat of a shovel and didn't finish his shift."[63]

The horses and mules were smart too. Cuter could tell time:

"With forty-five minutes to go before lunch time or tally, Cuter would go in to the farthest chute. With less time he would not go past the first one."

"Wednesday noon was the time to grease the axles of the train, and if he had not seen this done, he stayed out of the tunnel until it was."[64]

Figure 14   Underground Stable   Author
Pioneer Tunnel
Ashland, Pennsylvania 2000

In Bonanza, Colorado in the late 1890's a smart mule knew when additional cars were being pulled. If the miners added an extra car loaded with dull steels, they would have to push it a little so that the mule wouldn't know it was there.[65]

In 1878, 102 mules were working in the Sutro Tunnel. The men would share their lunches with their favorite mules. "The mules would get from one man a piece of pie and from another a cup of coffee."[66] In other mines the mules were given sweets, apples, figs, cookies, plug tobacco, and even an occasional bottle of beer.[67] A burro named Maudie (who replaced Prunes) refused to tram muck from the Hock Hocking mine without a plug of chaw.[68]

The mules showed the limits of their tolerance when the working conditions became severe for both man and animal. The extreme heat in the Sutro Tunnel prompted opportunistic behavior on the part of the tramming mules:

> "Mr. Bishop, a shift boss, tried to get his switch mule away from the blower and the mule bit Bishop's arm. If a mule saw a man with a piece of ice in his hand, the mule would make a grab for the ice and hold it in its mouth. The mules were given ice water to drink five or six times each shift and had their heads and lips rubbed with ice as well."[69]

Technology ultimately replaced the mine mule. For example, the Revenue Tunnel replaced its mules with an electric locomotive in 1896;[70] the Homestake introduced compressed air locomotives in 1901;[71] the Daly-Judge mine in Park City ordered their first electric locomotive in 1903.[72] Change was slow, however, and it wasn't until 1965 that laws were finally passed in Pennsylvania preventing mine mules from working underground.[73]

> My sweetheart's the mule in the mines
> I drive her without reins or lines
> On the bumper I sit
> I chew and I spit
> All over my sweetheart's behind [74]

How to get a Mule in the Mine

That is simple, if the mine has an adit – just lead him in. If the mine has a shaft, it is a little more complicated. Figures 15 through 19 illustrate how a mine mule was carefully restrained with straps, moved to the collar of the mine on a sled, and then slung from the cage for his trip below.

Arabian Nights

In March of 1855, the Senate authorized the expenditure of $30,000, by the War Department, for the purchase and importation of camels (23 plus a calf) and dromedaries (9). The camels were used as beasts of burden, carrying upwards of 600 pounds of supplies, whereas the dromedaries were used for express purposes. According to Major Henry C. Wayne, all of the animals outperformed even their most optimistic

Figure 15

Figure 16

Figure 17

Figure 18   Riding on the sled

Figure 19   Slung from the cage
Figures 15 through 19 Courtesy
World Museum of Mining, Butte, Montana

expectations, and it was claimed that three camels could perform the work of six horses or mules, and at twice the rate. After the expedition was complete, an attempt was made to use the camels in other capacities, but inexperienced handlers lead to the perception that they were of little value, and most were set free. [75]

In 1862, a Frenchman began using some of these camels for hauling salt from Rhodes Marsh to Virginia City.[76] Camels were introduced into the Austin, Nevada area in May 1863. The US Army surplus animals were used until about 1867 to haul salt mined near Walker Lake, ore, and freight from Virginia City to Austin.[77] In 1876, two Frenchmen rounded up about thirty head that were roaming the Arizona desert, and took them to Nevada to use for packing salt to the Comstock mills.[78]

The camels were prohibited on the streets of Virginia City during the day as they frightened the horses and mules, causing runaways. At night they could use the back streets.[79] Many other towns passed ordinances prohibiting them from entering town except at night. Nevada also enacted a state law providing for a fine of $100 for anybody that allowed his camels to run at large. At one auction in Virginia City they brought $250 each – about ½ that of a mule.[80]

Railroads

The development of the numerous railroads in the frontier West radically altered industry and society. Many mining camps were given a new lease on life by the arrival of a railroad. The arrival of a railroad meant vastly improved transportation and reduced freight rates and times. For example, before the arrival of the railroad, ore from the Galt mine in Neihart, Montana, was dragged down the mountainside in deerskins, packed on horseback to White Sulphur Springs, transferred to wagon for the trip to the railhead in Livingston, and then shipped by rail to the smelters in the Midwest, all of which was laborious, expensive, and time consuming.[81]

Camps would lustily compete for the railroad to select their community as its destination. The camp fortunate enough to have the railroad connection was very often transformed into a town of permanency and greater respectability – a newly acquired status that the neighboring camps envied, if they even survived at all. The camps vying for the road would all attempt to prove themselves worthy of the benefits of industrialized transportation. A strong assurance of plenty of passengers and freight going in, and industrial raw materials such as ore, concentrates, or timber coming out - all of which meant lucrative profits for the road, helped garner success.

The decision to bring a railroad into a camp was a difficult one for the railroad operators, and was something of a gamble. Building such a road was not a trivial or inexpensive process. This is especially true considering the fact that the mining camps always seem to be located in the most difficult terrain to build a road through: rugged mountains and scorched deserts.

By the time the railroad brought the first train into town, it might be too late. Many promising mining camps had fantastic surface deposits that simply didn't last. Some were stable communities, but were already past their peak and were beginning the inevitable decline[82] when the road finally arrived. Still others had plenty of ore, but economic conditions and metal prices made mining unprofitable, even with the advantages and reduced freight rates that a railroad brings with it. This was especially true for the silver mining camps.

It took years to plan and build the road. For example, in 1900 Tonopah Nevada was discovered. It wasn't until July 25, 1904 that the Tonopah Railroad was completed.[83] The rapid expansion and construction of some of the roads was often hasty and ill advised. Many railroads went into receivership as a result. In the Tonopah Mining Company's rush to build the last 4 miles of track into town, a four percent grade was used. This required, for the life of the track, that incoming freight and passenger trains be split into two sections, each brought in separately.[84]

Figure 20   The Joining of the Rails
Completing the Transcontinental Railroad
May 10, 1869 Promontory, Utah

Courtesy NARA

Transportation systems shifted considerably upon the arrival of the iron horse. When the railroad was finally completed from Reno to Virginia City on November 29, 1869, it replaced to a great extent the need for teams pulling freight wagons. At its peak, the 52.2-mile long road carried as many as 50 trains per day, though 36 – a considerable number, was the average. The cost of this line, complete with rolling stock, shops, real estate, and right-of-ways was variously placed at between $1,750,000 and $4,856,042 – a sizeable investment. Freight rates were significantly reduced: the cost of a cord of wood dropped from $15 to $11.50, and shipping of ore from $3.50 to $2 per ton. In 1870, the cost of mining materials had been reduced by 27% due to the arrival of the railroad.[85] The Virginia and Truckee Railroad transported wood from lumberyards south of Carson City to the mines of the Comstock at Virginia City. Their records for a six-year period are illustrated in table 1.[86]

The railroad only went as far as the station. Freight being delivered to the mines and ore being brought to the train still required transportation by the teamsters. The teamsters were not out of a job, though their numbers dwindled. The arrival of the railroad permitted the profitable development of nearby mining districts that may previously have been marginal or unprofitable. As a result, many of the teamsters found that their routes simply changed.

The mines – the big shippers and consumers, felt the greatest economic benefit from the trains. On July 8,1882 the Denver & Rio Grande (D&RG) railroad arrived in Silverton. Transportation rates from Silverton to the Pueblo smelters prior to the arrival of the railroad could be as high as $50-$60 per ton, but after the arrival dropped to $16 per ton, and shortly thereafter dropped to $12 per ton; thus allowing low-grade ores to be shipped economically.

The D&RG finished its line from Montrose to Ouray on December 15, 1887. Shortly afterwards, Otto Mears finished his Silverton Railroad, later called the *Rainbow Route*. The cost to build the Silverton Railroad, plus rolling stock and equipment, was $725,000. Passenger fare was set to a

Year	Lumber Board Feet	Fuel Cords
1874	52,220,801	139,808
1875	72,526,465	179,295
1876	71,633,072	212,279
1877	38,981,967	221,497
1878	34,427,502	205,311
1879	31,443,771	185,622
Total	301,233,578	1,143,812

Table 1   Virginia and Truckee Railroad Statistics

Drills And Mills

rather pricey 20 cents per mile for the 20-mile route.[87] Due to competition from Mears' railroad, the D&RG dropped its rates from Ouray to Denver to $8, $9, and $10 per ton for low, mid, and high-grade ores.[88]

When the D&RG finally reached Aspen on November 5, 1887, stockpiled ore shipped at the rate of 20 20-ton cars per day for 45 days. The railroad was not good news to everybody, however. The Aspen Mining and Smelting Company was forced to close because they could not compete with the combined cost of the railroad's cheap transportation of ores to the smelters in Denver and Pueblo, and the valley smelters' significantly lower reduction rates. Even after the arrival of the railroad, some 60-75 jack teams hauled supplies to and ore from nearby Tourtelotte Park.[89]

The availability of railroad cars, on demand, had much to do with the profit or loss at the mines. Ore that could not be shipped could not be smelted, and it was the smelter's payment to the mine that paid the miners. In 1890 there was a 30-day switchmen strike against the D&RG. This brought mining to a standstill, and the payroll loss, estimated at $40,000, crippled Aspen merchants. The strike ended and every mining camp along the line needed cars that were in short supply. The sudden resumption of shipping overloaded the smelters, and they in turn refused shipments.[90]

Shipping from Red Mountain to the Pueblo smelters before the railroad – by pack mule, had cost about $100 per ton, but with the railroad this dropped to about $40 per ton. The Red Mountain mines took full advantage of Mears' Silverton Railroad when it reached Red Mountain on September 19, 1888. By the early 1890's the mines were shipping via rail 2500 carloads of ore and importing 1500 carloads of coal annually.[91] Along this line, moving ore by rail from Chattanooga to Rickett's Mill in nearby Howardsville – a total of about 12 miles, cost $2 per ton.[92]

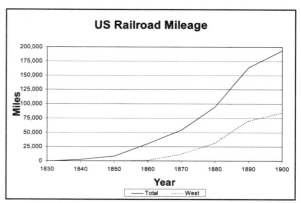

Chart 1

Shipping rates were at times set to capitalize on a boom – to gouge consumers. In 1870, shipment by rail over the Sierra Nevada Mountains to Reno cost $60 per ton. The same ton carried to Hamilton, Nevada cost $500 – less than three times the distance, but more than eight times the rate.[93]

Chart 1 shows the increase in railroad mileages in the U.S. as a whole, and that west of the Mississippi River.[94] Development of railroads in the West lagged behind the populated, industrial East, but the impact was extraordinary nonetheless.

Aerial Trams

Aerial trams were used in many of the mountainous mining districts throughout the west, especially those in rugged, inaccessible, and avalanche prone areas. They consist of an endless cable running on tower-mounted rollers, from which buckets were suspended – not unlike a ski lift or an amusement park aerial tram ride. See figure 21. Many operated by gravity – the weight of the descending, loaded ore buckets provided the motive power for the returning, empty buckets. Ore was loaded onto the buckets at a tram station at the mine and unloaded at the terminus, which was generally a mill. Depending on the local topography, intermediate tram stations were sometimes necessary for transferring buckets from one line to another.

Supplies such as coal or mine timbers were transported to the mine, this at considerable savings in freight expenses. Miners frequently rode to and from the mine in buckets – a potentially dangerous ride if one were not alert, but safer than taking long, snow-laden pack trails in avalanche country.

Grease Monkeys were responsible for keeping the tram system well lubricated.[95] Figure 22 shows a 20th century innovation used on the tram at the Mayflower Mill in Silverton – a tram *oiler* that would automatically dispense lubricant as it traveled along the tramline.

At White Pine, Nevada, a Hodgson[96] aerial tram was installed at the Eberhardt Mine during 1869 for an investment of $135,000. Steel cable, ⅞" diameter, ran for over two miles and traversed 2000' of elevation between the mine and the International Mill. Wooden buckets of 200 pounds capacity moved at three MPH, powered by a 16 HP engine located near the mill, and passed over 50 supporting towers that ranged in height from 20 to 130 feet, each built of 10" braced timbers. The towers also carried telegraphic lines and equipment for communication. It was the largest cable tramway in the US in the early 1870's. The company paid $1 per ton using the tram, where previously it had paid $3 per ton in the summer, and from $5-$7 per ton in the winter for freighting the ore.[97] Costs had dropped to about 65 cents per ton in 1871.[98]

The tensioning pulley had to be relocated to the mid-point of the tram due to temperature variations causing the cable to slacken. The buckets also hit the support towers on their descent, spilling precious ore, so only low-grade ore was transported on the tram. Shortly after the International Mill burned in August 1872, the wire cable broke.[99]

Hallidie's first tram installation may have been at the Freiberg Mining District, Nevada in 1872. In his design, the buckets were bolted to the cable.[100] Early single-rope tramways had very limited capacities; strain was kept to a minimum because the wire rope served to carry the load and transport it too.

In 1874, Theodore Otto and Adolf Bleichert demonstrated their first successful double-rope system. In this system, the cars had wheels that rolled on a very heavy, fixed cable that was suspended between towers, while a much lighter cable – the *traction cable*, pulled the car along. Detaching the cars was greatly simplified.[101] Charles M. Huson entered the growing aerial tram market in 1883. His design saw general use throughout the West.[102]

Figure 21   Aerial Tram   Author
Pioche, Nevada 2002

Figure 22   Tram Oiler   Author
Mayflower Mill, Silverton Colorado 1999

Aerial trams are very effective in transporting ore from mines located in inaccessible mountains down to mills located in a valley. Designing and erecting the tramways was a challenge, as was packing in the thousands of feet of cable.

In 1892, the Yellow Jacket mine, in the Loon Creek district west of Challis, Idaho, decided to reduce expenses by installing a Swem aerial tram. The 8400 feet of cable was brought in by company pack train in three trips. The problem was that the ⅞" wire rope was too stiff to be made into coils for each mule. Rather, a 2800-foot length was folded back and forth on itself six or seven times down the length of the main street in Challis.

Twenty mules were then lined up at intervals and the cable lashed to their sides. This proved to be quite a spectacle for the townsfolk, who all turned out to witness the event. As the pack train left for the mine, it soon proved comical for the teamsters, too. Whenever the train went through a depression, the mule in the middle was left suspended in midair.

On another occasion, one "wall-eyed cuss" decided to head down the side of the mountain, dragging the entire pack train 150 feet downslope. It took two days to disentangle the train. The wire was ultimately delivered to the mine, and when the aerial tramway was running the expense of transporting the ore from mine to mill dropped from $2.50 to $0.07 per ton.[103]

In 1897, 15,000 pounds of cable was transported from Telluride up to the Nellie Mine. The cable was pulled from the spool and coiled into 130 smaller coils spaced nine feet apart. Sixty-five mules were then brought up, and each was carefully fitted with two of these smaller coils, one on each side.[104]

Trams were not always used where they could be. In 1883, after considering the expense involved in constructing a tram, the Independence Mine on Galena Mountain, near Lake City, Colorado put in place a 1700-foot long ore chute instead.[105]

Figure 23   Mayflower Mill Tram Bucket   Author
Silverton, Colorado in the background 2002

- In 1888 the Aspen Mine constructed a tram, with 86 buckets of 150 pounds capacity each, for more than a mile up Aspen Mountain. 2000 tons of ore was moved every 24 hours.[106]

- At Eureka, Colorado in 1898 a Findlayson tram was built to connect the Sunnyside Mine to the Midway Mill, a distance of 8600 feet and a drop of 1600 feet, and a second segment connecting the Midway and Eureka mills, another 7100 feet. The cost of the tram, with terminals, was $75,000.[107]

- In 1898, a 9000-foot long gravity-powered Bleichert aerial tramway was built at the Camp Bird mine near Ouray, Colorado. The construction took 48 days, and required 300,000 board feet of timber for the 46 towers. The buckets had a capacity of 700 pounds, and delivered 12 tons per hour to the mill. The line had an angle station near the midpoint, where the buckets were transferred from one line to the other. The total drop was 1350 feet.[108]

- The Hector Mining Company, operating adjacent to the Smuggler-Union mine, made arrangements to use the latter's 6700 foot aerial tram, hauling sacked coal up from the Smuggler Mill in Pandora to the tram station and ore back down again. This was a cost-effective cooperative agreement between the two mines. The Smuggler made a small profit at the use charge of $1.50 per ton, and the Hector management ensured that coal could be delivered during the winter, a problem for pack trains in the avalanche-prone San Juan Mountains.[109]

- The Silver King mine in Park City, Utah, used a 7300-foot aerial tram – descending 1000 feet, of the Findlayson pattern. 80 buckets traveled at a little less than 2 MPH over 39 steel towers, carrying 500 pounds of ore down to an automatic unloading device, and returning with up to 325 pounds of coal. The cost per ton ranged from 17 to 22 cents.[110]

- In Bodie, California, the Standard mine moved ore to the mill via a Hallidie aerial tramway. This tramway, operational in February 1878, cost $9500 to erect, and had fifty buckets of 120-pound capacity supported by towers spaced 150 feet apart and carrying 5000 feet of ⅝" wire rope.[111]

- In 1904, the Old Hundred Mining Company in Silverton required a plethora of transportation modes to get materials up to their mine for construction of a tram system. The materials were first dropped off by train in nearby Howardsville, then transported by wagon to the mill site, taken by pack train up 6.5 miles of trails, then lowered by hand-cranked windlass down a 250-foot chute. Three trams were constructed to reach the various levels of the mine:

Figure 24   Tram Bucket   Author

  o The first was a 1450' 30° angle line, rising 670 feet. The capacity was 15 tons per hour using buckets of 1000-pound capacity.
  o The second line was 800 feet long, and rose 530 feet at a steep 48° angle. A 10 HP motor powered this ten-ton per hour capacity line.
  o The third line was 2000' long, averaged 40°, and rose 1400 feet reaching 12,630 feet in elevation. It had the lowest capacity, being five tons per hour.[112]

The Botched Jig-Back Inclined Tramway

At the New Almaden Mine, California, in an effort to reduce the expense of using teams and wagons to haul ore, engineers designed an inclined railroad – dubbed the "Cape Horn," for transporting the ore from the mine to the *planilla* (Spanish for ore-dressing floor or building).

The ore came from the Grey shaft and was loaded into cars, which were pulled by mules nearly ¾ of a mile to the top of the first incline. This incline – 500 feet long and having a 35° slope, was designed to use gravity, where the loaded car going downhill pulled an empty car uphill – a *jig-back tram*. A brake was used to regulate the speed of the cars, which shared the same track except where they passed each other at the midpoint.

A mule then pulled the loaded cars to the next incline some 1800 feet away. This incline was 800 feet long and had a 28° slope. Mules then pulled the cars over a rickety bridge crossing a ravine, and then on to the *planilla*, and returned with empty cars. The tracks were originally made of iron strapping nailed to redwood two-by-fours, but were later replaced with mine rail. About twenty men were required to operate this system.

Figure 25   Inclined Rail Tram ca 1871
Courtesy NARA

The original cost of the project was estimated at between $9,000-12,000, but when completed cost $35,000. After the installation was complete and put into use in 1864, it was determined that it was more expensive than using teams and ore wagons! In 1865, operation of the incline was suspended. Reverting back to using teams saved $40 per day.

One newspaper wrote:

> "It is a beautifully well-built piece of engineering that is a complete failure."

Concerning the occasional failure of the brakes on the incline and the subsequent somersaults and the crashing of the ore cars, author Schneider wrote:

> "As one can imagine, these acrobatics were not the most tranquilizing sport for the mule driver waiting at the bottom of the incline."

And concerning crossing the rickety bridge:

> "The mule driver stood on one bank and threw rocks at the mule until the train was safely over, then he took his chances and followed."[113]

Figure 26   1800' Inclined Rail Tram
Courtesy USGS

Power And Fuel

Steam Engines

Steam engines – the machinery that powered and helped make possible the Industrial Revolution, also powered numerous mines and mills. They came in many sizes; ranging from a few HP to giants over 200 HP. See figure 27. These engines were costly to install, operate, and fuel. They were required for hoisting in mines that reached significant depths, and to prevent flooding of the deep workings.

Steam engines were also used to power the machinery of the ore reduction mills, covered in the following chapters, and the locomotives that helped open up the West. Small engines even found use in tractors used to haul ore – see figure 28.

Steam engines also powered air compressors. The compressed air could be piped considerable distances with little loss in power. This proved advantageous in deep mines. On the Comstock compressed air was used not only to run the Burleigh drills, but also to run small hoists and provide much needed ventilation in the hot, cavernous stopes.[114]

On occasion, steam engines were located underground, as in the Bobtail Tunnel, Black Hawk, Colorado. The engine and boilers were used for hoisting and pumping, and were located 471 feet underground. The smokestack, made of brick and iron, extended up an old unused shaft.[115] Engineers tried using steam power on the 1465-level of the Ophir mine on the Comstock. A boiler and engine were installed, complete with a sheet iron smokestack to the surface. The heat it produced

Figure 27   Boilers and Engine
Source: Hatch, 1895

became unbearable to the men, so the practice was discontinued and the engine was removed. The boiler was then used as a compressed air reservoir.[116]

The 1880 Census reports that of 290 western deep mines, 392 steam-powered hoisting engines were reported, of which 360 were in use. The average horsepower per engine was 231 on the Comstock, and 29 in the rest of the west.[117] In Leadville, 231 steam engines were in use at the mines, with a total power of 5454 horsepower, or an average of about 24 HP – comparable to the 1880 Census figures.[118]

Steam engines, under the most ideal conditions, can generate one HP-Hour (a horsepower for an hour) using 1.5 pounds of "good coal".[119] By the early 1880's the boilers were ordinarily run at about 80 PSI.[120] Coal was used on the Comstock and in other mining districts where it was readily available and competitively priced. In 1873, for example, the Belcher and Yellow Jacket spent over $71,000 on coal.[121]

In 19th century "*Smokestack America*," the number of smokestacks – steam engines, was often used to judge the economic success of a town or mining community. Even fancy stock certificate artwork proudly illustrated black soot belching from industrial enterprises. See figure 29.

The steam engine did not last forever, and while it did it had competition. Waterpower was used in localities fortunate enough to have an adequate supply. Electricity and electric motors made their appearance during the last decade of the 19th century. At about the same time, the little marvel that would ultimately mobilize the masses made its appearance – the gasoline engine.

In 1890, a gasoline-powered diamond drill was used at the New Almaden mine. The engineers that installed it were apparently unaware of the fumes produced by the engine, and were almost overcome by them on its first use.[122] In 1900, C. S. Ford built a 10-stamp mill, powered by a gasoline engine – one of the first. It cost $8 to run the mill for 24 hours.[123]

The Pelton Wheel

Lester A. Pelton of Camptonville, CA, developed the *Pelton water wheel* in 1878.[124] See figure 30. Pelton performed numerous experiments in designing an effective water wheel, but the power delivered was not sufficient. Close examination of the jet of water hitting the iron buckets fastened to the wheel revealed that the water bouncing off of one bucket impeded the next. Time was spent trying to overcome the effect of this splashing.

Figure 28   Steam Traction Engine
Courtesy USGS

Figure 29   Stock Certificate Artwork   Author

Figure 30   Hug Turbine (Pelton Wheel)   Author

Jim Hutchinson, who worked with Pelton, describes how Pelton came up with the split-bucket[125] design:

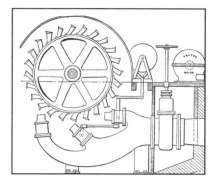

"Tired and worn out, Pelton thought a little relaxation might help him solve his problem. A trip visiting his neighbor and shooting the breeze might settle his nerves. As he approached his neighbor, who was out in the clover patch using a garden hose to drive a stray cow away, he observed that the stream of water coming from this garden hose hit the cow squarely on the sharp bone of its nose; the water divided as it struck, half going east and half going west with no water coming straight back. He saw immediately why his experiments were all failures."[126]

A valve controlling the water flow to one or more of the nozzles, as illustrated in figure 31, could regulate the power output of a Pelton wheel.[127]

Figure 31   Pelton Wheel
Source: Behr, 1896
Figure 32   Pelton Gearing

In 1894, the North Star Mining Company realized the need for a new power plant, and hired civil engineer Arthur De Wint Foote to design and construct the plant. Foote considered electricity, but abandoned that idea as being unreliable after having visited some of the power plants in the Lake Superior area. He settled on compressed air, where the compressors were to be powered by a Pelton wheel.

A pipe was installed for $27,000 to furnish the water. It was 7070' long, providing a head of 735' (about 335 PSI). An 18' 6" diameter Pelton wheel was installed, designed to operate at 110-120 RPM and limited by governors. See figure 33.

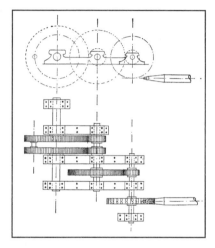

Edward A. Rix, in cooperation with Foote and E. F. Cobb, designed this Pelton wheel, which was fabricated at Fulton Engineering in San Francisco. Rix also designed the duplex compressors, which delivered 1412 cubic feet per minute at 90 PSI. The cost of the Pelton wheel and compressor was $7,410.

In 1898, the power plant was enlarged with the addition of a Pelton wheel of 30 feet diameter, the largest in the world at that time. This wheel turned at 65 RPM and produced up to 1000 HP. See figure 34. Cobb and Hesselmeyer of San Francisco built the wheel.[128]

Both of the Pelton wheels used a construction not unlike a bicycle wheel – tensioned spokes.[129] Many thought that it would fail: "The usual knockers lined the fences to see her blow up when started, but they were disappointed."[130]

◆ In 1888, when the Revenue Tunnel was started, the proactive management decided to use a six-foot Pelton wheel to power an air compressor, this supplying the air for four Rand Slugger drills. The volume of water available was insufficient except during the summer, however. Steam was used to power the drills during the rest of the year.[131]

◆ The last mill on the Comstock that used the Washoe process, the Nevada, was built in 1887 by Captain J. B. Overton to work Hale & Norcross and Chollar ore. This 60-stamp mill had a unique power plant. A 460-foot head of water, pro-

Figure 33   18.5 foot Pelton Wheel
Courtesy North Star Mining Museum
Grass Valley, California

vided by flume, powered an eleven-foot Pelton wheel. The water exiting the wheel was then piped 1630 feet underground to the Sutro Tunnel level, where it powered six forty-inch Pelton wheels, each wheel driving a dynamo. The electricity generated – about 65% of the power developed by the Pelton wheels, was used on in the mill.[132]

♦ The output of the Ontario drain tunnel in Park City, Utah was captured in a small reservoir, from which it fell about 125 feet and drove two three-foot Pelton wheels, producing 72 horsepower of AC. The electricity was used not only in the Ontario works, but also to power lights in Park City.[133]

♦ In the early 1900's, a Pelton wheel of 32 feet diameter and operating under a 1500-foot head was used to power a Rix 100-drill air compressor at the Morning mine in the Coeur d'Alene mining district.[134]

Electricity

In 1882, The Philadelphia Mining and Smelting Company's works in Wood River, Idaho, became the first to use electricity in Idaho.[135] In 1888, the first use of electricity in a mine in the U.S. had been successfully applied at the Veteran Tunnel in Aspen, Colorado, where a 7.5 HP streetcar motor was used as a hoist.[136]

In 1891, Lucius L. Nunn, with the assistance of his brother Paul H., built the world's first single-phase AC power transmission system at Ames, southwest of Telluride, Colorado. The power generated was used at the Gold King mill, located 2.6 miles away.

The plant operated on water at a head of 320 feet, driving a Pelton wheel connected to a 3000 volt, 133-cycle Westinghouse generator of Tesla's design. The Telluride Electric Power Transmission Company, incorporated in 1891, operated two dynamos, each with a capacity of 100 HP.[137] Two Pelton wheels were used, one 62 and the other 84 inches in diameter. Power was distributed up to about ten miles, and sold to about a half-dozen mining and milling interests.[138] See figures 35 and 36. A larger powerhouse replaced the first in 1895.

In 1897, Nunn also contracted with J. L. De La Mar to provide 500 HP of electricity to the Golden Gate Mill in Mercur, Utah. The power was generated at the Olmstead Generating Plant on the Provo River, and transmitted 32 miles – and at 40,000 volts, to Mercur. It was the first long-distance high-voltage project in the world.[139]

At the Revenue Tunnel in the early 1890's, long-range plans were being made for additional power. By the mid 90's these plans were realized, and included the original power station (mentioned above in *The Pelton Wheel*), plus two additional stations located near the Camp Bird mill complex, these designed to provide direct current. The electric power resulted in savings of over $1000 per month during the summer.[140]

Figure 34   Author
30-Foot Pelton Wheel, 2002

Figure 35
Ames Powerhouse
Courtesy Library of Congress

Figure 36
Switchboard and Generator
Courtesy Library of Congress

Wood

Wood was *the* raw material and fuel in the frontier West. Nearly all structures were built of it, mines were timbered with it, flumes were fabricated from it, boilers, cook stoves and fireplaces were fueled by it, and wagons, fences, furniture, and packing crates were fashioned from it. Even the railroads would not have been possible if not for the hundreds of millions of timber ties used to support the rails. Boomtowns sprung up as fast as sawmills could be erected and timber cut and sawed. In Aspen in 1881, Andy McFarlene's sawmill was kept running 14 hours a day to supply the demand.[141]

In the frenzy to mine the riches buried below, entire forests were denuded above. In the early days of mining at Park City, Utah, "an ample supply of admirable timber of even the largest dimensions" was available locally. As the mountains were stripped bare, timber was culled from the Uintah Mountains, and by the early 20th century, mine timber was imported from Oregon.[142] According to the *Mining and Scientific Press* in 1879, Virginia City, Nevada – alone, consumed about 300,000 cords of wood a year.[143] By 1871 the only wood suitable for charcoaling had been cut for a radius of 10 miles from Eureka, Nevada.[144]

Dan De Quille made the following enlightened observation concerning the forests of the Sierra Nevada adjacent to the Comstock:

> "The time is not far distant when the whole of that part of the Sierra Nevada range lying adjacent to the Nevada silver-mining region will be utterly denuded of trees of every kind. Already one bad effect of this denudation is seen in the summer failure of the water in the Carson River. The first spell of hot weather in the spring now sweeps nearly all the snow from the mountains and sends it down the valleys in one grand flood, whereas while the mountains were thickly clad with pines the melting of the snow was gradual and there was a good volume of water in the river throughout the summer and fall months. ... There must come a day when wood will be scarce and dear and some other fuel must be found."[145]

Historic photographs of mining communities often show the surrounding hills or mountains denuded of trees. Figure 37 shows Blackhawk, Colorado in 1911. Noticeably absent are most of the trees that normally thickly populate the slopes of the Rocky Mountains.

Figure 37   Black Hawk, Colorado 1911   Courtesy USGS

In the areas where some of the trees were spared, lives might be spared as a result. In 1899 at Tomichi, Colorado, the snow slide of March 3rd killed four people and destroyed all of the mine buildings. The nearby town was spared destruction due to a stand of pines preventing the initiation of an avalanche.[146]

The *Boise News* number of September 29, 1863, pleaded with the townspeople to try and preserve some of the trees in the area, if for no other reason than to provide some shady relief from the summer heat.[147]

Figure 38   Loggers ca 1885
Courtesy Library of Congress

Sawmills

At the beginning of the Comstock in 1859, there was perhaps a single sawmill. In 1860, lumber was priced from $160-$400 per thousand board feet. By 1861 there were three sawmills employing 100 men. By 1865, there were about a half dozen sawmills producing lumber that sold for $25 per thousand. By 1866 at least fifteen mills were in operation, the number of mills having doubled in two-year intervals. By 1870 there were 25 miles of logging flumes in use, transporting lumber valued at about $22 per thousand. This increased to 80 miles in 1880, transporting some 171,000 cords and 33,300,000 feet of lumber that year.[148]

Most of the tree was utilized:

Figure 39
Sledding logs to the sawmill ca 1885
Courtesy Library of Congress

♦ Cuts of the log down to 10" diameter went to the mill for saw logs, to be cut into timbers and planks of varying sizes, and sold by the board foot.

♦ 10"– 6" diameter lengths were used as mine stulls.

♦ 6"– 3" diameter pieces were used for lagging and mine rail ties.

♦ What remained was used as cordwood for sale and for the sawmill boilers.

♦ Sawdust was about all that was left, and was considered waste.[149] The sawmills in Aspen disposed of the sawdust by dumping it into the streams, thus fouling them.[150]

There was an occasional need for massive pieces of wood, such as the lengths used for Cornish System pump rods. In 1878 a bulkhead was installed in the Sutro Tunnel. The doors were made of solid sugar pine 30 inches thick, cut from a tree that was 495 years old.[151]

Whipsawed lumber cost $400 per thousand feet in the Owyhee district of Idaho during the winter of 1863-64; similar prices were to be found in Oro Grande, Idaho during the boom of 1869.[152] The cost of wood could vary considerably, even in the same locality. The Hale & Norcross mine on the Comstock paid $31.32 per thousand board feet for timber and $15.05 per cord in 1867. Three years later the prices dropped to $21.32 and $11.33, respectively.[153] During the White Pine rush, lumber fetched $175 per thousand board feet at the sawmill, but by the time it reached Treasure City where it was needed the cost rose to $200. When demand exceeded supply the price reached as high as $400. Fuel was fairly inexpensive at $6 per cord, however.[154]

Drills And Mills

Log Chutes

John Debo Galloway described the chutes used in the mountains surrounding Lake Tahoe:

> "Trees were felled by ax and saw, and the limbs trimmed from the trunk which was then cut into lengths from 16 up to 40 feet. The logs were dragged to the mill, when nearby, or transported on large wagons. Where the mountains were steep, logs were shot down the mountainside in a chute formed of two parallel lines of logs anchored to the ground. The friction of the moving log caused it to smoke, and with the accompanying dust presented an interesting sight. The chutes terminated in a pond or delivered the logs into Lake Tahoe, into which the logs plunged without injury. Daring individuals sometimes road the logs and received a wetting in the terminal pond."[155]

A log chute, built by Bob Rickard, was not quite as successful. The chute, an incline several thousand feet long, was built in the Pine Valley Mountains northwest of Silver Reef, Utah. Bob planned a grand celebration so that all could see this marvel of engineering. The guests "watched breathlessly as the first log came sliding down the incline at terrific speed." The following logs didn't fare so well – they smashed the chute into splinters. "In a matter of moments the grand opening became the grand closing of the timber chute venture. All guests were invited by Bob for a drink to celebrate the 'closing.'"[156]

The V-Flume

In 1864 the first *V-flume* was built near Carson City for transporting timber from the Sierra foothills to the valley below.[157] J. W. Haines was granted a patent for the invention of the V-flume in 1870. Testimony given in an 1872 infringement lawsuit stated that V-flumes had been built as early as 1864. The V-flume used two boards about 1.5" thick and two feet wide, joined at a right angle, forming sections. Each section overlapped the next. Later the width of the side boards were increased to about 30-32," and it was found that butt joints, if properly made, worked better than overlapping joints. The major advantage to the V-flume was that less water was required to float a log or stick of lumber, as the "V" shape more closely fit the shape of the piece of wood than a box flume did. A minor advantage was that slightly less lumber was required to build the flume, thus reducing construction and maintenance costs.[158]

A 15 mile V-flume, built in 10 weeks by the Pacific Wood, Lumber, and Fluming Company, was constructed of 2x24" planks and supported by trestles. It required 2,000,000 feet of lumber. Its capacity was 1000 cords of wood, or 500,000 feet of lumber, per day.[159] These flumes help supply the voracious maws of the mines and boilers on the Comstock. Estimates of 450-600 million feet of timber and 1.8-2.0 million cords of wood were used during the heyday of the Comstock. The Consolidated Virginia buried 6 million feet of timber annually.[160] Though the consumption of wood on the Comstock was enormous, it was not alone. All mines and mining communities used prodigious quantities of wood. For example, the Smuggler mine in Aspen used 100,000 board feet of lumber per month.[161]

Charcoal

Charcoal was extensively used throughout the West as a metallurgical fuel for smelting, and as a fuel for stoves. The manufacture of charcoal became an important industry, tied closely to the needs of smelters, the biggest consumers.

Charcoal *pits*, or more accurately, *meilers*, are circular mounds of wood covered with brush and loose earth. The wood was ignited, and draft holes along the periphery were used to carefully regulate the combustion of enough of the wood to sustain the formation of charcoal, but without burning the wood to ash.

Sometimes the wood would be stacked in long, narrow structures called *clamps* – up to 50 feet long, nine feet wide, and six high. The supporting structure was a combination of split wood, planks, and earth, with brush and earth covering the top. Ignition started at one end, and the charcoaling of the contained cordwood proceeded to the other end in about 5 days.[162]

These methods of charcoaling, while requiring little capital, were labor intensive. The charcoal was of an inferior grade – the dirt used to prevent the cordwood from igniting contaminated the product.

James C. Cameron, Jr., invented the *beehive* charcoal kiln in 1868,[163] where the Michigan Central Iron Works put it to the test. See figure 40. The kilns were fairly cheap to construct (about $600 in Michigan) and repair, easy to load the cordwood and unload the charcoal, and produced a quality product. A 35-cord kiln could produce 1750 bushels of charcoal in about 13 days. The beehive charcoal kiln was rapidly adopted throughout the east, and quickly spread to the West, where it helped satisfy the ever-growing demands for metallurgical charcoal.[164] Figure 41 shows the charcoal ovens at Ward, Nevada, which were operational from 1876-1879. [165]

Figure 40   Beehive Kiln   Author
Little Pinto, Utah 2002

♦ The Hecla Consolidated Mining Company in Hecla, Montana, operated 38 charcoal kilns on Canyon Creek. These kilns produced over one million bushels of charcoal annually for the nearby Glendale smelters, the charcoal selling for 11 cents a bushel. Canadian and French woodcutters performed most of the logging, while Italians handled the charcoaling.[166]

♦ Charcoal produced in the San Francisco district of Utah was made from piñon pine.[167] The wood was cut by Mormons for $1.25 per cord, and then hauled to the beehive kilns for $1.50-$2.50 per cord. About 50 bushels, each weighing 17 pounds, were produced per cord. Kiln hands were paid from $2.00-$2.50 per day. The cost per bushel, delivered in racks to the local smelters, was 18 cents.[168]

♦ In June 1873, Colonel Sherman Stevens built a sawmill, flume, and the Cottonwood charcoal kilns for producing mine timbers and charcoal to be used at Cerro Gordo. These products were hauled to Steven's Wharf on Owens Lake, then transported to the other side by the steamer Bessie Brady, and finally by wagon to the mines and smelters at Cerro Gordo.[169]

♦ In 1879, when Leadville nearly reached its peak of 16 smelters, local charcoal ranged from 10-18 cents per bushel.[170] The spruce and fir used made a poor product, however.[171]

Figure 41   Panoramic view of the Ward Charcoal Kilns, Ward, Nevada 2002   Author

Coke

Coal was converted to coke in beehive ovens in a manner not unlike that for charcoaling wood. See figure 42. For every ton of coal processed, about ⅔ of a ton of coke was created. Connellsville, Pennsylvania coke was preferred for metallurgical purposes because:

- ♦ It has the mechanical strength necessary to prevent being crushed in a smelter
- ♦ The size of the pieces were over two inches
- ♦ It could be handled roughly without breaking, unlike charcoal
- ♦ It has a higher degree of porosity than charcoal, which permits a greater reaction surface area
- ♦ It has a low ash content, typically less than 8%
- ♦ It has a low moisture content, typically under 1%
- ♦ It has a low phosphorous content, typically less than 0.02%
- ♦ It has a low sulfur content, typically less than 1.25%
- ♦ It has a high carbon content[173]

Figure 42   Coking Plant
Redstone, Colorado 1911
Courtesy USGS

Coke was an expensive commodity in the west. In 1872, metallurgical coke was available to the Salt Lake smelters – shipped from Connellsville, Pennsylvania, for $34 per ton.[174] Most of this price was for shipping: in Connellsville, coke cost but 90 cents a ton immediately following the Panic of 1873, then rose to a high of about $4-$5 per ton in the mid 1870's, and by 1880 had stabilized at $1.79 per ton.[175]

Leadville's smelters had an insatiable appetite for fuels. El Moro coke, produced 225 miles away in Trinidad, was preferred to local charcoal. Until railroad transportation reached the camp, the price varied greatly and depended in part on the condition of the roads and the season. During the summer it was $25 per ton, and in the winter as high as $60.[176] Colorado coal production is shown in chart 2.[177] Through 1900, Colorado produced less than 2% of the U.S. total.[178]

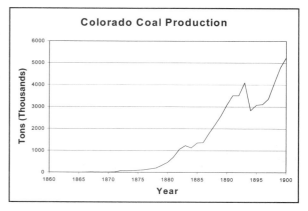

Chart 2

Charts 3 and 4 depict the total fuel consumption in the U.S. and the percentages of wood, coal, and petroleum consumption in the U.S. on an energy-value basis.[179]

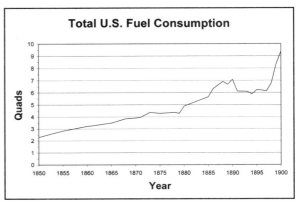

▲Chart 3   ▼Chart 4

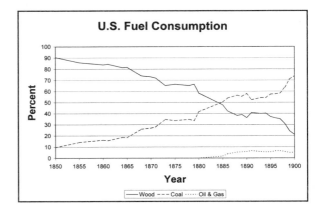

Alternate Fuels

Lack of wood for mine timbers – the nearest being sixteen miles away, slowed development of the mines in the Cornucopia mining district in Nevada.

Wood was so expensive that the 10-stamp Leopard Company mill burned sagebrush for fuel. The mill started up in December of 1874, but burned down in July 1875 – sparks ignited a pile of sagebrush stacked against the side of the mill. Sagebrush was also used for fuel in Tuscarora, Nevada due to the scarcity of wood.[180]

156 pounds of sagebrush has roughly the same fuel value as 100 pounds of cedar.[181]

The White Hills Company – about 50 miles northwest of Kingman, Arizona, used Joshua trees and yucca as fuel for the steam hoists.[182]

Fire

With all of the wooden structures and wood-burning engines, stoves, and fireplaces, fires were bound to happen, and they did with appalling regularity. Very few of the western mining camps escaped the ravages of fire, and some experienced fires more than once. Fires destroyed Mokelumne Hill, California in 1854, 1864, and 1874.[183]

Grant Smith witnessed the great fire of Virginia City on October 26, 1875:

> "The awesome scene reached its height when the fire caught the great Con. Virginia and Ophir hoisting works and millions of feet of piled lumber and thousands of cords of wood burst into flames. The heat was so intense that brick buildings went down like paper boxes 'and railroad car wheels were melted in the open air alongside of the works.' Fortunately there had been ample time to get the men out of the mines."[184]

In 1880, there were 2200 buildings in Virginia City, but only 92 – a scant 4%, were of brick.[185] It seems the residents didn't learn their lesson, even after being burned out of house and home.

♦ Park City, Utah burned to the ground on June 19, 1898. Most of Main Street was destroyed; Chinatown was gone, as were 75 homes on nearby Rossie Hill. 500 people were left homeless and more than $1,000,000 of property was lost. Fitting for the spirit of a mining town, the first new building to be built was a saloon.[186]

♦ Colorado certainly had its share of fires. On June 5, 1892, Creede Colorado was burned to the ground. Cripple Creek burned on April 25, 1896, destroying 15 acres of the town. Four days later a second fire wiped out pretty much all that was left standing after the first fire. On August 21, 1899, much of neighboring Victor was destroyed by fire.[187]

♦ Mercur, Utah was burned to ashes on June 26, 1902. Figures 43 and 44 show two spectacular views of Mercur. The first was taken two days before the fire. The second shows Mercur two and a half hours after the fire. The massive Golden Gate Mill in the background and a few of the homes were spared.[188]

♦ The great Pioche, Nevada fire of September 1871 began in a restaurant where a celebration was underway. It quickly spread to the neighboring buildings, including the Felsenthal Store, which was supposedly a fireproof stone structure. It was not, as was evidenced by the ignition and explosion of 300 barrels of blasting powder, which shot a 1000-pound door over the town and to the Burke Mine, and rained stone, timbers, and burning debris over the town, touching off new fires.[189]

Figure 43 ▲   Mercur, Utah June 24, 1902
Figure 44 ▼   Mercur, Utah June 26, 1902

Fires in hoisting works could drop burning debris down into the shaft, which would in turn ignite the shaft timbering and destroy it too.[190] Prospectors often viewed wildfires with indifference. Some found the fires to be convenient. The fire

"let daylight and sunlight into the dark recesses, burns off the turf and accumulated matter on the surface of the ground clear down to the rocks and gravel thus greatly facilitating prospecting."[191]

In the Caribou, Colorado area prospectors intentionally burned up the forest just to clear away the brush; thus making prospecting easier.[192]

Assays

How does one determine if precious metals are present in a rock? If the gold isn't visible to the naked eye, then an assay is required. The Homestake in Dakota employed a simple method of assaying their ore, which was still being used after at least twenty years of operating the legendary mines. Every day, two-pound samples were taken from every working face, crushed mechanically, and then panned. The man panning could process 60 pans per day, and by eye could estimate the value of the ore to within 25-50 cents. Periodic checks by fire assay confirmed this.[193]

Two types of assay were commonly performed: The first, which might be termed a *field assay*, was performed onsite by a prospector with simple tools. It wasn't very sophisticated, but it would reveal the presence of silver adequately. The *fire assay*, which is performed by a professional assayer in a mining camp or community, is far more accurate, and is used to detect and accurately measure the amounts of gold and silver in the rock. The fire assay is still used today for the determination of precious metals in ores.

Field Assay

Small flecks of gold might be seen in a specimen of rock with either the naked eye or a hand lens.[194] Additional testing was required to better determine the amounts and types of precious and base metals contained within. The sample was finely ground using one stone against another. The resulting powder was placed in a split ox horn, and washed in a manner similar to that used for panning gold.

Silver was determined by washing this residue into a flask, and nitric acid was added. The flask was heated until the escaping fumes changed from red to white, with silver nitrate being produced if silver was present. The chemical reaction is:

$$Ag + NO_3^- \quad \blacktriangleright \quad AgNO_3$$

After cooling, the solution was poured into a test tube, and a solution of ordinary salt was added.[195] The reaction that followed

$$AgNO_3 + NaCl \quad \blacktriangleright \quad NaNO_3 + AgCl$$

precipitates silver chloride as an ultra-fine white powder. Exposure to light would cause the silver chloride to turn an unmistakable dark purple. Washing the precipitate would assist in dissolving lead chloride, if present. The silver chloride could be reduced to metallic silver by placing it in a small, hollowed out section of charcoal and then heating it by candle flame – this would produce a small bead of silver.[196] If copper were present, an iron wire or knife blade would be plated when immersed in the solution. Silver chloride present in the original ore could not be determined in this fashion – it required the more sophisticated Fire Assay.[197]

Figure 45   Medieval Assay Lab

Source: Lazarus Ercker's
Treatise on Ores and Assaying

The Fire Assay

Much of the following description of the *fire assay* comes from Van Loon and Barefoot's comprehensive *Determination of the Precious Metals – Selected Instrumental Methods* and from Young and Lenon's *Western Mining*.[198]

The fire assay has been used for hundreds of years. The first comprehensive treatment of gold and silver assaying was by Ercker in 1574 in *Treatise on Ores and Assaying*. See figure 45. It is interesting to note that the fire assay has never failed to identify a paying ore. Successful application of the fire assay requires the skill and experience of the assayer.

One of the most difficult decisions for the person selecting the sample was to choose a representative one. If the claim or mine owner wished to sell, the choice was easy: find the most valuable piece of ore possible, have it assayed, and use the artificially high results to influence the decision of the unwary buyer. In 1868 at Meadow Lake, California, it was reported that a ½ walnut-sized piece of ore assayed $93,770.97 per ton! Over a 60-year period, the entire Meadow Lake district produced barely twice that amount. Another assay, seen in the box to the right, was apparently performed there as well.[199]

Mines carefully selected large numbers of small ore samples. When reduced to powder and thoroughly mixed, the varying precious metal content of the individual pieces would provide a reasonable average value for the current workings. Mills collected frequent and small samples from the output of the crushing machinery for the same purpose.

Preparation

The first step is to prepare the sample, which was generally performed by the assayer's assistant. Larger samples were cobbed into pieces small enough to fit into a *chipmunk* – a small, hand-cranked jaw crusher. See figure 46. Jaw crushers are described in the last chapter. The rock fed through the chipmunk emerges about pea-sized.

Portions of the crushed rock were then placed on a small, iron *bucking board* that has sides that curve slightly upward. A cast iron *muller* – a heavy iron shoe of about 20 pounds fixed to the end of an axe handle, was used to grind the sample down to grit by repeatedly sliding the muller back and forth and with a slight side-to-side rocking action over the sample. See figure 47. Final preparation of the sample was made with a mortar and pestle, reducing the sample to *rock flour*.

Each sample to be assayed was then carefully divided into three or more parts. The first was used for the assay, and the second for a re-assay if the first showed anomalous results. The third was kept as a reference, or in the case of a custom mill purchasing a lot of ore from a mine, for a third-party and independent assayer to provide a check if the buyer and seller disagreed on the principle assayer's results. A *riffle splitter* was sometimes used to split larger samples into multiple parts. See figure 48.

Figure 46 ▲   Chipmunk   Author

Figure 47 ▼   Muller   Author

The samples were then carefully weighed to 29.167 grams – an *assay ton*. One ton of ore contains 29167 *troy ounces*. The assay ton simplifies the calculation of ounces of precious metal per ton, as each milligram of precious metal in the assay ton represents an ounce per ton of ore. Precision balances were used for all steps requiring weighing, especially those used to measure the pinhead-sized bead of precious metal described later. The scales were kept in cases behind glass doors, and as far away from dust as possible – a difficult requirement in a business that crushes rock to flour all day. See figure 49. Sensitive and accurate balances were not cheap. The Eureka Consolidated paid $250 for an Oertling assay balance in 1871.[200]

HASH
"Fire Assay"

The following "assay" was made of hash served at a restaurant in Meadow Lake, California:

Hair	7
Gum Boots	3
Potatoes	60
Flies	2
Yellow Jackets	1
Pork, Very Old	15
Beef	10
False Teeth	2

The assay samples were then poured into fire clay *crucibles* – small ceramic cups, for subsequent *fusion* – melting. *Fluxes* were added, the individual amounts determined by the nature of the ore and by experience. Successful collection of the gold and silver present in the sample required considerable experimentation with fluxes and assay conditions. Typical fluxes used included:

- Litharge PbO
- Silica SiO_2
- Borax $Na_2B_4O_7$
- Soda ash Na_2CO_3
- Niter KNO_3
- Wheat flour A reducing agent

The litharge (lead oxide) is used to collect the gold and silver – it is the *collector*. For an extremely high-grade bonanza ore sample of, say, 20 ounces of gold and 500 ounces of silver per ton, the assay ton would contain 520 milligrams of precious metal. Note that at least 165 grams of litharge is used as the collector in an assay of a low-sulfide assay ton-sized sample. In this example, that is over 300 times as much litharge as precious metal. This ensures the complete collection of all of the precious metals. Likewise, high percentages of lead or copper were required for successful smelting of many silver and gold ores.

Figure 48 ▲   Riffle Splitter   Author
Figure 49 ▼   Balance   Author

The silica is used to create a glassy slag of the unwanted minerals. Borax, which is acidic, forms complex compounds and lowers the fusion temperature of the slag. It is useful when an improved recovery of the precious metals is required. Soda ash (sodium carbonate), which is strongly basic, promotes the formation of sulfides. The flour is used to reduce the litharge to lead. Some ores – especially those very high in sulfur content, may require additional oxidizer, such as niter (potassium nitrate). See table 2 for typical ore-flux mixtures used for an assay ton.[201]

Inquartation

If the ore or concentrate sample has a silver-to-gold ratio less than about 3:1, then *inquartation* is required. This is the addition of an *inquart* – a known weight of silver, either a needle-like crystal of pure silver, or a carefully measured length of lead-silver alloy rod. The silver added is designed to bring this ratio to at least 3:1, and preferably 5:1. This serves three purposes:

Weights in grams	Low sulfide	High sulfide
Ore	29.167	29.167
PbO	165	400
SiO_2	19.4	21.9
Na_2CO_3	41.0	58.3
KNO_3	1.9	23.3
Flour	2 - 6	

Table 2
Typical flux amounts
for an assay ton

- Reduces gold losses during the cupellation step.

- Allows trace amounts of gold to be transferred from the cupel during the parting process.

- Provides the silver-gold ratio required for effective dissolving of the silver during parting.

Too much silver will allow the gold to *flour* during parting. This may have been unavoidable for many ores or concentrates.

Drills And Mills

Classic Lead Assay

The samples are placed in a *muffle furnace* – see figures 50 and 51, on the lower, reducing deck[202] at an initial temperature of about 1040° C, and then quickly raised to 1150° C. The flour reduces the litharge, forming molten lead droplets. This reaction, where the active part of the flour is its carbon content, is:

$$PbO + C \quad \blacktriangleright \quad Pb + CO$$

The droplets of lead collect the gold and silver from the fusing mass as they sink to the bottom of the crucible. A glassy slag forms and floats above the dense lead. The slag carries with it the unwanted metals such as iron, which may be present in the form of pyrite, and is not collected by the lead. After about 30 minutes at this temperature, the fusion is complete. The mechanism by which lead collects noble metals is not clear, even to this day.

The glowing fusion mass is poured into an inverted conical-shaped mold made of cast iron, possibly coated with a thin film of iron oxide (Fe_2O_3) to prevent the solidified mass from adhering to it. See figure 52. The dense lead solidifies at the point of the cone, the slag above. After cooling, the mass is removed from the mold, and the slag is separated from the lead *button* by gently tapping it with a small hammer.

Cupellation

Cupellation is the next step, and requires the use of *cupels* – small cups made from bone ash. Bone ash has the interesting property of readily absorbing lead oxide, but not lead, gold or silver. They are fashioned in a wooden mold – see figure 53.

The lead button is carefully hammered into a small cube, making sure that no slag is attached in the process. Meanwhile, the cupels are pre-heated to about 1000° C, and are sometimes arranged with *deadheads* – blank cupels, used as "shields" around the perimeter. Without these deadheads, relatively cold and undesirable air currents near the furnace door can cause *freezing* – lead oxide covering the molten lead, thus preventing further oxidation. These shields diminish and pre-heat the air currents entering the door.

The cubes are quickly added, one to each cupel. After about five minutes of *opening* the bead – bringing it to a molten and glowing state, the furnace door or air draught is opened to admit air (oxygen) to *drive* – oxidize, the sample. The temperature is allowed to drop rapidly to about 820° C, and over a period of about 30 minutes it is slowly raised to the finishing temperature of about 880° C. If the temperature is allowed to get too high, volatilization of the silver occurs.[203]

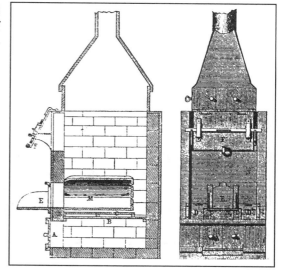

Figure 50   Muffle Furnace
Source: Eissler, 1889

Figure 51   Muffle Furnace   Author

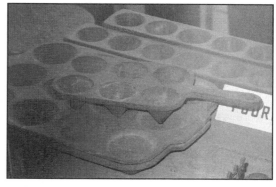

Figure 52   Iron Assay Molds   Author

During this time the molten lead is oxidized back to litharge – about 98.5% is absorbed by the cupel, and 1.5% volatilizes. For this reason, it is extremely important that the furnace be adequately exhausted. When the very last of the litharge is absorbed by the cupel, the small *prill* – bead, of molten gold and silver would *blick* – give off a flash of light, as it solidified.[204]

Parting

The cupels are then removed and allowed to cool. The very tiny prill that remains in the cupel contains the *doré* – gold and silver, present in the original sample, plus the silver inquart if added. The prill is very carefully weighed, then hammered and flattened to the point of being paper-thin, and dissolved in warm nitric (or sulfuric) acid. This is known as *parting* the silver and gold. The silver was completely dissolved from the doré only if there was a sufficient amount present, which created the interstitial pathways for its removal from the flattened bead; thus the requirement for inquartation for some ore samples. The remaining residue is the gold.[205] It is weighed after being collected, washed, dried and annealed. The difference between the prill's original weight and the gold remaining after parting is the silver present, less the weight of the inquart if one were added. The assayer then filled out the assay slip for his customer, and it was on to the next batch of samples.

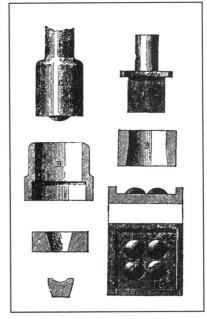

Figure 53   Cupel Molds
Source: Eissler, 1889

Samplers

An extension of assaying, but on a greater scale, is the service provided by the *sampler*. Samplers created a local market for the ore sellers – the mines, and for the ore buyers – the mills and smelters. Part of their function was to *sample* – assay, lots of ore independently from the buyers and sellers. Samplers also acted as on-site ore purchasing agents for large ore reduction concerns such as smelting companies, which required a variety of different types of ore to conduct their operations successfully. The sampler would negotiate favorable contracts with a number of mines, buying the different ore in quantities suitable for the economic reduction of the minerals. The economy of scale offered by sampling works translated to reduced expenses, such as favorable railroad rates and rebates, and this in turn translated to competitive prices for the mines.

Figure 54   Eagle Sampler
Goldfield, Colorado, 1903
Courtesy USGS

The J. R. Nichols Metallurgical Works, built in Sandy, Utah, was perhaps the largest sampler in the Great Basin in the mid-1870's. Ore was received by the Utah Central Line railroad, where it was either put in bins or piled outside. The sampling works – a behemoth at three stories, 60x80 feet, and requiring a half million bricks and 260,000 feet of lumber to build, cost $125,000.

Inside, the ore – actually, every tenth shovel full, was used as the starting point for the sample. The hard ores present were crushed in a Cornish roll;[206] any sands were thoroughly mixed with the ore thus crushed, the whole lot being dried. This sample was then quartered, crushed finer through another set of rolls, and again quartered.

At this point, about six-tenths of one percent of the original ore made up the sample. A portion of this was taken, ground still further to pass a 70-mesh screen, and split into thirds; one portion to be assayed by the smelter, one portion to be assayed by the owners of the ore, and the last portion to be assayed independently if the first two assays disagreed significantly. The average of the assays was then used as the basis for the sampler's purchase of the lot of ore.[207]

The Taylor & Brunton Sampler at Cripple Creek used a similar method. The ore was crushed in a two-stage set of rolls (42 and 36 inch), from which 20 percent was sampled. This sample was then crushed in another set of rolls (27 inch), 20 percent sampled and crushed (20 inch), and 20 percent sampled. The total sample, weighing from 20-50 pounds, was now about eight-tenths of one percent of the original ore lot, and crushed to about one-sixteenth of an inch (0.0625") in average size.

It was dried, ground in a rotary grinder, and broken down to a 30-ounce sample using a large riffle splitter. The sample was then ground to pass a 110-mesh screen by using a muller. It was then split into four parts, one of which was assayed, one sent to the shipper, and two held in reserve in case of disagreement.[208] Table 3 lists required sample sizes based on how finely the rock is crushed.[209]

Piece Diameter, Inches	Minimum Sample Weight, Lbs
5.5	79300
4.0	69109
3.5	44958
2.5	16384
1.25	2048
0.67	256
0.33	32
0.17	4
0.083	0.5
0.040	0.0625

Table 3
Sample weight based on particle sizes

Metalliferous Murphy

Mark Twain, in *Roughing It*, wrote the following concerning a particular assayer:

"Assaying was a good business, and so some engaged in it, occasionally, who were not strictly scientific and capable. One assayer got such results out of all specimens brought to him that in time he almost acquired a monopoly in the business. But like all men who achieve success, he became an object of envy and suspicion. The other assayers entered into a conspiracy against him, and let some prominent citizens into the secret in order to show that they meant fairly. Then they broke a little fragment off a carpenter's grindstone and got a stranger to take it to the popular scientist and get it assayed. In the course of an hour the result came – whereby it appeared that a ton of that rock would yield $1284.40 in silver and $366.36 in gold! Due publication of the whole matter was made in the paper, and the popular assayer left town 'between two days'."[210]

Metalliferous Murphy may have been a real assayer, trained in Scotland, who worked in Pioche, Nevada. The trick described by Twain may have indeed happened, where Murphy proclaimed the rich silver values found in the sandstone fragment.

Some claim he was hanged on the spot, others that he was run out of town. But one ending is that he

"traced the origin of the grindstone to the Leeds, Utah area, where he promptly went, located his claims and became fabulously rich."

Leeds – the Silver Reef area, had silver bearing sandstone that assayed $500 silver to the ton![211]

Figure 55   Assay Lab   Author

Endnotes

1 Sometimes referred to as a *tipple*, but that is more properly applied to coal-storage bins.

2 Used until 1976.

3 TAYLOR01989 page 13

4 GARDINER2002 pages 15, 25, 47

5 SAVORY1970

6 The following is provided for clarification. When a male donkey breeds with a female horse, a *mule* is the offspring. When a male horse breeds with a female donkey, the offspring is a *hinny*. Contrary to popular belief, all mules are not sterile; *male* mules and hinnies are sterile; *females* are not. Spanish donkeys were preferred for breeding mules. In the U.S. in 1920 there were 5.43 million mules; 1931, 5.13 million; 1948, 2.54 million; and by 1954 only 1.6 million. SAVORY1970

7 SAVORY1970

8 RAGSDALE1976 page 47

9 SAVORY1970

10 SOWELL1976 pages 28,29

11 BACKUS1969 pages 45,48

12 BACKUS1969 page 90

13 WOLLE1963 page 291

14 JESSEN1994 pages 215-217. An earlier owner was Ed Snell, who had a jack train in Alma.

15 BACKUS1969 page 259

16 SOWELL1976 pages 28,29. Crack of dusk, too. And for that matter, during the day.

17 NORTHROP1975 page 10. The salt was required for the *Patio Process*, described in the following chapter.

18 NORTHROP1975 page 15

19 GALLOWAY1947 page 39

20 NORTHROP1975 page 22

21 JACKSONW1963 pages 47,48

22 BLAIR1980 page 92

23 ROHRBOUGH1986 page 58

24 SMITHP1994 page 42

25 NORTHROP1975 page 29

26 GREGORYD1996 page 82

27 BIRD1986 page 43

28 CARPENTER1953 pages 21,23

29 BAILEY2002 page 41

30 JACKSONW1963 pages 36,118

31 TAYLORJ1964 page 92

32 RAYMOND1873 page 238

33 JACKSONW1963 pages 47,48,192,205

34 ROHRBOUGH1986 page 57

35 ROHRBOUGH1986 page 110

36 Now a part of the spectacular Million Dollar Highway.

37 SMITHP1994 pages 39,42,90,91,100

38 RANSOME1908 page 80

39 WELLS2002 pages 21, 22

40 WOLLE1963 pages 312-313

41 BLAIR1980 page 92

42 SOWELL1976 pages 28,29

43 BLAIR1980 page 92

44 TAYLORJ1964 page 92

45 CARPENTER1953 pages 10-11

46 RAGSDALE1976 page 48

47 DEQUILLE1959 page 162

48 The end of the whip had a silk "popper" used to make the characteristic cracking noise; hence the expression.

49 BENNETT1966 pages 18-19

50 TAYLORJ1964 page 37

51 JACKSONW1963 page 63

52 TAYLORJ1964 page 63

53 SAVORY1970

54 BACKUS1969 pages 49,104

55 WOLLE1977 pages 229,230

56 MCQUISTON1986 page 18, YOUNGO1972 page 162

57 VOYNICK1984 page 47

58 STEWART1962 page 109, SAVORY1970, YOUNGO1972 page 162

59 RINGHOLZ1972 page 20

60 RINGHOLZ1972 page 20

61 POLINIAK1970 page 20

62 DICICCIO1996 page 110

63 BENNETT1966 page 178

64 BENNETT1966 page 178

65 WOLLE1977 page 230

66 STEWART1962 pages 109, 156

67 POLINIAK1970 page 21

68 JESSEN1994 pages 218-219

69 STEWART1962 page 147

70 GREGORYD1996 page 115

71 FIELDER1970 page 176

72 THOMPSON1968 page 123

73 POLINIAK1970 page 21

74 POLINIAK1970 page 21. YOUNGO1972 page 162 has a similar version.

75 FARISH1915 pages 354, 355, 360. On page 360, mention is made that about 1863, the remaining 14 animals were turned loose in Arizona.

76 TINGLEY1990, DEQUILLE1959 page 281

77 WIER1957 page 292, ABBE1985 page 47

78 FARISH1915 page 360

79 DEQUILLE1959 page 281

80 TAYLORJ1964 pages 7, 313. Other animals were used for mining-related transportation. Dogs were used to pull sleds in the Alaska goldfields. The author has a photograph of Jersey cows pulling slabs of marble in Vermont.

81 MONTANADEQ.41

82 Molinelli, in his promotional piece *Eureka and its Resources*, said, "While there is some difference of opinion as to the exact character of the main lode here, all are agreed that the ore deposits are of a permanent kind." MOLINELLI1997 page 39

83 WIER1957 page 294, CARPENTER1953 page 16 During these first five years, Tonopah produced over $6.3 million. CARPENTER1953 page 149.

84 CARPENTER1953 page 45

85 GALLOWAY1947 pages 53-56

86 GALLOWAY1947 page 101

87 Four dollars for a twenty-mile ride, this during the days when good wages for a miner were also about $4 per day.

88 SMITHP1994 pages 159,168,177

89 ROHRBOUGH1986 pages 157,158,159,171

90 ROHRBOUGH1986 pages 209,210

91 SMITHP1994 pages 34,91,166,170,176, RANSOME1901 page 22

92 SLOAN1975 page 131

93 JACKSONW1963 page 151

94 BRITANNICA1958, *Railroad*, page 918

95 FETCHENHIER1999 page 41

96 Charles Hodgson received a patent on July 20, 1868, for a tram that utilized friction – in the form of a leather-lined notched piece of wood, to transport the bucket. TRENNERT2001 page 14. The Treasure Hill tramway, 11,000 feet long, was also a Hodgson design and was put in operation in late May 1871. TRENNERT2001 page 16

97 JACKSONW1963 pages 177-178

98 RAYMOND1873 page 190

99 JACKSONW1963 pages 178,182

100 TRENNERT2001 pages 11, 17

101 TRENNERT2001 pages 29-30

102 TRENNERT2001 page 21

103 WELLS2002 page 102

104 TRENNERT2001 pages 54-55

105 MORSE2000 page 36

106 ROHRBOUGH1986 page 169

107 BIRD1986 pages 61,66

108 BENHAM1980 page 45

109 GREGORYD1996 pages 128-130

110 BOUTWELL1912 page 24

111 WASSON1878 page 28, WEDERTZ1996 page 183

112 FETCHENHIER1999 pages 36-38

113 SCHNEIDER1992 pages 65-67. The North Star mine utilized a 2000-foot jig-back aerial tram, where the descending loaded bucket brought up the empty one, and then the direction of the buckets reversed when the next loaded bucket was sent down. When the loaded bucket reached its terminus, the contents were transferred to a second 3.2-mile conventional aerial tram and transported to the Contention mill on the Animas River.[113]

114 DEQUILLE1959 page 374

115 MANRY1999 page 115

116 DEQUILLE1959 page 241

117 EMMONS1885 page 133

118 BANCROFT1890 page 622

119 BEHR1896 page 95

120 EMMONS1885 page 246

121 GALLOWAY1947 page 75

122 SCHNEIDER1992 page 101

123 HALL1998 page 76

124 KIROY1961, MCQUISTON1986 page 36

125 Patented in 1880. ASME.H157

126 KIROY1961. Patent #223,692 for the splitter principle, October 26, 1880.

127 BEHR1896 page 97

128 ASME.H157

129 The bicycle was arguably the most technologically advanced machine in its day, if one considers the research, patents, metallurgy, and other efforts that furthered its design and engineering. The Wright Brothers – bicycle mechanics, used a lot of its technology in developing their airplanes.

130 CARMAN1963 pages 1-5, MCKINNEY1995 page 28, GARDNER2001. An attempt was made to reactivate the Pelton wheels in the 1950's. Due to age and leaks in the pipeline, and the 344% increase in the cost of the water to power them, the wheels were finally retired.

131 GREGORYD1996 pages 154-155

[132] SMITHG1998 page 256, DE-QUILLE1974 page 79

[133] BOUTWELL1912 pages 22-23

[134] RANSOME1908 pages 87, 88

[135] WELLS2002 page 154

[136] BENHAM1980 page 37

[137] 1000 HP per USGS1897. The plaque on the Ames powerhouse states 100 HP.

[138] HAER01, GREGORYD1996 pages 161-163, USGS1897 page 755 all give 1890 as the date. The plaque on the Ames power-house states "Electricity produced here in the spring of 1891."

[139] ALDER1961 page 37

[140] GREGORYD1996 pages 155-158

[141] ROHRBOUGH1986 page 43

[142] BOUTWELL1912 page 23

[143] BAILEY2002 page 172

[144] RAYMOND1873 page 174

[145] DEQUILLE1959 page 179

[146] WOLLE1977 page 140

[147] WOLLE1963 page 230

[148] GALLOWAY1947 pages 81-83, 88-89

[149] SOWELL1976 pages 42,43

[150] ROHRBOUGH1986 page 112

[151] STEWART1962 page 146

[152] WELLS2002 pages 36, 98

[153] RAYMOND1873 page 145

[154] JACKSONW1963 pages 116,119

[155] GALLOWAY1947 page 85

[156] PROCTOR1991 page 163

[157] WIER1957 page 292

[158] GALLOWAY1947 page 86

[159] GALLOWAY1947 pages 100-101

[160] SMITHD1993 pages 12-13, SMITHG1998 page 247, DEQUILLE1959 page 174

[161] ROHRBOUGH1986 page 192

[162] BAILEY2002 pages 148-149

[163] BUTLER1913 page 114 gives 1868; BAILEY2002 page 160 gives "1867 or 1868"

[164] BAILEY2002 pages 160, 163-164

[165] The ovens are 30 feet high and 27 feet in diameter at the base, with walls 20 inches thick. Each oven held about 35 cords of wood and produced about 1750 bushels of charcoal. WARD2002

[166] MONTANADEQ.10

[167] A cord of nut pine produces anywhere from 18 (ANGEL1973 page 438) to 28 (BAILEY2002 page 86) bushels of charcoal.

[168] BUTLER1913 page 114

[169] CERES.537. The Bessie Brady was built by James Brady and launched June 27, 1872. It was destroyed by spontaneous combustion on May 11, 1882.

[170] FELL1979 page 103

[171] GARDINER2002 page 50

[172] ANGEL1973 page 438, BANCROFT1890 pages 284-285, ONEILL1986 pages 14-15. The Tybo-Hot Creek area also had problems with charcoalers, but this time they were Chinese. Ultimately they were driven out, replaced by *Carbonari* and Indians. ONEILL1986 page 15.

[173] DICICCIO1996 page 69

[174] BAILEY2002 page 179

[175] DICICCIO1996 pages 40, 70

[176] FELL1979 page 100

[177] BAKER1927 pages 548, 551

[178] DICICCIO1996 pages 31, 62 for U.S total, BAKER1927 pages 548, 551 for Colorado total, which is 55,783,400 tons.

[179] Data from http://starfire.ne.uiuc.edu/ne201/course/topics/resource_usage/each_fuel.html. A *quad* is a quadrillion BTU's. The West used greater percentages of wood than coal, whereas the heavily industrialized East – in close proximity to the developing coalfields of Pennsylvania, used greater percentages of coal.

[180] HALL1998 pages 18,20,70

[181] EMMONS1885 page 246

[182] WOLLE1963 page 80

[183] CERES.269

[184] SMITHG1998 page 192

[185] SMITHG1998 page 232

[186] THOMPSON1968 pages 160, 164, 167

[187] There are many books that mention fires in Colorado camps. All those that the author has read agree on the dates for these particular facts, so no specific references were selected.

[188] ALDER1961 page 39, inside front cover.

[189] LINCOLN page 11. Three separate photocopies available at the Lincoln County Museum list dates of September 15, 16, and 23 for the fire, one being an eyewitness account by hay farmer/teamster Peter Gottredson.

[190] TAYLOR01989 page 106

[191] DUNCAN1990 page 66

[192] SMITHD1993 page 55

[193] IRVING1904 page 59

[194] The first application of the microscope to the study of chemically etched and polished minerals was made in New Mexico in 1885. NORTHROP1975 page 30

[195] Muriatic acid was sometimes substituted for salt.

[196] The blowpipe assay was also performed. A small sample of the crushed mineral to be assayed was placed in a depression on a block of charcoal, sometimes covered with sodium bicarbonate. A flame heated the charcoal, and the assayer blew a stream of air to increase the temperature – acting as the bellows for the blacksmith's forge. The metal was smelted, and the color revealed the metals present:

Ag, a silver bead

As, fumes with a garlic odor at lower temperatures

Au, a gold bead

Cu, a red bead – especially if reduced with sodium bicarbonate

Pb, a metallic bead, but also white-to-yellow depending on the sulfur content

Sb, a dense white Sb_2O_3 sublimate lacking a garlic odor (from **As**, if present, which is driven off at a lower temperature)

Te, white

Zn, in a reducing flame, canary yellow (hot) or white (cold).

Other metals can be more complex – for example, Ni produces a violet (hot) or brown (cold) bead from an oxidizing atmosphere, but a grey bead in a reducing atmosphere. This method was slow and best suited for high-grade silver ores and base metals.

[197] DEQUILLE1959 pages 70-72

[198] LOON1991 pages 106-136, YOUNGO1972 pages 34-39

[199] FATOUT1969 pages 107,145; 70 for "hash assay."

[200] RAYMOND1873 page 176. $3521 in 2002 dollars.

[201] Table adapted from LOON1991 page 113, and converted to a rounded assay-ton basis. Telluride ores can be problematic, having a tendency of drawing off silver and gold during cupellation. A strongly oxidizing flux can help eliminate this effect. CHEMEX2001.

[202] The lower deck does not have a draught of air supplied like the upper deck does. It has a higher concentration of carbon monoxide, and is at a higher temperature than the upper deck; thus it is a reducing environment and the upper deck is an oxidizing environment.

[203] About 2% of the silver present volatilizes under nominal conditions. CHEMEX2001.

[204] The liquid state of the bead only existed due to the presence of the lead – the alloy had a far lower melting temperature than gold or silver. The *blick* – flash of light, is caused by the loss of energy when the gold and silver bead transitions from liquid to solid. The bead is small enough for this change to occur almost instantly. A similar phenomenon was seen when refining silver, and the last of the litharge was blown off the surface – it was called the *brightening*.

[205] And platinum, palladium, etc if present.

[206] A gradual reduction in particle size, and the attendant reduction in fines being produced, was accomplished more successfully by using multiple sets of rolls, such as three sets, as opposed to two. DAY1892 page 149

[207] BAILEY2002 pages 119-121

[208] LINDGREN1906 page 138

[209] HAMILTON1920 page 152

[210] TWAIN1980 page 195

[211] PROCTOR1991 pages 26,39. A photocopy from an unidentified source, available at the Lincoln County Museum in Pioche, Nevada, stated "230 ounces of silver to the ton." The author has seen other values while thumbing through the plethora of ghost town tomes written over the years. For example, WOLLE1963 page 386 lists the sources of the grindstone as Isaac Duffin of Toquerville in one version, and Alima T. Angell of Leeds in another. She states that the assay was 200 ounces silver to the ton. It would seem that every retelling of this yarn changes the purported value of the grindstone assay, perhaps Twain's being the most outlandish considering the specific values – to the penny. ☺

Mill Processes

Figure 1   Humphrey Concentration Mill, Creede, Colorado 1905   Courtesy USGS

Mills are mineral treatment plants that crush and extract the desired minerals or metals from the ore. This process of extraction is referred to as *winning* the metal. Part of the process is to separate the valueless gangue from the desired metal or mineral. This separation is *milling* or *dressing* the ore. Some mills do not extract the metal, but instead concentrate the valuable minerals by discarding most of the worthless ones. The *concentrates*, or *con*, would receive additional processing at other mills or smelters. Facilities that perform this function are known as *concentration mills* or *concentrators*.

Some processes may have had roots in the 19th century, but were not made practical for milling until the 20th century, and for this reason are not discussed in this book. For examples, a jigging method of electrostatic separation for minerals was patented by Carpenter in 1886, but was not applied successfully until 1907 on sphalerite-pyrite ores. The Bessel brothers conceived flotation in 1877, but its first use was in Australia in 1905.[1] This "Australian Flotation Process" was tried in Rico, Colorado, in 1906. It wasn't until 1912-1914 that it was applied successfully in Colorado mills.[2] George Backus adapted the flotation process to work with molybdenum ores in 1917.[3] In 1918, the new 500 TPD Sunnyside Mill in Eureka, Colorado, successfully applied the flotation process.[4]

This chapter outlines the *physical* and *wet – lixiviation* (leaching), metallurgical processes that found widespread use in the mills for winning gold and silver. *Dry* processes, such as smelting and roasting-condensing, are covered in the following chapter. The mills crushed the ore to varying degrees of fineness prior to applying these processes. Each process required different types of machinery for the particular task. This chapter outlines the general mill plan and the processes used; the machinery involved in the process is merely mentioned. A selection of these machines is covered in greater detail in a later chapter.

Mill Processes

Many processes, and process peddlers, have come and gone. For example, in the Meadow Lake, California mining district between 1868 and 1880, the following people – and their processes, failed to economically win gold from the refractory, sulphuret ores:

> Burns, Churchill, Crail, Crosby, Doling, Fryer (claimed 90% recovery), Gleason, Gould, Green, Hagen, Hartley, Maltman (a chlorination process), and Willard.[5]

Millmen quickly became skeptical of anything new or touted as a solution to their problems, as most of it was *snake oil*. Instead they fell back on the tried and true processes known to work. Some of the processes that produced hundreds of millions of dollars in gold and silver were merely mechanized versions of simple processes developed hundreds of years before.

Amalgamation

Amalgam, strictly speaking, is a naturally occurring alloy[6] of mercury and silver. The term is generally applied to any alloy of mercury. Mercury is also called *quicksilver*, and the two names are used interchangeably. *Amalgamation* is the production of a mercury alloy.

The discovery that mercury has the unusual property of wetting or adhering to silver and gold is lost to antiquity. This discovery is of great importance for the recovery of precious metals. Gold or silver may be recovered using the *amalgamation process*. The ore, finely divided and suspended in water – called *pulp*, is passed over the surface of, or agitated with, mercury to form an amalgam. A fire-refining process is then used to recover the gold or silver.

Quicksilver, as mentioned in the first chapter, was used by the Argonauts in their sluices. It was also employed by the millmen for recovery of gold and silver. This might be accomplished in the simple *arrastra* mill, or on the inside of *stamp batteries* and on mercury coated *copper amalgamation plates* over which the pulp flowed from the stamps.[7] See figure 2. Mills that use stamp batteries for crushing and amalgamation for gold recovery are often called *quartz mills*.

The percentage of the gold that actually amalgamated was quite variable and subject to numerous conditions. Fire assays are very accurate and determine the total amount of gold and silver present in the ore. This is accomplished by fusion, which frees all of the precious metals for the assayer. Mills, with the exception of smelters, rely on crushing the ore to liberate the gold.

Those ores that are directly amenable to crushing and amalgamation are called *free milling ores*. As the ore is crushed into very fine particles, ranging from coarse sand-sized to flour, the small bits of gold locked in the ore are freed as tiny particles. When these particles come into contact with mercury, the mercury wets the surface and draws the particle into the droplet or film, thus amalgamating it.

If the gold is exposed on the surface of a particle, the mercury will wet it, but will be unable to amalgamate the entire mass. This accounts for some of the small mercury losses from stamp milling. If the gold is enclosed within the grain, it passes over the mercury with no effect. If the particle of gold is coated with some other substance – often called *rusty gold*, then the mercury will not amalgamate it. In rare cases, the gold is chemically bound to tellurium, as in calaverite ($AuTe_2$), and will not amalgamate.

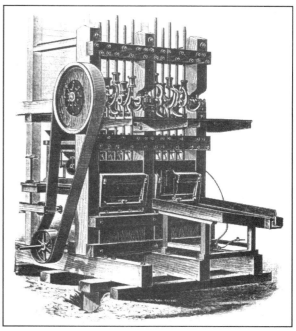

Figure 2   10-Stamp Battery
Source: Allis-Chalmers, 1903

Retorting

After a *cleanup* had been completed – see figure 3, the amalgam was usually strained through a chamois to free excess mercury. It was then ready for *retorting* – heating it in an iron pot until the mercury was vaporized from the mass, and conducting this gas away through a pipe.

The mercury was condensed for reuse by either exhausting the gas directly under water in a bucket,[8] or by condensing it in a section of pipe cooled by a water jacket.

There are two basic types of retorts: *Cylindrical retorts*, mounted horizontally in a furnace, and small *pot retorts*, which are usually placed over a blacksmith's forge.[9] See figure 4. The larger retorts were luted and swabbed-out with a mixture of salt and ashes.[10]

It took quite some time to bring the entire mass of amalgam up to the temperature at which the mercury vaporized. The

Figure 3   Cleanup at the Homestake
Terra Gold Stamp Mill
Terraville, Dakota 1888
Courtesy NARA

small retorts take about seven hours for completion. It also took a significant amount of fuel to maintain this heat – about ¼ cord was required to retort one thousand pounds of amalgam;[11] thus squeezing out the excess mercury from the amalgam saved both retorting time and fuel.

The presence of tellurium or selenium in the ore will foul the mercury, causing it to become black and frothy. These are volatile elements, which condense with the retorted mercury. The mercury was cleaned with nitric acid or potassium cyanide, and then the surface wiped free of the contaminants.[12]

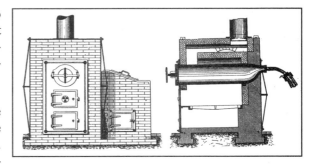

Figure 4   Retort Furnace
Source: Miller, 1906

When the retorting was complete and the vessel cooled and opened, a *retort sponge* was left inside in the shape of the inside surface of the retort. The porous nature of the sponge occurs because that is the space that the mercury occupied in the amalgam prior to retorting, and the temperature of retorting was nowhere near that required to melt the bits of gold and silver into a solid mass. The sponges would be locked away until enough had been collected to melt into bullion.

Melting

The *melting furnaces* that were used were generally very small, being about 16 inches square and 18 inches deep. They were made of firebrick with a cast iron door, and held together with wrought iron ties. The *crucibles* used for melting the gold and silver were made of black-lead (graphite).[13]

Fluxes were added to the melt to form a slag of impurities. The melted bullion was sometimes cast directly into bars if experience showed that upon melting, no impurities were present. At some mills the gold was cast into a conical iron mold, point-side down. Once the mass cooled it was broken loose and the slag chipped off. The doré was collected and melted for casting into bullion, and the slag sent back to the mill for reprocessing along with the ore. The bullion was then ready for shipment and sale. See figure 5.

The Homestake in South Dakota still used amalgamation in 1963, and it was responsible for 71.55% of the recovery, cyanidation recovering 25.4%, for a total of 96.95%. Mercury was lost at the rate of 0.23 troy ounces per ton.[14]

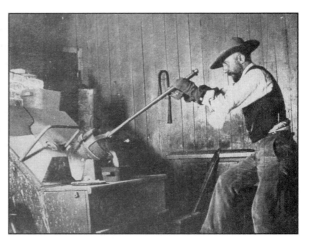

Figure 5   Thomas Marshall pouring
gold into bars at the North Star mill
Grass Valley, California

Courtesy North Star Mining Museum
Grass Valley, California

Slippery Stuff

In July 1883 Homestake millmen discovered that a small hole in the back of the Highland mill's retort allowed 47 pounds of amalgam carrying 36 pounds of bullion to leak out.[15]

In 1903, while making repairs to the Ontario mill in Park City, Utah, it was discovered that quicksilver had been leaking from the storage tanks. The topsoil was sluiced, and 575 flasks were recovered.[16]

The Patio Process

Bartolomé de Medina developed the *Patio Process* around 1555-1557. This process was also called *beneficio en frío* (the cold process) because the ore was not heated. It was exactly what was required in the New World, especially when labor, power, water, fuel, and other resources are considered. The patio process was employed as the basis for silver recovery in Mexico and Peru up until the late 19th century.

The silver-bearing ore was brought from the mines to the *hacienda de beneficio* (refining plant). There it was crushed to pebble-size, capable of passing through a screen made of perforated cowhide. Workers – often Indians or women, hammered the rocks piece by piece to accomplish this; though at larger facilities crushing machines were used, generally man or mule powered in Mexico and water-powered in Peru. The high-grade ores thus concentrated – those containing 100 or more ounces of silver per ton, were set aside for smelting, a costly process reserved for these ores due to the scarcity of fuel.

The lower grade ores were then reduced to sand in *arrastras* – circular crushing apparatus described in the last chapter, this taking about a day. The pulp was dumped in piles in a *patio* (courtyard), hence the name for the process. These patios were sometimes up to two acres in size. When enough crushed ore had accumulated to make a *torta* (cake), ranging in size from fifteen to about one hundred feet in diameter by two feet thick, the *azoguero* (amalgamator) began his job.

He would attempt to determine how the cake reacted when salt was added. If the cake were "too hot," he would add lime to "cool" the mass; if "too cool," *magistral* (copper pyrite, $CuFeS_2$) was added.[17] The specified amounts of water, salt, lime, and magistral were then thoroughly worked into the mass, forming a muddy paste. The mass was then allowed to "cook" or "sweat" for a few days. The azoguero would then judiciously sprinkle quicksilver onto the torta. Quicksilver was a very expensive commodity monopolized by the crown (Government of Spain). He was expected to yield, more or less, an ounce of silver for every six ounces of quicksilver used.

The azoguero then carefully monitored the progress of the chemical digestion and amalgamation of the silver in the torta. He would take up samples into his *jícara* (gourd), wash the tailings away, and examine the color and consistency of the droplets of the mercury that remained, all the while making adjustments to the mass if it were "too hot" or "too cold." Mules – or men, were frequently brought in to tramp through the cake, kneading and agitating the mass, redistributing the chemical reagents, and exposing fresh surfaces to the air, sunlight, and rain. See figure 6. The process would continue in this fashion until the azoguero decided the job was complete, this taking anywhere from a few weeks to five months, five weeks being typical.

The torta was shoveled up and carefully washed in vats to recover the *pella* ("lumps"; amalgam). The pella was squeezed through cloth sacks to recover excess quicksilver. At some haciendas the pella was molded into small pyramids, neatly arranged on a metal platform. A charcoal fire was built beneath the platform, and a *capellina* (a bronze bell) placed over the whole affair. The mercury in the pella vaporized, condensed when it came into contact with the capellina, rolled down the interior side, and was caught in a little trough beneath. At other refineries the mass was placed into a crucible and retorted, the recovered silver conforming to the characteristic shape of the crucible and called a *piña* (pineapple). The porous silver alloy remaining was then melted down into bullion and cast into bars.[18]

Alvaro Alonzo Barba invented an adaptation of this process in the late 1590's,[19] the *beneficio de cazo* (the dipper process). It was conducted in large copper-lined wooden tubs, and became known as the *Cazo Process*. The pulp, water, and salt were charged into the pan and brought to the boiling temperature of the pulp. Mercury was then added, and the pulp stirred continuously. The tailings were washed away and the amalgam recovered. It was much faster than the patio process, taking about 10-20 hours to achieve what the patio process did in so many weeks. It consumed less quicksilver, but required significant amounts of expensive fuel.

The cold process recovered a greater percentage of the silver than did the cazo process, however, and for that reason the latter was only infrequently adopted. A hybrid of the two processes would prove to be the cornerstone of silver milling carried out at a later time.[20]

The patio process was relatively simple and required no fuel except that which was used for retorting. It was very labor intensive, however. It was well suited to the environments where it was used. The crude methods and equipment used led to a considerable loss of silver and mercury. The mercury loss accounted for at least 11% of the recovered values,[21] and amounted to about 1-2 ounces per ounce of silver recovered.[22]

Regarding the chemical reactions taking place, they

> "have been but little studied; indeed, chemists have not yet reached definite conclusions as to the essential reactions of the patio process, a subject to which a number of elaborate investigations have been devoted."[23]

The silver sulphurets, namely argentite (Ag_2S), were converted to chlorides by reaction with the salt and air:[24]

$$Ag_2S + 2NaCl + 2O_2 \quad \blacktriangleright \quad Na_2SO_4 + 2AgCl$$

The silver chlorides were then reduced to metal by the mercury:

$$2AgCl + 2Hg \quad \blacktriangleright \quad 2Ag + Hg_2Cl_2$$

Much of the mercury was converted to calomel (Hg_2Cl_2) in this way and was lost.[25] The excess mercury then amalgamated the silver. Adding magistral (copper sulfate and copper sulfide) assisted the process with additional chemical reaction pathways leading to metallic silver:

$$CuSO_4 + 2NaCl \quad \blacktriangleright \quad CuCl_2 + Na_2SO_4$$
$$2CuCl_2 + 2Hg \quad \blacktriangleright \quad Cu_2Cl_2 + Hg_2Cl_2 \quad \text{(mercury lost)}$$
$$CuS + CuCl_2 \quad \blacktriangleright \quad Cu_2Cl_2 + S$$
$$AgCl + CuCl \quad \blacktriangleright \quad Ag + CuCl_2 \text{ [26]}$$

Additional reactions for silver minerals, which lead to the formation of silver chloride, are:[27]

Argentite

$$Ag_2S + CuCl_2 \quad \blacktriangleright \quad 2AgCl + CuS$$
$$Ag_2S + 2CuCl_2 \quad \blacktriangleright \quad 2AgCl + Cu_2Cl_2 + S$$
$$Ag_2S + Cu_2Cl_2 \quad \blacktriangleright \quad 2AgCl + Cu_2S$$
$$Ag_2S + Cu_2Cl_2 \quad \blacktriangleright \quad 2AgCl + CuS + Cu$$
$$Ag_2S + Cu_2Cl_2 \quad \blacktriangleright \quad 2Ag + CuCl_2 + CuS \text{ [28]}$$
$$2Ag_2S + Cu_2Cl_2 + 2Hg \quad \blacktriangleright \quad 4Ag + 2CuS + Hg_2Cl_2 \quad \text{(mercury lost)}$$

Proustite

$$4Ag_3AsS_3 + 4CuCl_2 \quad \blacktriangleright \quad 8AgCl + 2Ag_2S + 4CuS + 2As_2S_3$$

Pyragyrite

$$2Ag_3SbS_3 + 3CuCl_2 \quad \blacktriangleright \quad 6AgCl + 3CuS + Sb_2S_3$$
$$2Ag_3SbS_3 + Cu_2Cl_2 \quad \blacktriangleright \quad 2AgCl + Ag_2S + 2Ag + 2CuS + Sb_2S_3$$

The Washoe Process

When the dark clayey ores of the fabulous Comstock Lode were finally recognized as being something other than "that damned blue stuff" that clogged the sluices – namely, unbelievably rich silver ores, a scramble ensued to find or discover a suitable method of recovering the phenomenal silver values from the enormous surface deposits.

Until that time, the only practical methods for silver recovery available to the millmen were the patio and cazo processes, both far too time consuming and inefficient for the demands of the mine owners, and for the rapid pace of development along the lode.

The mines were producing ore at rates that far exceeded the capacity of the primitive milling methods then in use. Something needed to happen to accelerate the recovery of the silver, and it needed to happen soon.

A great deal of experimentation commenced, notably by Almarin B. Paul in 1860,[29] and what distilled from this was the *Washoe Process* – essentially a mechanized version of the 250-year old cazo process, one that would have a lasting impact on mining history and on events that were unfolding at that time – the Civil War and the fate of the Nation.

Figure 6 shows a remarkable view of the more primitive patio process still being used as the new Washoe process mills were shifting into high gear.

Figure 6   Patio Process in the foreground
Gould & Curry Mill in the background
Virginia City, Nevada ca 1865

Courtesy Library of Congress

The machinery and methods quickly evolved into what became known as the Washoe process. Fifteen years later, the combination of the Washoe process and the astonishing ore production of the Big Bonanza would produce almost half of the annual precious metals production of the U.S.[30]

Quite by accident, the machinery used to mechanize the process of winning the gold and silver values from the ore added the ingredient crucial to achieving the goal of faster milling and enhanced recovery, and it added this component simply by wearing down: Iron.

Iron added the following *very* favorable chemical reaction to the host of others already at work:[31]

$$2AgCl + Fe \quad \blacktriangleright \quad 2Ag + FeCl_2$$

Best of all, most of the iron came from the pans and mullers – a serendipitous use for the stuff of normal wear and tear.

"Iron is one of the important factors in the amalgamation of silver ores. It is used in various forms; in the first place as cast iron in the material of the pans. As wrought iron, in the form of rings, it is sometimes put in the pans, and it is occasionally added to the charge in the form of shavings, filings, etc."[32]

The Manhattan mill in Austin, Nevada added ten pounds of iron turnings to a charge, which were almost always consumed, thus sparing the cast iron components of the pan to some extent.[33]

William H. Howland, in 1860, modified the pan, as designed by Henry Breevort, for rapid and fine grinding – what was needed for the Comstock ores. A year later he devised the steam jacket that was attached beneath the pan, its purpose being to control the temperature of the pulp. Chemical reactions, as a general rule, occur faster at higher temperatures. There was still considerable experimentation going on with machinery, processes, and in particular chemicals used in the processes.

Figure 7   Austin, Nevada ca 1868
Courtesy NARA

The Sagebrush Process

Regarding all manner of chemicals added to the various processes, Samuel Franklin Emmons stated, in *Statistics and Technology of the Precious Metals*:

"As a curiosity the following list of chemicals which are used at a mill in Arizona may be mentioned: One and a half hours after charging, 20 pounds of salt, 3 ounces of cyanide of potassium, 2 ounces of sulphuric (sic) acid, 1 ounce of nitric acid, 1 ounce of hydrochloric acid, and ¼ pound of carbonate of lime. The superintendent does not profess to know what reactions are produced."[34]

Perhaps in jest, J. V. Tingley mentioned that tobacco juice and sagebrush were used in attempts to improve the Washoe process.[35] Dan De Quille made the following tongue-in-cheek statements regarding the unbridled scramble for novel and improved milling processes:

"Not content with blue-stone (sulphate of copper) salt, and one or two other simple articles of known efficacy, they poured into their pans all manner of acids; dumped in potash, borax, salt-peter, alum, and all else that could be found at the drug-stores, then went to the hills and started in on the vegetable kingdom. They peeled bark off the cedar trees, boiled it down till they had obtained a strong tea, and then poured it into the pans, where it would have an opportunity of attacking the silver stubbornly remaining in the rocky parts of the ore."

"...It was not long before a genius in charge of a mill conceived the idea of making a tea of this and putting it into his pans. Soon the wonders performed of the 'sagebrush process,' as it was called were being heralded throughout the land."[36]

Consolidated Virginia Mill

Now let us follow the flow of the Washoe process, as practiced in the West. First, we will examine the Consolidated Virginia Mill, circa 1876. Between 1873-1882, 809,275 tons of ore was reduced using the Washoe process, yielding bullion worth $29,168,227 in gold and $31,959,256 in silver.[37]

The following description of the Consolidated Virginia, except where noted, is based on that given by Dan De Quille in *The Big Bonanza*.[38] Dimensions of the various departments are included to provide the reader a sense of the size of the mill works.

The ore is taken from the shaft hoist house to the ore house by means of a mule-drawn train of 10 cars. To keep the stamps busy, one carload of ore is required every five minutes, day and night. The ore is dumped into chutes, at the bases of which are grizzlies with a 3" gap. The undersize ore drops into the bin below through distribution chutes. Blake jaw crushers crush the oversized ore[39] before it is sent to the 110 feet long ore bin.

Ore leaving the ore bin feeds twelve Tulloch self-feeders, invented by James Tulloch of California. Only two men are required to monitor the automatic feeding of the 60 stamps. The battery room, 100x58 feet, has 60 stamps, arranged in 6 batteries of 10 stamps. Each stamp weighs 800 pounds. The batteries are powered by belt, which is 14" wide and 60 feet in length, and is connected to a counter-shaft positioned in front of the stamps. The belt that connects the engine and the counter-shaft is 24" wide and 160 feet long, and runs at 3600 feet per minute (41 MPH). See figure 8.

Figure 8   Counter-shaft   Author

The pulp flowing from the stamps is sluiced (two sluices; one each for 30 stamps) to settling tanks located at the next lower level – the amalgamating room, which is 120x92 feet. There are 17 [40] settling tanks. When the pulp has settled to a consistency of mortar, it is shoveled out of the settling tank and onto a platform above the amalgamation pans. See figure 9.

The amalgamation pans are 5.5 feet in diameter. There are 32 total – two banks of 16 pans. Water is added to the pan to bring the 3000 pounds of pulp to the proper consistency, and the required amount of salt,[41] copper sulfate, and a small amount of quicksilver is added. The mullers are then lowered and set to revolving – grinding the ore, and thoroughly mixing the ore with the added chemicals. Steam is admitted directly to the pulp, and also beneath the pan. After about 2.5 hours the mullers are raised and about 300 pounds of quicksilver is added,[42] the charge being agitated for an additional 2.5 hours.[43]

The charge is then drawn off and transferred into settling pans located on a platform next to and lower than the amalgamation pans. There are 8 settlers 9 feet in diameter and about 5 feet deep – one settling pan for two amalgamation pans. The settling pans are similar to the amalgamation pans in that a muller rotates, but the speed at which it does is much slower and the mullers set much higher. This allows the dense amalgam to settle to the bottom of the pan over a period of a couple of hours. The amalgam so collected is drawn from the base of the settling pan and run through strainers. The strainers – *amalgam safes*, have iron covers and are kept locked. See figure 10.

The pulp is then sluiced to the agitator room, 92x20 feet in size, which contains four circular agitators. Large rakes slowly agitate the pulp, allowing any remaining amalgam to settle and be recovered.

Figure 9   Brunswick Mill Pan Room
Carson River, Nevada ca 1875

The pulp is then discharged from the mill through a long flume. A large array of blanket sluices, located some distance from the mill, caught some of the amalgam and sulphurets that escaped the mill. Hundreds of tons passed daily through these wide, shallow-graded sluices, some covered with from 5-6 *miles* of blankets across their surfaces.[44] See figure 11. The woolen blankets were rinsed in a vat, and the concentrates thus collected were returned to the mill to be reworked.

A 600 HP engine, requiring 8 boilers, each 54" diameter and 16 feet in length, and burning 28 cords of wood per day, powered the mill. The engine weighed about 50 tons, and was built upon a masonry foundation weighing in excess of 600 tons. The flywheel was 18 feet in diameter and weighed 16.5 tons, and directly drove the stamp batteries. The room enclosing the power plant was 92x58 feet, with a roof 50 feet high.

The amalgam collected in the strainers was sent to the retort house, 20x60 feet, for retorting. The retort sponges collected were then melted in a small furnace and poured into brick-shaped molds. A small ladle was dipped into the bullion as it was poured into the mold. This sample was cast into a bucket of water, forming what are known as *granulations*, to be used for assaying the fineness and value of the bullion.

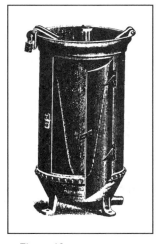

Figure 10
Amalgam Safe

Source:
Allis-Chalmers 1902

Stanford Mill

Now let us visit a mill that processes silver chloride ores, and examine the workings to gain a better understanding of the processes and equipment involved. Many features will be recognized from those used in the Washoe process.

For this tour we visit the 30-stamp Stanford Mill,[45] located in Eberhardt, Nevada, as it appeared in 1871. This description is based on that reported by Rossiter W. Raymond in *Statistics of Mines and Mining in the States and Territories West of the Rocky Mountains*.[46]

The great rush to the White Pine district, from 1866-1876, produced over $8.8 million from 147,000 tons of ore. See chart 1.[47]

The remains of the White Pine district and the Stanford mill may still be seen today. See figure 12.

Figure 11   Brunswick Mill Blanket Sluices
Carson River, Nevada ca 1875

The silver chloride ore is hauled to the mill dump-floor by teams, where it is dumped into the 350-ton capacity ore house (58x24 feet). A Varney and Nix rock-breaker crushes it to egg-size, and discharges the broken rock onto an apron. It is then carted by wheelbarrow to the drying room (58x16 feet) to be dried in a 10x52 foot dryer, turned manually until dry, and then transferred by wheelbarrow to the battery room (58x48 feet) and dumped into Stanford self-feeding hoppers on the stamp batteries. Thirty stamps, weighing 750 pounds each,[48] *dry-crush* the ore to 40-mesh, crushing on average 50 TPD. The sand leaving the battery is caught in cars, and when full, is weighed and moved to the pan room.

Drills And Mills

The pan room (58x60 feet) contains 16 pans with steam chambers, 4.5 feet in diameter and 32 inches deep. Each receives a charge of 2500 pounds of pulp, water, 20 pounds of salt, and ¼ pound of potassium cyanide. The mullers revolve rapidly at 57 RPM.[49] After 4.5 hours, 250 pounds of mercury is added, and grinding continues for another hour. The muller is then raised for two hours to give the amalgam a chance to settle and collect. Sixty pounds of mercury are then added, and water is introduced to thin the pulp. Eight hours after charging the pan, the contents are transferred to the settlers.

Eight Beldan settlers are used, each 7.25 feet in diameter, 2.5 feet deep, with wooden mullers revolving slowly at 11 RPM. Two pans feed each settler. The amalgam settles, and is discharged through a siphon and into a tub. Six hours after charging, a plug is drawn near the top of the settler and a stream of water is admitted into the tank. The overflow of water with suspended *slimes* – extremely finely ground particles, and sands flows to the agitators. There are two settlers for each agitator. After another hour, plugs located lower than the first are opened, permitting most of the settled sands to flow into the agitators. Every 48 hours, the heaviest sands that accumulate in the bottom of the settlers are removed by opening a plug located on the side of and at the base of the settler. These sands are charged back into the pans with fresh sand from the stamps.

Below the settlers are 4 agitators, 6.5 feet in diameter and 2.5 feet deep, making 17 RPM, and discharge into the tailrace, which is located 44 feet below the dump-boards of the ore house. The agitators provide a final opportunity to catch suspended amalgam and heavy sands that escaped the settlers. Every day the deposited sands are removed and recharged into the pans with fresh sand from the stamps. These heavy sands assay 50% of the ore-value.

The amalgam collected in the tubs is strained through canvas strainers,[50] and then cleaned in two Knox pans, 4 feet in diameter. It is diluted with additional mercury and water, and a small amount of potassium cyanide is added. The mullers are set in motion for a few hours. Magnets are used to remove iron. The amalgam is then strained to be as "dry" as possible.[51]

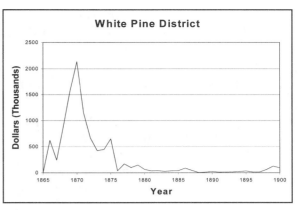

White Pine District

Chart 1

Figure 12   Silent Sentinel   Author

The remaining stamp battery king pieces of the Stanford mill in the foreground, the tailings dump of the Eberhardt workings on the hill in the background.
Eberhardt, Nevada 2002

After about 1000 pounds of amalgam has accumulated, four retorts, 6 feet long and 14 inches in diameter, and located in the retort and melting room (58x16 feet) are used to recover the mercury. Graphite crucibles are used for melting the bullion in the two furnaces. Mercury losses averaged about one and ¾ pounds per ton milled.[52]

Sampling is made every half-hour by collecting a small sample of sand from the discharge of the stamps. After 12 hours, the samples are thoroughly mixed and assayed. Samples are also collected from the drain of the agitator to determine the loss in the tailings. If the tailings assay exceeds 20% of the sand assay, then the ore is not being amalgamated well, and steps are taken to remedy the situation. Nearly 86% of the assay value of the ore was recovered.

A 140 HP engine located in the engine room (42x16 feet), and three boilers – each 52 inches in diameter and sixteen feet long and located in the boiler room (42x22 feet), furnish power for the mill.

Quicksilver Loss

Quicksilver losses during the height of the Big Bonanza averaged about 2-3 pounds per ton of ore milled – about 10-15% of the cost of milling.[53] Loss of quicksilver was attributed, in part, to the inability to separate the amalgam from the sands in the settlers. When using the Washoe process for slimes about 4 pounds of mercury was lost per ton milled.[54] Emmons noted that,

> "In the patio process of amalgamation a very large amount of quicksilver is converted into calomel and lost. In the pan process it is highly probable that one or both chlorides of mercury form to some extent, but these compounds are, for the most part, reduced by iron. Were this not the case, the loss of quicksilver would be far greater than that actually sustained."[55]

Dan De Quille observed that enormous amounts of quicksilver were lost from the mills, but mistakenly thought that it was purely due to being "almost invisible and immeasurable globules of mercury." Later, he writes of the discovery that mercury amalgam had coated iron nails in a flume downstream of other mills. He hypothesized that the mercury plating was due to the lucky timing of tiny pebbles impacting the droplet of mercury just as it passed over the head of the nail! The formation of a soluble form of mercury as a side effect of the Washoe process was not suspected, nor was its subsequent plating on the iron nails.[56] He further states, "There is for millmen food for reflection, and for inventors a field of profit and distinction." He then estimates an annual loss of 734,400 pounds of quicksilver – food indeed![57]

Strangely, there are no popular accounts of this observation leading to any novel mercury recovery methods being employed at the Comstock. There were some methods for saving mercury tried elsewhere. R. T. Gillespie, superintendent of the Christy Mill in Silver Reef, Utah, experimented with the new-fangled Rae Electric System in 1887.[58] It was designed to recover more than 50% of the floured mercury lost in the mill. Gillespie confirmed a savings of over $1000 a month on 1800 tons of ore milled.[59] The district quicksilver loss was from ¾ to 1.5 pounds per ton.[60]

De Quille commented on a novel use for the amalgam that escaped the mills along the Comstock:

> "After freshets in the canyon the miners used to go out and collect amalgam by digging it out of the crevices in the rocks with knives or scooping it out with spoons. Having retorted this, they would take it to a blacksmith's forge and make rings out of it by melting it and pouring it into a mold cut in an adobe or piece of brick. In this way they made rings that would weigh an ounce or more, and of nights, when going into town to have a good time with the "boys," would slip three or four of these rings upon the fingers of their right hands, for use in lieu of brass knuckles."[61]

Washoe Process Résumé

During the early years 1859-60, milling costs were initially $100 per ton but quickly dropped to $50 per ton. Cordwood from the vicinity was priced at $4.50, but rapidly rose to $15 due to scarcity.[62] The price of fuel and other supplies affected the cost of milling, and often dictated which ores could be profitably milled. The milling charges were periodically adjusted – $12 in October 1876, about $10.50 in 1877, and $9 in 1878, the basis of which factored in the cost of quicksilver.[63] The price per flask of quicksilver during these years was about $44, $37, and $33 – prices that reflect the decrease in the milling fees.[64]

In an eight-year period of milling 300,000 tons of Comstock ore, the Hale & Norcross recovered 76% of the gold and 61% of the silver.[65] The Savage recovered 76% of the gold and 87% of the silver from slimes that assayed $42 per ton. Other mills had similar slime recoveries.[66] Comstock mill recovery was, overall, about 75% of the total value as of 1880.[67]

The bullion produced varied from mine to mine, and also within each mine as the composition of the various ore bodies changed. For example, the Belcher had bullion as high as 50% gold, while in the Consolidated Virginia it sometimes ran as low as 10% of the value.[68] Savage bullion from slimes was gold 005 fine, silver 537, and the remainder base metals.[69] For the years 1873-1882, the Consolidated Virginia produced approximately 17.5 ounces of silver for every ounce of gold.[70] In 1880, the overall production from the Comstock was 17.3 ounces of silver for each ounce of gold.[71]

A significant fraction of the values present in the ore were washed away in tailings, which were periodically reworked at the mills,[72] but the recovery rarely exceeded 50% of the assay value. There was a point where "it often becomes advisable to sacrifice a certain percentage of the value for the sake of working a greater number of tons per diem." This is evident in chart 2 where working the tailings longer than a few hours would not return enough additional silver to justify the expense.[73] See figure 13.

> "Had any man thought of saving these tailings in the early days of milling, by putting a flume into Gold Canyon and running them to some flat or valley where they could have been dumped in a great heap, all that is now lost would have been saved, and the originator of the enterprise would have made half a dozen big fortunes."[74]

Freight on bullion averaged about 1.25% of its value – small shippers paid perhaps 2%, large shippers such as the Savage paid about 4/10 of 1% of the value of the bullion in Wells Fargo freight expenses.[75] See figure 14. Charts 3 and 4 illustrate the phenomenal tonnages milled and the values won on the Comstock.[76]

The Washoe process found widespread use throughout the west. It was a proven technology with a good track record. The following facts provide a sketch of a few of the many places where it was used.

♦ The Gold Hill mine at Placerville, Idaho, commenced operations in 1869, and by 1873 had recovered $300,000. That year the Washoe process was adopted. The Gold Hill produced an additional $1,950,000 by 1896.[77]

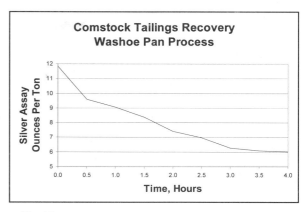

Chart 2

Figure 13 Sacking tailings at the Gould & Curry
Virginia City, Nevada ca 1865
Courtesy Library of Congress

Figure 14   Wells Fargo bullion express 1890
Courtesy Library of Congress

- When describing the early developments in Tombstone, Arizona, Patrick Hamilton stated, "The silver occurs as a chloride with very little base combinations, and can be worked by pan process, to 90 percent, and upwards."[78]

  Perhaps the stated recovery was overly optimistic. According to the 1880 census, 18,123 tons of ore was raised during the census year, carrying an average of 0.6 ounces of gold and 65 ounces of silver per ton. From this 12,380 tons was milled, recovering 64% of the gold and 77% of the silver.[79]

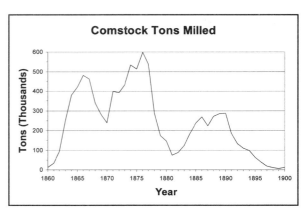

Chart 3

- In 1868 the Stanford Mill reduction costs ran about $65 for ore worth $160 per ton. By 1869 wage reductions, better freight rates, and other factors reduced milling costs to $35, then to $20. White Pine competitors charged from $12.34 to $14.60 per ton, where from $4-$5 of this were freight charges. 1870 assay figures showed the silver content at $50.31 per ton, but the nearby International Mill recovered $38.84, or 77%. Total expenses were $32.07 per ton, leaving a very small profit. The Stanford mill, in 1872, was recovering 87% of the value, and kept all of the excess above the agreed-upon 82.5% recovery. This was profit in addition to the milling charge of $13 per ton.[80]

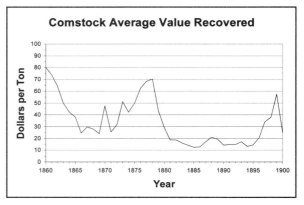

Chart 4

- In the Silver Reef mining district of southwestern Utah, the Washoe process was successfully applied to silver-bearing sandstone ores. Tailing losses were moderate at over 20%. The Stormont 10-stamp mill used six sluices, each 130 feet long and 13 inches wide, to capture values leaving the mill. What wasn't recovered in the mill or the sluices wound up in tailing piles or the Virgin River. *Chloriders* occasionally reworked the tailings – the term possibly originated in the area. Silver Reef's production is shown in chart 5.[81] The district's overall recovery was about 75%. The bullion was 820-930 fine, the remainder mostly copper.[82]

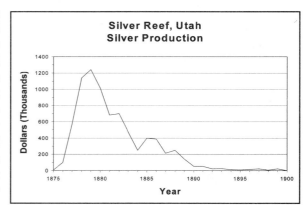

Chart 5

Roasting

Roasting was an essential preliminary step for many of the processes that follow. The purpose of roasting is to completely remove anything that can be volatilized, especially sulfur, tellurium, arsenic, and antimony, and to convert iron, copper, lead, zinc and other metals into oxides, leaving the gold in a metallic state.[83] *Sulphurets* – those ores containing sulfides, always required preliminary roasting. A *chlorodizing roast* – roasting ore with added common salt (NaCl), was required for ores that contain lime (CaO), talc ($Mg_3Si_4O_{10}(OH)_2$), calc-spar (calcite, $CaCO_3$), and heavy spar (barite, $BaSO_4$). If the ore contained lead or antimony, salt was not added.[84]

Two popular revolving roasting furnaces, *Brückner's Cylinder* and the *White-Howell* furnace, are covered in greater detail in the last chapter. See figures 15 and 16.

Roasting ores could cause significant losses of lead and gold. Stetefeldt found that Mexican ores roasted in a reverberatory furnace lost from 53-88% of their gold, the loss associated with the volatilization of copper chlorides. In another instance, copper-free ores lost 80% of the silver and from 68-85% of the gold in a chlorodizing roast. Küstel reported a loss of 8% of the gold from a chlorodizing roast of telluride ores.[85]

Ores containing a significant amount of pyrite either needed an immediate roasting, or, kept damp while stored. If not, lumps would form that prevented a *dead* – complete, roast.[86] Pan tailings required drying, and then pulverizing and sifting to about twelve-mesh before roasting, otherwise they would bake into hard lumps unsuitable for chlorination.[87]

Roasting, as carried out at the Eureka mine in Grass Valley, California generally took about twenty hours for one ton of sulphurets, with three men required for the stirring and raking. The Eureka used a double furnace, with one hearth located above the other. A one-ton charge was loaded through a hopper located at the end of the upper hearth opposite the flue. The upper hearth held nine tons of ore, which was slowly raked towards the flue leading to the lower hearth. This took 24 hours to perform.

As the ore moved towards the flue, the temperature of the furnace and the completeness of the roasting increased. A *rabble* – a hoe, made of ⅝" round iron and about six feet long, was used for *rabbling* – stirring and raking, the ore through the furnace. Rabbling was performed at fifteen-minute intervals, this being "necessary for the relief of the roaster."

The lower hearth – for *finishing,* was kept hotter than the upper hearth, and about one ton at a time was worked through it, this taking about twelve hours. The ore was turned frequently so that all surfaces were exposed to the flue gases; thus ensuring a dead roast.

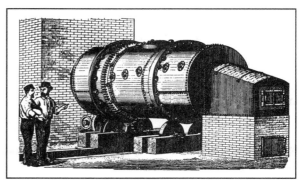

Figure 15   Brückner Cylinder
Source: Eissler, 1889

When the ore was completely roasted, it was raked into a car located below the hearth. The car was then rolled to an area where the roasted ore was spread out and cooled. About two tons per day were roasted by three shifts, each with two roasters.[88]

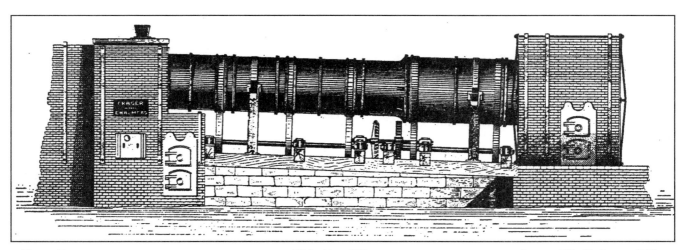

Figure 16   White-Howell Furnace   Source: Allis-Chalmers, 1903

At the Plymouth Mine's mill in California, *reverberatory furnaces* were used for roasting ores. See figure 17. The ore was rabbled from one compartment to the next. These were called *drying*, *burning*, and *cooking* compartments. One man worked a 2400-pound charge through the furnace per shift.

The sulfur in the ore, about 20%, burned in the second compartment. This generated considerable heat – enough to sustain combustion of the ore.[89] Towards the end of the burning ¾ of 1% of salt was added to the roast. The ore was moved to a cooling floor after roasting. When four tons accumulated it was chlorinated.[90]

Figure 17   Reverberatory Furnace
                   Kilton Chlorination Works
                   Boulder, Colorado 1898

Courtesy Carnegie Branch Library for Local History, Boulder, Colorado

The Reese River Process

In May 1862, William M. Talcott found a silver bearing outcropping in what he named Pony Gulch.[91] That same month the Reese River mining district in Nevada was organized, and a rush ensued when ore samples were taken to Virginia City. The town of Austin and other smaller communities rapidly formed. The first silver brick was made in the burgeoning camp on May 28, 1863 from ore worked by arrastra on the Tesora claim. Much of the ore was shipped to Virginia City for processing as plans were being made to erect mills. The first stamp mill, owned by Buell & Co., began crushing ore in early August 1863. Within a few years, 29 mills were dropping 444 stamps. The cost of reduction was $75 per ton in March 1864, $40 in 1866, and about $36 in 1868. Mining costs in 1869 averaged $30 per ton. Only high-grade ores could be worked at a profit, from which about 80% of the silver was recovered.[92]

Problems with milling began as the oxidized surface ores, which persisted to depths of only 50-100 feet, were depleted. Allan A, Curtis, manager of the Manhattan Silver Mining Company, wrote in 1869,

> "I am forced to believe that the veins of Lander Hill instead of becoming richer as they are worked down on become poorer and change rapidly after reaching a certain depth."[93]

Reese River ores proved to be far more complex than the ores found at the Comstock. In 1864, the Oregon Company solved the major technical problem of how to process the refractory silver ores found at depth in the Reese River district: roasting. A complete roasting eliminated the antimony and arsenic present in the ores. The addition of common salt during roasting converted the silver sulfides to chlorides, which made the ore amenable to the Washoe process of pan amalgamation. Reverberatory furnaces were initially used, but proved costly in fuel, time, and labor.

In the summer of 1869 Carl A. Stetefeldt built an experimental furnace in Reno. This furnace was vertical in design, the charge of finely ground ore and salt falling for a few seconds through the high temperature flue gases, then left to sit for about 45 minutes in a hopper where the residual heat, salt, and silver could react. This chlorodizing roast resulted in up to a 90% chlorodized product, suitable for pan amalgamation. The furnace was also more economical with fuel than other designs then in use. Even so, roasting added to the expense of ore reduction – additional machinery, fuel, and salt were required.

In March 1870, the Manhattan Company – the biggest ore processor in the Reese River district, sent ore samples to be tested. The results were so satisfactory that the company closed its mill in April and remodeled it for the Stetefeldt furnaces.

By June the mill was back in operation, and by August it was determined that roasting costs had been reduced by 50%, silver recovery was increased, and lower-grade ores could at last be worked at a profit, even after a $2 per ton royalty was paid to use the furnaces.

The Manhattan Company management secured an exclusive right to use the process in the district; thus cornering the milling market. This became known as the *Reese River Process.*[94]

Other mining districts used the Reese River process: Georgetown, Caribou, and Silver Cliff, Colorado, for example. Depending on the nature of the ore, furnaces other than Stetefeldt's were sometimes used. The time required for the roasting was variable. Ore from Caribou required from 8-11 hours, whereas that from Georgetown required 10-20 hours.[95]

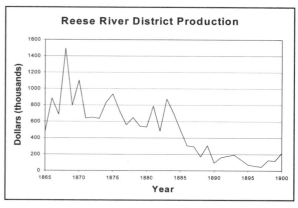

Chart 6

Figure 18   Caribou, Colorado 1911
Courtesy USGS

The Freiberg and Augustin Processes

The *Freiberg*, or *European Barrel*, process used a chlorodizing roast followed by amalgamation. The roasted ore, water, salt, iron, and mercury were introduced into a barrel and it was set into motion. The brine dissolved the silver chloride, which was reduced to the metallic state by the iron, and was subsequently amalgamated. This process could recover up to 80% of the silver values, but lost part of the gold. In practice, up to 40% of the values washed away with the tailings. It was expensive, time-consuming, and was generally reserved for high-grade silver ores. On the Comstock Lode, the Ophir, Mexican, and Gould & Curry discontinued using the process after their rich ores were exhausted. Especially high-grade ore was still reserved for treatment – at $50 per ton, at Dall's Freiberg custom mill up until about 1870.[96]

The *Augustin* process amounted to roasting the *argentiferous* – silver-bearing, ore with salt, which formed soluble silver chloride. The silver chloride was then dissolved by hot brine, and precipitated by copper.[97]

The Chlorination Process

The *Chlorination Process*, also called the *Barrel Chlorination Process*, and the *Plattner Process* after the inventor, Karl Friedrich Plattner, recovers gold by reaction with chlorine gas, forming water-soluble gold chloride, which is subsequently precipitated by other chemical reactions. Gold forms very few chemical compounds, gold chloride and gold cyanide being two of the handful readily created. The gold dissolving power of a 1% solution in 1-¼ hours is 4.49% for chlorine, 6.46% for bromine,[98] and 0.57% for cyanide.[99]

Plattner introduced his process in 1848.[100] Chlorination was first used to treat arsenical ores in Silesia, Czechoslovakia, in 1848.[101] G. F. Deitken and O. Maltman were the first to use Plattner's Process in the U.S. at the Pioneer Reduction Works, Nevada City, California in late 1858, and by 1860 had applied it commercially and successfully.[102]

The chlorination process may be successfully applied to a variety of ores, but more frequently than not the ores required a preliminary roasting. Many developments were made to streamline the process, some of which permitted improved extraction from *refractory* ores – the more *rebellious* ores. Some of the more important process developments and enhancements are highlighted later.

The chlorination process is most amenable to ores carrying gold alone.[103] Ores having coarse particles of gold are generally not satisfactory for chlorination as there is insufficient time for the chlorine and gold to react – the particles are incompletely penetrated. Ores that have large quantities of silver are not suitable either – the silver forms an insoluble chloride that coats the gold, preventing effective extraction. This effect was reduced to some extent with the introduction of barrel chlorination, or from a thorough, chlorodizing roast. Special care was taken during roasting – a significant amount of gold could be volatilized with the silver during roasting.[104]

Ores where the gangue contains large amounts of hydrated iron oxides are well suited for barrel chlorination,[105] but those containing iron sulfate are not suitable, unless the sulfates are converted to oxides by complete roasting. Metallic iron from grinding and stamping operations must also be converted to oxides.[106] "The roasting is the most important part of the whole operation – that on which the success of the chlorination principally depends." Success in the chlorination process depends on a dead or *sweet* – complete, roasting of the ore.[107]

Roasting was responsible for about 50% of the cost of chlorination,[108] where the chief item of expense was salt if chlorodizing roasting was performed.[109] In some locations, roasting was very expensive due to the costs of fuel and labor. In other places it was considerably cheaper. In the Cripple Creek district, the cost was 30 cents per ton. In other localities the price ran as high as $3.75 per ton.[110] Reverberatory furnaces required about 600 pounds of wood to dead roast a ton of ore.[111]

To determine if the roast was complete, a small sample of the roasted ore was stirred into a glass of water. After the solids settle, a drop of potassium ferrocyanide ($K_4Fe(CN)_6 \cdot 3H_2O$) was added, and if a strong blue or green color appeared, the roasting was incomplete.[112]

The roasted ore was spread in a box about 8-10 feet square. About 4-5% of water was sprinkled onto the ore, care being taken to continuously rake and mix it such that it was evenly wetted. The ore was moist enough to form a loose ball when squeezed, but otherwise would crumble. This reduced packing, and permitted the chlorine gas to permeate the charge.[113]

Leaching Vats and Charging

A typical *leaching vat* was about seven feet in diameter and three feet high, capable of holding about three tons of roasted ore. Larger capacity vats were made longer and wider, but not deeper. See figures 19 and 20. This prevented the compaction of the ore charge, which would occur if vats of greater depth were used. All of the interior surfaces of the vat were coated with a mixture of pitch and tar, applied by brush while hot, or lined with sheet lead of ten pounds per square foot.

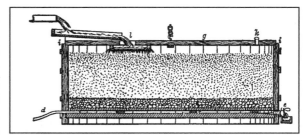

Figure 19   Chlorination Leaching Vat
Source: Eissler. 1889

Above the bottom of the wooden vat was an empty space about one inch thick, over which rested a false bottom of closely spaced boards. Half-inch holes were bored every foot in the false-bottom boards. The false bottom rested on short pieces of wood for support, with space sufficient for the passage of the chlorine gas, which was piped into the empty space.

A filter was made by placing coarse quartz gravel over the false bottom to a depth of about two inches. Over this finer gravel was layered, until finally sand covered the filter, the entire depth being about 4-5 inches. Care was taken to avoid disturbing the filter when the charge was removed. Strips of wood were laid on the filter to help prevent disrupting the surface of the filter, and to furnish a convenient surface for shoveling out a spent charge. Filters lasted up to 50-60 charges.

The vat had two ports on opposite sides – one to admit the chlorine gas, and the other to drain the tank. The tank was inclined ½ inch from the drain side to the gas side to facilitate draining.

Figure 20   Chlorination leaching Vats
Source: Electrochemical Industry, 1904

When charging a vat that was previously used, the filter was still very wet, and the water would wet the ore and hinder chlorination. Dry ore was sifted loosely over the wet filter to a depth of 8-10 inches, and allowed to stand for 6-8 hours to absorb some of this moisture. If too wet or dry, the appropriate ore was carefully mixed in to make it right. Then the remaining pre-moistened ore was sifted in to complete the charge, care being taken to achieve the required loose condition for effective permeation of the chlorine gas. The sieve used for sifting was a frame of about one by two feet in size, five inches deep, and with a coarse two- to eight-mesh screen. The sieve was either positioned on a couple of boards that were placed across the top of the vat, or suspended by four ropes above the vat.[114]

Chlorine Gas Generation

The *chlorine gas generator* was made almost entirely of lead, costing about $120 to build. See figures 21 and 22. The vessel was surrounded by a water chamber, in which the edge of the lid was immersed, forming a gas-tight seal. A funnel built into the lid, used for adding the acid, also had a trap that could be filled with water.

Charging the vessel was very tedious, taking from one to two hours. A lead-coated iron stirrer was used to mix the charge. The generator was either equipped with a jacket for steam heating, or sat in a sand bath over a fire as seen in figure 21.

Chlorine gas sufficient for three or four tons of roasted ore was made using:

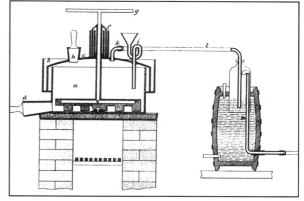

Figure 21   Chlorine Gas Generator
Source: Aaron, 1881

- 30 pounds of manganese peroxide (manganese dioxide, MnO_2)
- 40 pounds of salt (NaCl)
- 36 pounds of water (H_2O)
- 70 pounds of sulfuric acid (H_2SO_4, three bottles).

All of the quantities were somewhat variable due to the quality of the chemicals used. The salt, manganese peroxide, and water were put in the generator and stirred to mix them together. The lid was put down and the water joints filled.

When the chlorine gas (Cl_2) was required, a bottle of sulfuric acid was slowly poured into the funnel as the stirrer was turned. The reaction produced a significant amount of heat, so no external heating was required. A fire was made (or steam introduced into the jacket, if so equipped) after the last bottle of sulfuric acid had been used.

The reaction producing the chlorine is:[115]

$$4MnO_2 + 2H_2SO_4 + 2NaCl \quad \blacktriangleright \quad Cl_2 + 2NaSO_4 + 2Mn_2O_3 + 2H_2O$$

A second method of generating the chlorine was to use

- ◆ 1 part manganese peroxide
- ◆ 2 parts muriatic acid (HCl)
- ◆ 1 part sulfuric acid diluted with 1 part water.

The reaction is:[116]

$$MnO_2 + 4HCl \quad \blacktriangleright \quad Cl_2 + MnCl_2 + 2H_2O$$

Figure 22   Chlorine Gas Generators
Courtesy Mount Morgan Historical Museum, Inc.

A third way of generating chlorine was to mix about

- ◆ 50 pounds of lime chloride ($CaCl_2O$)
- ◆ 60 pounds of sulfuric acid

in a lead-lined iron cylinder. The reaction is:

$$CaCl_2O + H_2SO_4 \quad \blacktriangleright \quad Cl_2 + CaSO_4 + H_2O$$

A fourth method – the Pollok process, invented by J. H. Pollok of Glasgow University, used sodium bisulfate and chloride of lime, the sodium bisulfate being cheaper to ship than sulfuric acid:[117]

$$NaHSO_4 + CaCl_2O \quad \blacktriangleright \quad Cl_2 + CaSO_4 + NaOH$$

The chlorine gas produced was first conducted to a purifier (right side of figure 21), which amounts to an inverted bottle with water in it, designed to dissolve and remove any hydrogen chloride present in the gas.[118] The water has a limited capacity for absorbing the acid – it was renewed once or twice during a charging operation. The purifier also revealed the rate of generation of the chlorine gas by how vigorously it bubbled, and this was used to determine when to add additional sulfuric acid to the generator.[119]

Chlorination

The chlorine gas was then admitted to the vat. It took from three to six hours for the chlorine to reach the top of the charge. Its presence could be detected above the surface of the roasted ore. A glass rod dipped into ammonia and held over the ore gave off white ammonium chloride fumes in the presence of chlorine. Chains were used to lower the lid. To prevent the escape of chlorine, the edge of the lid was luted with a paste made of wheat flower or a mixture of bran and leached sand. It took a few hours to prepare the lid. Leaks could be detected and fixed using the previously described method.[120] The chlorine was then allowed to perform its work for between one half to two days.[121] During this time, the chlorine gas reacted with the gold, forming gold chloride:

$$2Au + 3Cl_2 \quad \blacktriangleright \quad 2AuCl_3$$

The gold chloride thus formed needed to be removed from the vat for subsequent precipitation and refining. In earlier incarnations of the process the vat lid was removed to conduct these operations. This was a hazardous procedure, as vividly described by Aaron:

"At this point a difficulty arises, from the fact that a large quantity of chlorine remains in the vat, the escape of which is not desirable. If the cover of the vat be raised, the gas is visible like a green sea above the ore; a pestilential sea whose waves, surging forth upon the slightest disturbance of the air, threaten to envelope and suffocate the workman, unless he hold his breath while hoisting the cover and fastening the tackle, and then retreat in haste till the storm is over; and even then the same trouble recurs while he enters, and displaces the chlorine still remaining beneath the filter, and permeating the loose mass of damp ore."[122]

After removing the lid and giving sufficient time to exhaust away the remaining gas, the vat was carefully and slowly filled with water. The gold chloride quickly went into solution. Water was added until it completely covered and soaked into the ore, and no bubbles were seen rising to the surface. This *liquor* was then drained and run into a trough or lead pipe to a settling tank. A steady stream of wash water replaced the liquor being drained, always keeping the ore completely immersed.

Washing continued until the wash water showed that chlorine was no longer present. A simple test was made by sampling the liquor in a glass, and adding to this a small amount of a prepared iron sulfate ($FeSO_4$) solution. If a dark precipitate formed, the solution still contained gold chloride. If the water remained clear, the gold chloride had been completely washed from the vat, and washing ceased. This step of the process took about 4-5 hours.

Later installations fixed a wood or lead vent pipe to the side of the vat near the top. As the wash water was admitted, it displaced the gas, which vented outside the mill. The lid was removed only after the vat was completely filled with water.[123]

Settling and Precipitation

Settling tanks were designed to hold at least a day's worth of liquor. If the liquor showed significant amounts of suspended solids – a cloudy or muddy quality, sulfuric acid was added to precipitate the impurities (as insoluble sulfates, like gypsum) in the settling tank. Otherwise, these impurities would contaminate the gold precipitate. The clear solution was then carefully siphoned or discharged from the settling tank and run into precipitation vats. The time spent settling varied from a few hours to a day.[124]

Figure 23   Precipitation Vats
Source: Electrochemical Industry, 1904

The accumulated liquor, once settled, was drawn off into precipitation tanks. See figure 23. These wooden tanks were generally from 3 to 8 feet in diameter, four feet deep, and were lined with lead or a pitch-tar coating. A smooth surface was desired, this making the removal of the precipitate easier. Each tank held the liquor produced from three tons of ore. A ferrous sulfate ($FeSO_4$) solution was used to precipitate the gold from solution. The precipitation reaction is:[125]

$$AuCl_3 + 3FeSO_4 \quad \blacktriangleright \quad Au + FeCl_3 + Fe_2(SO_4)_3$$

Ferrous sulfate (also known as *copperas*) was made by putting about 50 pounds of scrap iron into a small wooden tank. A few buckets of water were poured in, and then 20-30 pounds of sulfuric acid were carefully added. The reaction is:

$$Fe + H_2SO_4 \quad \blacktriangleright \quad FeSO_4 + H_2$$

Batches of ferrous sulfate solution were usually prepared a couple of days in advance of use.

The ferrous sulfate solution was poured into the precipitation tank, and then given sufficient time to react with the gold chloride. A sample of the tank solution would be taken and tested (described earlier). This would be repeated until the gold precipitation reaction ceased. Up to three days were allowed for the ultra-fine suspended gold particles to completely settle to the tank bottom.

When the precipitate had settled, the *barren* solution was carefully drawn or siphoned off, and a fresh solution added to the precipitation tank. The accumulated precipitate was periodically collected, and allowed to settle in smaller lead-lined boxes. For this reason the precipitation tanks were kept covered and locked.[126]

Refining

The gold precipitate was washed with boiling water to remove any iron salts, collected and dried on filters, and then melted into bullion. The fluxes used were borax, salt, and potassium nitrate. By carefully skimming the molten gold, bullion of 990 fineness or higher could be produced. The bullion produced from ferrous sulfate precipitation can easily be 950-990 fine, but that produced from hydrogen sulfide precipitation (described later) is not as pure – it is usually between 800-950 fine.[127]

Process Improvements: Barrels

Aside from the time spent roasting the ore and precipitating the gold from solution, the vat chlorination process required at least four days – one to clean up the previous charge and then recharge the vat, two for the chlorination, and one for dissolving the gold chloride and draining the vat. For this reason, four leaching vats would be used, one for each day. To increase the capacity of the mill, a large number of vats and tanks would be required – mill floor space that was generally unavailable or costly. There certainly was room for improvements and streamlining of the process.[128]

The Mears Process

B. H. Mears, M.D., of Philadelphia, was performing experiments on ore chlorination in his lab at his home. The experimental vessel used for chlorination exploded shortly after charging due to a clogged pipe. Despite the setback, he collected up the scattered ore fragments to determine if there had been any exposure to the chlorine gas in such a short time. Much to his surprise, he discovered that the degree of chlorination from a few minutes exposure to pressurized chlorine was as great as would be expected from hours of conventional vat-type exposure. The *Mears Process* quickly developed from this serendipitous discovery and found widespread use.

The lead-lined barrel was made of cast or sheet iron and built to withstand pressures up to 60 PSI. It revolved about a hollow trunnion at 15-20 RPM, this keeping the roasted ore in constant agitation. The chlorine gas, externally generated as in vat chlorination, was pumped into the cylinder through the trunnion. See figure 24.

The tumbling of the ore helped to mechanically wear away the gold chloride formed on the surface of the gold particle, exposing a fresh gold surface to the attacking chlorine gas. This accelerated the chlorination and enhanced the overall recovery of coarse particles of gold. Many gold ores have silver in substantial percentages alloyed with the gold (*electrum*). This same abrasive effect applied to the formation of silver chlorides, which in the vat process created a coating that greatly hindered chlorination of the gold. The pressure of the chlorine gas, pumped in, also hastened the process.

The roasted ore was moistened with a small amount of water and charged into the barrel through an access door. The door was bolted shut and the barrel set to revolving, and within *two hours* the chlorination was complete. The barrel was stopped, and the access door was unbolted and water added to the pulp. It was then discharged into a filtering vat like that previously described, to be washed, precipitated, etc.

The Mears process decreased the time of chlorination from two days to so many hours. It was not without its difficulties, however. The seals on the trunnion were difficult to maintain, with chlorine gas leaking into the mill works. Discharging the pulp was clumsy. Repair costs were also high. Further improvements could be made, and were.[129]

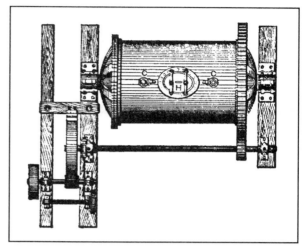

Figure 24   Mears Chlorination Barrel
Source: Wilson, 1907

The Thies Process

Carl Adolph Thies set about to streamline the Mears process. His significant improvements led to the *Thies Process*. Much of his work was carried out at the Haile Gold Mine in South Carolina.[130]

First, and perhaps most significantly, he dispensed with the external chlorine gas generator, gas storage tank, pump, and hollow trunnion by simply generating the gas within the barrel itself. He also tapered the barrel ends. This more effectively drained the liquor from the center of the barrel. Early models had a single door and took a one-ton charge, but later models with greater capacity were made. A five-ton barrel was five feet in diameter and nine feet long, had two charging doors, and could chlorinate up to six charges – 30 tons, per day, though three or four charges per day was typical. There was also an optional framework for supporting a sand filter in the barrel itself. See figure 25.

The barrel was partially filled with water, to which sulfuric acid was carefully added. An excess of sulfuric acid was usually added, otherwise calcium sulfate could precipitate with the gold. The roasted ore was charged next. Chloride of lime (bleaching powder) was added last, and the charging ports were bolted shut. The barrel was then set to revolving. This mixed the ore and the chemicals that were charged separately; the chlorine gas was generated, and pressurized the barrel to about two atmospheres. The chlorination time was about six hours – not as fast as Mears, but far more streamlined.[131]

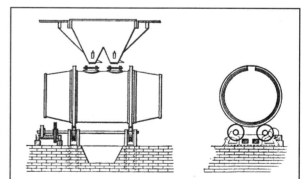

Figure 25   Thies Chlorination Barrel
Source: Wilson, 1907

A small pop-valve allowed the chlorinator to test for the presence of chlorine gas without having to open the barrel up. When the chlorination was complete, the barrel was stopped, and enough water was added to almost fill it. It was set to revolving again to wash the ore and dissolve most of the gold chloride. It was stopped, and the solution drained and sent to shallow filter beds. A second wash was then run through the barrel after the first. Lastly, the pulp was discharged, and the barrel rinsed out and prepared for the next charge.

Water could be conserved in the process. After draining the concentrated solution from the barrel, an additional 120 gallons of water per ton of ore would be added to the barrel. The barrel would then be pressurized, and this wash water would be forced from the barrel, through a hose, and into a tank positioned higher than the barrel. The next ore charge to be processed would use this weak wash solution instead of fresh water.[132]

Results on dead roasted and very fine ores showed a recovery of no less than 96%, the gold obtained being 978 fine. The total cost of treatment was only $4 per ton.[133]

Precipitation Improvements

Ferrous sulfate was not used on a large scale due to the time required to effect complete precipitation – at least 24 hours for precipitation and another two days to allow the gold to settle. An improvement in precipitation was the use of sulfur dioxide (SO_2) and hydrogen sulfide (H_2S) gases. This method gained favor due to the simplicity and economy of generating the gases, and the faster recovery of the gold. Only about five to six hours is required for complete precipitation when using hydrogen sulfide.

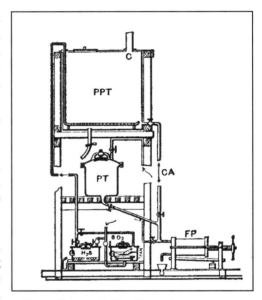

Figure 26　　Golden Reward Precipitation System
Source: Wilson, 1907

The Golden Reward Gold Mining Company chlorination works in Deadwood, South Dakota, which began using barrel chlorination in April 1891,[134] used this process, as introduced by W. Langguth. The following process outline is based on this arrangement. See figure 26.

The gold chloride solution was pumped into a lead-lined, wooden storage tank of about 7000 gallons capacity – sufficient for holding the solution from twenty tons of ore. A lead pipe ran the width of the tank, a few inches above the floor. It had small, closely spaced holes for admitting the gas into the tank. The pipe was connected to two gas generators.

The first step was to remove any free (uncombined) chlorine present in the solution. A gas generator, about 2.5 feet in diameter and 4 feet high, used compressed air to burn roll sulfur, creating sulfur dioxide gas:

$$S + O_2 \quad \blacktriangleright \quad SO_2$$

The sulfur dioxide – under pressure, was admitted into the tank, where the chlorine was rapidly removed by the following reaction:

$$SO_2 + Cl_2 + 2H_2O \quad \blacktriangleright \quad H_2SO_4 + 2HCl$$

Excess gas escaped through a pipe in the top of the tank.

The next step was to precipitate the gold chloride from solution. Hydrogen sulfide was generated by combining sulfuric acid with iron matte (iron sulfide) in a lead-lined gas generator of dimensions similar to that used for generating sulfur dioxide. [135]

$$H_2SO_4 + FeS \quad \blacktriangleright \quad FeSO_4 + H_2S$$

The hydrogen sulfide, pumped into the tank, precipitated the gold:

$$2AuCl_3 + H_2S + 2H_2O \quad \blacktriangleright \quad 2Au + 6HCl + SO_2$$

After sufficient time was allowed for complete precipitation – about an hour, the solution was allowed to settle for two hours. The gold precipitate was in a finely divided state, much of which settled to the floor of the tank, but a significant portion remained in suspension in the solution.

The solution was drained from the tank, to about four inches above the gas-pipe, and into the pressure tank. From there it was forced, using compressed air, through a filter press to collect the suspended solids. This required about three hours. A total of about six hours was required to precipitate and collect the gold.

A cleanup was made twice a month. The precipitated gold resting on the bottom of the tank was washed into the pressure tank, where it was then forced through the filter press. The collected gold was refined into bullion.[136]

Charcoal was also used to precipitate the gold from solution, it being patented in 1880 by Professor Koenig, of the University of Pennsylvania.[137] Charcoal was perhaps the safest and simplest precipitation method of the three – ferrous sulfate, hydrogen sulfide, and charcoal, in use. At cleanup time, the charcoal was simply dried and then carefully burned to recover the gold.[138] Even so, in many mills ferrous sulfate was still preferred over charcoal.[139]

The Rothwell and Newberry-Vautin Processes

J. E. Rothwell devised a barrel that used a built-in filter. The barrel had a charging-discharging port on one side of the barrel, and a series of drainage holes on the opposite side. The filter originally used was made of woven asbestos cloth, which lasted for about 50-60 charges, but was expensive. He devised a sand filter that proved satisfactory, lasting about a month before requiring replacement. Both filters were secured in the barrel by means of a wooden frame. It was impregnated with tar or asphalt to enhance its life. These innovations became known as the *Rothwell Process*.[140]

The *Newberry-Vautin Process* streamlined barrel chlorination, washing, and precipitation further yet. Compressed air was added after charging the barrel. A rubber hose was connected to a valve on the barrel for this purpose. This brought the pressure in the barrel up to as high as 60 PSI – like the Mears process; higher pressures meant shorter chlorination times. Pressures of from 30-40 PSI could reduce the time for leaching to as little as 40 minutes, depending on the nature of the charge.[141] The barrel rotated at about 10 RPM.

After chlorination, the compressed gases were vented to the outside of the mill using the valve and a second rubber hose. The charging port was removed, and the barrel set in motion. On each revolution, a portion of the pulp discharged into a chute leading to a leaching vat located on the floor below. After most of the charge was emptied this way, the barrel was stopped, a few buckets of water thrown in, and it was started again to clear the remaining pulp out.

The leaching vat was a lead-lined iron box, built on a pivot. Connected to the false bottom was a vacuum pump. This accelerated the rate at which it was drained, the process taking about an hour. The solution was sent to a solution tank. After washing and draining the vat, it was tipped on its side. The tailings were emptied into a car positioned on a track located on a lower deck and run to the tailings heap.

The gold-bearing solution was drained from the base of the solution tank and run through a charcoal filter. The gold collects on the surface of the charcoal, but the copper, zinc, magnesium, and calcium salts pass through; thus purifying the bullion.[142]

Chlorination Résumé

One objection to using the chlorination process was the acid; the transportation was both costly and troublesome.[143] Other difficulties included the use of very toxic chlorine and hydrogen sulfide gases, the cost of preliminary roasting of the ore or concentrates, the time and manpower required to treat a ton of ore, and the equipment and installation costs. Even so, the chlorination process – in its myriad forms, was one of the very few practical wet-chemistry processes for gold recovery for 30 years, and it was indeed effective if performed properly. Chlorination was attempted in many mining districts, but was often abandoned just as quickly due to the aforementioned concerns regarding its practical implementation.

Overall, the various chlorination processes were capable of recovering about 95% of the gold from the ore,[144] and the bullion produced was of a very high fineness. There were exceptions, however. At the Alaska Treadwell mine, amalgamation recovered 50% of the gold, whereas chlorination recovered only 62%.[145]

Cripple Creek

In 1893, Edward Holden erected the first chlorination works in Cripple Creek. By 1895, works of 50 TPD using barrel chlorination were operating in nearby Gillett, and the Metallic Extraction Company built their cyanide mill near Florence. In 1896[146] there were five stamp mills that produced $144,500 from 11,800 tons of ore, or $12.25 per ton. It is doubtful that the recovery exceeded 55%. Two cyanide works recovered $864,000 from 48,400 tons, or $17.85 per ton. Two chlorination works recovered $476,000 from 15,600 tons, or $30.51 per ton.

Some of the Cripple Creek chlorination mills bought ore at $19 per ounce of gold in addition to a $7 per ton milling fee.[147] This does not mean that 92% of the gold value was recovered (92% of $20.67 is $19), but merely a guaranteed rate paid to the mine. If more than 92% could be recovered, it would mean additional profit for the mill, whereas less recovered would go against the fixed $7 charge. Thus the $7 charge covered treatment costs, gold paid for but lost, and profit.[148]

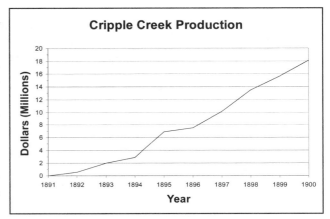

Chart 7

In 1902, chlorination was processing most of the district's ore. By 1904, chlorination works had an aggregate capacity of 1750 TPD whereas cyanide plants had 450. About one-sixth of the ore was shipped to smelters. But, the writing was on the wall: "In the opinion of some able metallurgists the cyanide process is much better adapted to the ores and will eventually displace chlorination." The fight was on between chlorination and cyanidation, but by 1911, the days of chlorination were over in Cripple Creek – cyanidation had finally won.[149]

Cripple Creek's phenomenal gold output – over $77 million in the first decade, is graphed in chart 7.[150] In the year 1900, at the peak of production, nearly 23% of the gold produced in the U.S. came from the Victor-Cripple Creek goldfields, and nearly all of this was won using the chlorination process.

Figure 27   Golden Cycle Mine   Courtesy USGS
                   Victor, Colorado 1903

The Kiss Process

The use of alkaline earth hyposulfites for silver extraction was first proposed by Percy in 1848 and put in practice by Von Patera at Joachimsthal (Jachymov), Czechoslovakia in 1858. This became known as the *Von Patera Process*. Sodium hyposulfite and sodium polysulfide were used. Kiss, in 1860,[151] substituted calcium salts, and this became known as the *Kiss Process*.[152]

Gold-silver ores that underwent a chlorodizing roast and the chlorination process contained insoluble silver chloride (AgCl). It was not lost, however. If the ore was sufficiently rich, it could be recovered after the gold chloride leaching was complete.[153] For silver ores, a chlorodizing roast was performed on the argentiferous tailings first. The water-soluble base metal chlorides were then removed by vat leaching, leaving behind the insoluble silver chloride. Leaching took from 4-10 hours.[154]

A solution of calcium hyposulphite (CaO_3S_2, calcium thiosulfate) was used to leach the silver chloride:

$$2AgCl + CaO_3S_2 \quad \blacktriangleright \quad Ag_2O_3S_2 + CaCl_2$$

Testing if the leach was complete used one of two different tests: The taste of the solution, or chemical precipitation. When the sweet taste of the solution went away, leaching was complete. The chemical test used the same chemistry for precipitation, description following. The leaching could take from 8 hours to 2-3 days depending on the nature of the ore.[155]

The calcium polysulfide (CaS)[156] could be made onsite by boiling two parts of lime with one part of sulfur for 3-4 hours. The consumption of sulfur and lime varied with the ore, but ranged from 2-7 pounds for the former, twice that for the latter.[157]

The solution obtained was run to a separate precipitation vat. Calcium polysulfide was then added to precipitate the silver as silver sulfide (Ag_2S), the reaction being: [158]

$$Ag_2O_3S_2 + CaS \quad \blacktriangleright \quad Ag_2S + CaO_3S_2$$

Care was exercised in adding the calcium polysulfide; any more than was necessary to effect a nearly complete precipitation would wind up being recycled into the leaching vat when the solution was reused, causing a precipitation and loss of silver values into the tailings. Using less than that required for complete precipitation did not lose silver; the silver was recycled in soluble form ($Ag_2O_3S_2$, silver thiosulfate) back into the leaching vat too.

The precipitate, looking like dark mud, was washed, filtered, and dried into a cake. It was then carefully roasted in a reverberatory furnace – a temperature high enough to drive off some of the sulfur, but not high enough to melt the cake. This was sometimes difficult due to other sulfides and metals being present, notably lead, which reduced the melting temperature of the cake. The cake was then ready for melting. The fluxes used included borax and scrap iron. The iron would combine with the remaining sulfur, forming a matte that was skimmed away.[159]

O. Hofmann, in about 1880, used a combination of sodium hyposulfite and calcium polysulfide. This became known as the *Hofmann process*.[160] Küstel and Hofmann successfully applied this process in Mexico and southern California, and there it became known as the *Mexican Process*.[161] The cost varied from $5-12 per ton, and recoveries could be as high as 80-90% under optimum conditions.[162] In practice the Kiss process and its derivatives were not very successful in extracting the silver from complex ores, and only recovered a portion of any contained gold.[163]

The Cyanide Process

Eighteenth century alchemists knew that gold was soluble in potassium cyanide (KCN) solutions. Scheele noted this effect in 1783. In 1846 Elsner recognized that atmospheric oxygen was essential for dissolving gold with cyanide, but he did little more than report this fact. It wasn't until 1887 – 41 years later, when John S. MacArthur and brothers Robert and William Forrest were awarded their patent that a commercially successful process was made available to the mining industry, a process that is used to this day.[164]

The *MacArthur-Forrest Process*, later to become known simply as the *Cyanide Process*, was developed and patented in England by MacArthur and the Forrests in October of 1887. An additional patent was granted for the use of lime in the process, and more importantly, the use of zinc for precipitation, in 1888. They then secured a patent in the U.S. in May of 1889.[165]

The process was first used experimentally to treat tailings from a 10-stamp mill at the Crown Mine, Karangahake, New Zealand, in 1889. In 1890 it was adapted to treat the Robinson Gold Mines ores from the Witwatersrand gold fields of the Transvaal, this being the first commercial use of the process. The Gold Recovery Syndicate, representatives of the Cassel Company (owners of the MacArthur-Forrest patents), implemented this very successful commercial venture in South Africa.[166] The cyanide process made its debut in the U.S. in 1891, when William Orr introduced it to the management of the Mercur Gold Mining and Milling Company in Mercur, Utah, for use at the Manning Mill. [167]

Either sodium (NaCN) or potassium cyanide may be used in the process. The choice was generally determined by price and availability.[168] In the following chemical reactions, the positive ion – sodium (Na) or potassium (K), is omitted for clarity, but may be added to those reactants or products with a negative charge (superscript). The first set of reactions illustrates the dissolution of the gold by cyanide. Note that oxygen (O_2) is required:[169]

$$2Au + 4CN^- + O_2 + 2H_2O \quad \blacktriangleright \quad 2Au(CN)_2^- + 2OH^- + H_2O_2$$

Hydrogen peroxide (H_2O_2) is produced as an intermediate product, and then becomes a reactant:

$$2Au + 4CN^- + H_2O_2 \quad \blacktriangleright \quad 2Au(CN)_2^- + 2OH^-$$

Combining these two equations

$$4Au + 8CN^- + O_2 + 2H_2O \quad \blacktriangleright \quad 4Au(CN)_2^- + 4OH^-$$

produces Elsner's equation from 1846. The fact that Elsner's published equation predated the MacArthur patent by 41 years no doubt contributed to the inability of MacArthur to deflect legal attacks against the validity of the patents that he was awarded.

Silver minerals are also dissolved by cyanide solutions:[170]

- ◆ Native silver: $4Ag + 8CN^- + O_2 + 2H_2O$ ▶ $4Ag(CN)_2^- + 4OH^-$
- ◆ Ceragyrite (Horn silver): $AgCl + 2CN^-$ ▶ $Ag(CN)_2^- + Cl^-$
- ◆ Argentite: $Ag_2S + 4CN^-$ ▶ $2Ag(CN)_2^- + S^{2-}$

The relative solubility of various metals in a cyanide solution, in decreasing order, is:[171]

Mg, Magnesium ▶	Al, Aluminum ▶	Zn, Zinc ▶	Cu, Copper ▶	Au, Gold ▶
Ag, Silver ▶	Hg, Mercury ▶	Pb, Lead ▶	Fe, Iron ▶	Pt, Platinum

Any metal listed tends to displace any metals already in solution listed after it; thus zinc will replace and precipitate copper, gold, silver, etc., but not magnesium or aluminum. Gold is the important metal to be recovered by cyanidation; thus one of Mg, Al, Zn, or Cu must be used to precipitate it. Of these, zinc had the virtue of being cheap and very effective.[172]

The precipitation of gold and silver by zinc is shown in the following reactions:[173]

$$2Au(CN)_2^- + Zn \quad \blacktriangleright \quad Zn(CN)_4^{2-} + 2Au$$
$$2Ag(CN)_2^- + Zn \quad \blacktriangleright \quad Zn(CN)_4^{2-} + 2Ag$$

Free cyanide may then be regenerated because in a basic solution the following reaction takes place:[174]

$$Zn(CN)_4^{2-} + 4OH^- \quad \blacktriangleright \quad Zn(OH)_4^{2-} + 4CN^-$$

These equations are, naturally, ideal. In practice, significantly more cyanide was required due to base metal contamination and other effects. Cyanide consumption at the Empire Mine in Grass Valley, California was between 0.75-0.90 *pounds* per ton on sands and slimes assaying about 0.10 *ounces* gold.[175]

Cyanidation is a relatively inexpensive process due to the low cost of the cyanide and zinc. Free-milling gold ores are the most suitable for this process. Auriferous ores work better than argentiferous ores, but for the latter, no special treatments are required. As with the chlorination process, ore with large, granular particles of free gold take longer for the cyanide to dissolve.

Difficulties arise when crushed ores remain relatively impermeable to the cyanide solution. Slimes may prevent uniform percolation. Ores containing organic matter – wood from cribbing or mine timbers and from reworked tailing heaps, adsorbs the gold from solution in a manner similar to charcoal. About 10-15% of the Kendall mine, Montana gold ore was often associated with bitumen, called "black ore," which could not be treated with cyanide unless a preliminary roasting was performed.[176]

Neutral ores are best; sulfide ores that consequently form sulfuric acid are best neutralized with lime or a caustic soda wash prior to treatment. Tellurium and antimony interfere with the process, though roasting makes the ore amenable to treatment, albeit at additional cost. Ores containing appreciable amounts of copper, especially carbonates and oxides, interfere with cyanidation. Oxidized zinc and copper, and other metals, are called *cyanicides*. They cause excessive consumption of cyanide. Chromium compounds are "some of the worst interfering substances."[177]

Other chemical reactions impede the dissolution of gold, or require excessive amounts of cyanide to be used. Because oxygen is required, anything that consumes oxygen hinders the process. For example, pyrrhotite (FeS)[178] is present in many ores, and in an aqueous solution leads to the formation of ferric hydroxide $(Fe(OH)_3)$ through the following two reactions, the second of which consumes the oxygen:[179]

$$FeS + 2OH^- \quad \blacktriangleright \quad Fe(OH)_2 + S^{2-}$$

$$4Fe(OH)_2 + O_2 + 2H_2O \quad \blacktriangleright \quad 4Fe(OH)_3$$

The presence of the cyanicide sphalerite (ZnS) serves as an example of the formation of an cyanide-consuming complex, as in the following reaction:[180]

$$ZnS + 4CN^- \quad \blacktriangleright \quad [Zn(CN)_4]^{2-} + S^{2-}$$

The formation of films on the surface of the gold particles interferes with their dissolution. Sulfides, present in concentrations of as little as 0.5 PPM (Parts Per Million), cause the formation of insoluble gold sulfide. At concentrations of 20 PPM, the rate of dissolution for gold drops by about 30%. Excessive amounts of lime used to adjust the ph lead to the formation of calcium peroxide on the surface of the gold, inhibiting dissolution.[181]

Silver dissolves at about half the rate that gold does, on a weight-basis.[182] The rate that cyanide leaches gold for very coarse ore[183] is shown in chart 8. Similar curves result from leaching sands and agitated slimes, but at much shorter time-scales.[184] The Empire Mine's cyanide plant (ca 1929) processed sands in about 3-4 days.[185] Temperature also affects the rate that cyanide dissolves gold, as is seen in chart 9.[186]

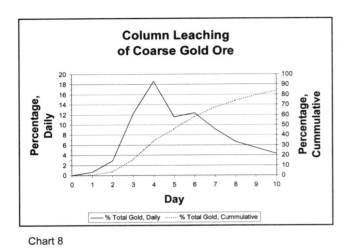

Chart 8

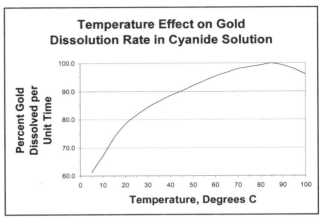

Chart9

The Process

MacArthur describes the cyanide process:

> "The ore is placed in vats, provided with a false bottom covered with canvas or other similar material to act as a filter,[187] and treated with the cyanide solution... In the case of poor ores and tailings the total time of lixiviation and washing occupies seldom less than thirty-six hours, which time is often increased in richer ores or when the material is coarse. The gold-bearing solution, as it comes from the vats, is caused to flow through a tank containing ... layers of spongy zinc. The precipitation goes on continuously and is only interrupted once or twice a month for a clean up. The amount of zinc actually consumed... amounts to ten or fifteen times the weight of the gold deposited. At each clean up the gold is shaken off the zinc ... and contain a large quantity of base metal which would be removed either by purification with acid before smelting, or by oxidising (sic) the slimes and mixing with suitable fluxes. In smelting, the fluxes generally used are sand, soda, fluor (sic) spar, and borax."[188]

The total amount of cyanide solution used was about twice the weight of the sands charged into the vat. About 24 hours were required for cyaniding. The vat was then drained of the *pregnant solution* and then washed with water recycled from the precipitation tanks. The gold was precipitated in a series of interconnected *zinc boxes* composed of a long, narrow steel trough separated by partitions, each having a screen in the bottom on which the zinc shavings rest. See figure 28. The arrangement was made such that the solution flowed up through one compartment and down through the next.[189] Complete precipitation resulted in a *barren solution*.

The zinc shavings used in precipitating the gold from the pregnant solution were often turned from a rod of zinc chucked into a small lathe. See figure 29.[190] Ideally, the shavings are 1/32 inch wide and 1/1260 inch thick, thus making

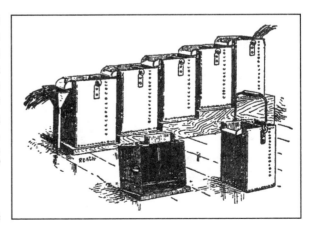

Figure 28   Zinc Boxes
Source: Miller, 1906

156

1630 square feet of surface area to the pound of zinc.[191] The precipitate washed from the zinc shavings was allowed to settle, then was treated with 10% sulfuric acid to dissolve the zinc, forming soluble zinc sulfate.[192]

Filter presses were used to collect the particles of precipitated gold that remained suspended in the barren solution after reacting with the zinc. The presses varied greatly in their dimensions, depending on the requirements of the milling operation. Typical Allis-Chalmers presses from the turn of the century could be as small as weighing 532 pounds, with 12" square filter plates, each having six chambers and 0.4 cubic feet of filtering capacity, on up to models weighing 50,000 pounds, with 48" square plates, each with 48 chambers and a total capacity of 88 cubic feet. The cake that built up on the filters was about 1" thick, and the presses operated at about 100-150 PSI.[193] See figure 30.

Table 1 provides representative mill horsepower requirements for the various stages of the process. An average of only 2 horsepower per ton was required overall. 73% of the power required was for crushing and grinding of the auriferous ore.[194]

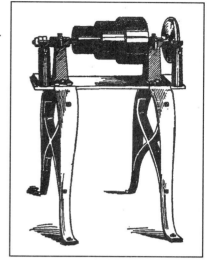

Figure 29   Zinc Lathe
Source: Miller, 1906

Mill	TPD	Crush	Grind	Thicken	Filter	Agitate	Precip.	Tailing	Misc	Total	Per Ton
DeSantis	150	48	128	8	48	24	4		89.5	349.5	2.3
East Malarite	1050	602	615	19	146	58	27	7.5	127.5	1602	1.5
Gunnar Gold	150	43	154	14	34	21	6	5	27.5	304.5	2.0
Kerr Addison	650	459	497.5	28.5	138.5	62	27		83	1296	2.0
Lebel Oro	80	53.5	77	12	34	30	4	5	10.25	225.8	2.8
Morris Kirkland	150	72	156	8	39.5	31	8	7.5	19.5	341.5	2.3
Sladen Malartic	500	193	472.5	10	44	8	37.5	10	6.5	781.5	1.6
Total	2730	1470.5	2100	99.5	484	234	113.5	35	363.8	4900	1.8
Percent		30	43	2	10	5	2	1	7	100	2.0

Table 1

Cyanide Résumé

The Cyanide Process quietly spread throughout the West, destined to dominate gold recovery methods through the 20th century and into the 21st. By the early 20th century, most gold ore was worked by a combination of amalgamation and cyanidation. It wasn't until 1911, for example, that cyanidation finally displaced chlorination in the Victor-Cripple Creek gold fields.[195]

Some ores were not amenable to the treatment, and other recovery methods were required: In 1900, Broadway mine refractory ores valued at about $20 per ton were processed in the Cherry Creek 20-stamp amalgamation-cyanidation mill, located in the Silver Star district of Montana. Despite utilizing both of these processes, only 60% of the values were recovered, the tailings being sent to Butte for smelting.[196]

Figure 30   Filter Press
Source: Allis-Chalmers, 1903

A few milestones in the steady advance of cyanidation are outlined below.

1891 Only a short time after the introduction of cyanidation in Mercur, the process was introduced at the Utica Mine in Calumet, California.[197]

1892 The first cyanide works in Cripple Creek were established.[198]

The Black Hills Gold and Extraction Company built a small cyanide plant in Deadwood. Early attempts cost more than what was saved, however.[199]

1893 The Gilt Edge mill, rebuilt for $35,000, was possibly the first cyanide plant built in Montana, working 100 tons of $20 ore per day.[200]

1895 The Yellow Jacket 30-stamp 200 TPD cyanide mill, located near Challis, Idaho, had a milling cost of only $2.67 per ton.[201]

1896 The first cyanide plant in Nevada was constructed at Silver City by R. D. Jackson to treat Comstock tailings.[202]

Retreatment of tailings generated a series of mini-booms throughout the West. Massive piles of mill sand, containing significant and previously unrecoverable gold and silver values, begged to be processed using the new technology, as did low-grade ore dumps.

1899 Stamp milling with a cyanide solution rather than using plain water was introduced at the Homestake.[203] In this way the ore was brought into contact with the cyanide at the earliest – and most convenient, time. This resulted in the dissolving of from 70-80% of the gold and 5-25% of the silver before the pulp even reached the cyanide leaching tanks.[204]

1901 Charles W. "Cyanide Charlie" Merrill successfully adapted the cyanide process to treat Homestake tailings in the 1200 TPD Number One Sand Plant.[205] Prior to the introduction of cyanidation, the Homestake mills recovered 75-80% of the values.[206] By 1904, that figure rose to 94%.[207]

Figure 31   180° panorama of the Hendricks Cyanide Mill, Bannack, Montana 2001   Author

Thieves' Stinkin' Socks

"An example of one form of theft was the practice of suspending a sock full of zinc shavings or dust in a pregnant cyanide leaching tank to collect or precipitate gold, which was then taken home and melted into bullion."[208]

Endnotes

1 ARBITER1964 page 7
2 HENDERSON1926 pages 14-15
3 BACKUS1969 page 260. Pine oil was probably the reagent used – see Voynick's *Climax* page 17. Flotation was destined to dominate ore concentration in the 20th century.
4 SLOAN1975 page 319
5 FATOUT1969 pages 108-111, 115, 120-127
6 Pseudoalloy
7 The copper plates used were frequently electroplated with silver to the amount of about an ounce per square foot, and then coated with mercury. ALLIS1902 pages 66-69.
8 The Homestake had mercury vapor condense in a bucket of water, for example. FIELDER1970 page 101
9 RICHARDS1925 page 63
10 EMMONS1885 page 267
11 EMMONS1885 pages 246,284
12 MILLER1906 pages 197,198
13 EMMONS1885 page 267. The crucibles lasted from 15-25 melts for silver bullion.
14 ARBITER1964 page 272
15 FIELDER1970 page 121
16 THOMPSON1968 page 133
17 Sulfides, in the presence of humid air, form sulfates. Both were important components of the patio process chemical reactions.
18 MOTTEN1972 pages 22-23, FISHER1977 pages 54-55
19 DENNIS1963 page 285 lists 1609.
20 DENNIS1963 page 285 lists 1609, FISHER1977 page 55
21 FISHER1977 page 55
22 DENNIS1963 page 285
23 EMMONS1885 page 264
24 WASHOE2000. The reaction $2AgCl + Hg \rightarrow 2Ag + HgCl_2$ no doubt occurred to some extent, but was thermodynamically less favorable with a net free energy change of +41 kJ/mole as compared to the formation of calomel having a net change of +9. $AgCl + CuCl \rightarrow Ag + CuCl_2$ is also unfavorable with a net free energy change of +54.
25 EMMONS1885 page 265
26 WASHOE2000, DENNIS1963 pages 283-284, PROCTOR1991 page 72, 1911ENC.Silver
27 1911ENC.Silver. These reactions were not checked for their thermodynamic spontaneity.
28 Unfavorable – net free energy change of +49 kJ/mole.
29 TINGLEY1993 page 12, SMITHG1998 page 41
30 TINGLEY1993 page 41. In 1876, the Comstock contributed 55.1% of the silver and 42.9% of the gold – 47.6% total, to the US Treasury.
31 WASHOE2000. -82.7 kJ/mole net change.
32 EMMONS1885 page 265
33 EMMONS1885 page 265
34 EMMONS1885 page 264

35 TINGLEY1990
36 DEQUILLE1959 page 92
37 SMITHG1998 page 260
38 DEQUILLE1959 pages 255-265
39 SMITHG1998 page 43
40 16? 18?
41 SMITHG1998 page 43. In 1861, salt was mined in Dixie Marsh, where it was shipped to the mills in Virginia City for processing Comstock ore. Rhodes Marsh also produced salt, which in the early 1860's was shipped to Virginia City by camel. Additional discoveries were made: Sand Springs Marsh in 1863; Eagle Marsh in 1870, which had the benefit of being close to the Central Pacific Railroad. TINGLEY1990
42 Average quicksilver charge was 10% the weight of the ore, and even more added for especially rich ore. SMITHG1998 page 43.
43 In practice, it took perhaps a half hour to charge and discharge a pan, bring it up to temperature, etc., so the actual time spent for treatment probably didn't exceed 3.5-4 hours. RAYMOND1873 page 428.
44 SMITHG1998 page258
45 There were only two mills in Eberhardt, Nevada: The *California, Stanford, International*, and *Eberhardt*. Confused? So was I, but thanks to Shawn Hall, the mystery was cleared up. The Stanford brothers built the *California* mill. It was later renamed the *Stanford*. The *International* mill processed ore from the Eberhardt mine, the two connected by aerial tramway. Because of this, it became known as the *Eberhardt* mill. The *Stanford* is located on the east side of the drainage, and the *International* is located on the west side, and to the north of the *Stanford*. HALL2003.
46 RAYMOND1873 pages 190-194
47 COUCH1943 page 149
48 Stem 286 lbs; boss 230; shoe 120; tappet 114. Shoes and dies last about five months, and cams about fifteen months.
49 Shoes and dies last about four months.
50 Canton flannel was used in Bodie. Hot straining – at temperatures near the boiling point of water, was used for a while, but was abandoned due to the "ruinous effect that it had upon the health of the men." EMMONS1885 page 266.
51 Hydraulic presses were infrequently used. The silver amalgam contained about 7 parts mercury for each part of bullion. After compressing the amalgam at about 100 PSI, it was reduced to about 3.5 parts. This saved considerable fuel retorting. EMMONS1885 pages 266-267.
52 Iron discs were sometimes placed in the retort to facilitate the separation of the bullion for melting. Mercury losses from retorting were relatively small. The California mill lost ½ pound per 1000 pounds of amalgam. EMMONS1885 page 267.
53 SMITHG1998 page 177
54 RAYMOND1873 page 429
55 EMMONS1885 page 265
56 Mercuric chloride, $HgCl_2$. The mercury would give up its chlorine to the iron.
57 DEQUILLE1959 pages 96-97
58 Far too late to do much good for the Comstock.

59 PROCTOR1991 page 180
60 EMMONS1885 pages 480-482
61 DEQUILLE1959 page 95
62 BANCROFT1890 page 111
63 SMITHG1998 page 177
64 During this three-year period, average milled ore values *increased* from $62.65 to $68.26 to $70.40 per ton. The 1878 value of $70.40 per ton was the highest since 1861, and would remain so.
65 EMMONS1885 page 264
66 RAYMOND1873 page 429. Slimes sometimes carried greater values than did the coarse ore.
67 EMMONS1885 page 310
68 SMITHG1998 page 260
69 RAYMOND1873 page 429
70 Based on the previously cited production, and assuming the silver was valued at $1.2929 (coinage value) per ounce, which was typical for the time. The difference between the coinage value and that actually received was generally included under *Discounts* on the financial statements.
71 MAB.1881-5. Assuming the coinage rate of $1.2929 for silver.
72 EMMONS1885 page 268, RAYMOND1873 page 431
73 RAYMOND1873 page 431
74 DEQUILLE1959 page 94
75 TWAIN1980 page 282, RAYMOND1873 page 159
76 Data derived from COUCH1943 pages 133-135. *See page 97, endnote 13.* Note that chart 2 represents *tons milled*. Tonnage at the mill was based on the ore *dry* weight; mine tonnage is based on *wet* weight, where the ore has perhaps 10% moisture. The mill tonnage also includes tailings that were reprocessed. What was mined was not necessarily milled. A lot of gangue and low-grade was used as fill.
77 WELLS2002 page 16
78 HAMILTONP1881 page 36
79 EMMONS1885 page 320
80 JACKSONW1963 pages 6,14,122,137,181
81 PROCTOR1991 pages 69-72,82, chart from one illustrated on page 190, EMMONS1885 page 479 for 1877-1880. The amount given for 1879, $517,444.73, was for the first 5 months of the year. This was annualized for the value graphed. Blanket sluices: Proctor states 14 *feet* wide, and also 130 feet in length. Emmons gives 120 feet long. EMMONS1885 page 479
82 EMMONS1885 pages 480-482. And possibly a little bit of uranium.
83 ROTHWELL1896 page 261
84 KUSTEL1868 page 240
85 EISSLER1889 pages 204,205. EMMONS1885 page 274
86 EISSLER1889 pages 207-208
87 KUSTEL1868 page 232
88 KUSTEL1868 pages 237,239-240
89 This would become the basis for *pyritic smelting* – utilizing sulfur to sustain combustion.
90 EISSLER1889 pages 191,208
91 Named after his employer, the Pony Express.
92 ROSS1953 pages 24-25, 26, 28, 29
93 ROSS1953 pages 26, 28-29

[94] ABBE1985 pages 18, 28-29, ROSS1953 pages 29-30, 32, ELLIOTT1973 page 103. BAILEY2002 page 65 states that Stetefeldt invented his furnace at Austin in 1867. The use of steam chests on the pans was not as prevalent in the Reese River process as it was in the Washoe process. Less water was required in the pan than in the Washoe process. 1911ENC.Silver

[95] MANRY1999 pages 43,47

[96] 1911ENC.Silver, SMITHG1998 pages 45, 85

[97] HUTCHISON2003.1

[98] In 1903, the Telluride mill near Colorado City was completed. It was unique in that it utilized bromine instead of chlorine to treat ore. HENDERSON1926 page 13

[99] WILSON1907 page 2

[100] MANNIX1913 page 86. WILSON1907 page 6 gives 1856.

[101] MCQUISTON1986 page 13. KUSTEL1868 page 225 gives 1851.

[102] WILSON1907 page 98, states Deitken and Grass Valley. MCQUISTON1986 page 29, states December 8,1858 at the Pioneer Reduction Works, SW of Nevada City. KUSTEL1868 page 225 spells Deetken, and in 1858. USGS1896 page 24 spells as G. F. Deetken and also O. Maltman, but in 1860. PAUL1965 page 142 states that it was first tried in 1858, but wasn't successful until 1860.

[103] ROTHWELL1896 page 261

[104] EISSLER1889 pages 174-176. Sandy pulp, with the smallest amount of dust or slimes, is the most suitable for chlorination. DAY1892 page 149

[105] ALLIS1903 page 48

[106] EISSLER1889 page 175

[107] KUSTEL1868 pages 231-232 quote, ALLIS1903 page 44, DAY1892 page 149

[108] KUSTEL1868 page 238

[109] EMMONS1885 page 274

[110] WILSON1907 page 107

[111] EMMONS1885 page 274. The Stetefeldt furnace was the most economical in terms of fuel, requiring only about 200 pounds of cordwood to roast a ton of ore. It was built of solid brick; thus retaining its heat better.

[112] EISSLER1889 page 190

[113] WILSON1907 page 62, EISSLER1889 page 192, KUSTEL1868 page 241

[114] WILSON1907 page 75-76, EISSLER1889 pages 192-195, 209, KUSTEL1868 pages 242-244

[115] The net free energy change is −768 kJ/mole. This is one of many possible reactions that took place. For example, with the formation of Mn_3O_4 instead of Mn_2O_3, the revised reaction has a net free energy change of −754 kJ/mole. Undoubtedly, this reaction as well as several others occurred.

[116] This is essentially the Weldon process, which at best converts only about ⅓ of the hydrogen chloride to chlorine gas.

[117] JOHNSON1898.7

[118] KUSTEL1868 page 226. If the hydrogen chloride is allowed to pass, it will react with metal sulfides, if present from incomplete roasting. Hydrogen sulfide and metal chlorides are produced by this reaction. The hydrogen sulfide will then precipitate the gold chloride, causing its loss.

[119] AARON1881 pages 37,38,51, EISSLER1889 pages 195-198, 219, KUSTEL1868 pages 244-247

[120] EISSLER1889 pages 198, 209, WILSON1907 pages 63,64, KUSTEL1868 pages 246-248

[121] EISSLER1889 page 198, WILSON1907 page 63

[122] AARON1881 page 54

[123] WILSON1907 pages 63,64, EISSLER1889 pages 199,200

[124] WILSON1907 pages 64, 81, EISSLER1889 page 210

[125] BULLION2001

[126] WILSON1907 pages 81-83, EISSLER1889 pages 200-201, 210, KUSTEL1868 page 249

[127] WILSON1907 pages 83,92, EISSLER1889 page 202, KUSTEL1868 page 250

[128] WILSON1907 page 62

[129] EISSLER1889 pages 212-214, 218, 221, WILSON1907 pages 65-67

[130] About 1877. Thies was the manager and metallurgist, and retired in 1904. His son, Captain Ernest Thies, took over – he was killed in a boiler explosion on August 10, 1908.

[131] DAY1892 pages 149-150

[132] DAY1892 page 150

[133] ROTHWELL1896 page 261, ALLIS1903 pages 45, 78, WILSON1907 pages 65, 67, 70, 72, 98, EISSLER1889 pages 221-223

[134] IRVING1904 page 117

[135] Burning a mixture of sulfur and paraffin could also produce hydrogen sulfide gas. The *ideal* reaction would be $CH_2 + S + O_2 \blacktriangleright CO_2 + H_2S$. DAY1892 page 150

[136] BULLION2001, ALLIS1903 page 46, WILSON1907 pages 83-88

[137] BULLION2001, MAB.1882-10 page 231

[138] MORGAN2001, EISSLER1889 pages 219,225

[139] EISSLER1889 page 214

[140] ALLIS1903 page 46, WILSON1907 pages 78-79

[141] DAY1892 page 149

[142] EISSLER1889 pages 223-225

[143] AARON1881 page 142

[144] WILSON1907 page 64, EISSLER1889 page 210

[145] ROSENTHAL1970 page 215

[146] By 1896 the installed chlorination plants in the U.S. had a capacity of about 1000 TPD. ROTHWELL1896 page 261

[147] Other mining districts had different rates. The charge for treating one ton of sulphurets was frequently $16-$20. Mines with their own chlorination works reported the cost per ton as $8-$9. USGS1896 page 24. In California the cost was about $10 per ton. EMMONS1885 page 268

[148] ROTHWELL1896 page 261

[149] HENDERSON1926 page 13, 15, LINDGREN1906 pages 139-140. ROTHWELL1896 page 245. Lindgren dedicates two-pages to describing the Standard chlorination works' process which recovered 95% of the values – roasting, chlorination, precipitation using hydrogen sulfide, and also Wilfley tables used to concentrate

[150] gold values trapped in magnetite (as a result of roasting pyrite) that were then smelted.

[151] USGS1902 page 122. Note that these figures represent all methods of gold recovery: amalgamation, chlorination, and cyanidation.

[152] 1911ENC.Silver

[153] AARON1881 page 142

[154] EISSLER1889 pages 219-221

[155] ALLIS1903 page 52

[156] EISSLER1889 pages 219-221, ALLIS1903 page 53

[157] Strictly speaking, calcium polysulfide would be written as CaS_N, not as CaS. The subscripted N represents a variable – and possibly fractional, formula. Calcium sulfide was used in the equations for simplicity and clarity – the actual chemistry is more complex. Silver thiosulfate is more properly written as $Ag(O_3S_2)_N$.

[158] ALLIS1903 page 53

[159] The interesting part of this reaction is that the calcium hyposulphite was *possibly* restored for reuse. "If the precipitation is carefully performed, no additional calcium hyposulphite will be required for years." ALLIS1903 page 52

[160] EISSLER1889 pages 219-221

[161] In 1884 Russell used sodium hyposulfite and cuprous hyposulfite, however this resulted in the precipitation of cuprous sulfide. This process substituted the double salt sodium-copper thiosulfate, the reaction being $2NaS_2O_3,3Cu_2S_2O_4 + 3Ag_2S \blacktriangleright 2NaS_2O_3,3Ag_2S_2O_4 + 3Cu_2S$. This is the *Russell process*. 1911ENC.Silver. Ores containing lead or zinc sulfide, antimony, arsenic, and bismuth proved unsuitable for the Kiss process alone. After a preliminary leaching using this method, a second leaching followed using the Russell process. This was then followed by precipitation with sodium sulfide. HUTCHISON2003.1

[161] AARON1881 page 142

[162] ALLIS1903 page 50

[163] KUSTEL1868 page 256

[164] HABASHI1967 pages 3-5. It is interesting to note that MacArthur and the Forrests were unaware that oxygen was required; their proposed reaction showed hydrogen gas being evolved. The patent also stated that cyanogen gas could dissolve gold, which is not so. In 1896 Bolander suggested that hydrogen peroxide was formed as an intermediate product, having detected it experimentally, which is true. In 1905, MacArthur proposed that potassium cyanate was responsible for the dissolution; again, not so. Credit should be given where due: MacArthur and the Forrests developed the most commercially effective process for recovering gold, which to this day is the backbone of gold recovery.

[165] LESCOHIER1993 pages 16-17

[166] ALLIS1903 page 11: New Zealand in 1889 to treat the tailings from a 10-stamp mill. In 1890 introduced to the Witwatersrand gold fields of the Transvaal. LESCOHIER1993 page 17. PEELE1966 page 33-06: 1889 Crown Mine, New Zealand, MCQUISTON1986 page 48

[167] ALDER1961 pages 34-36; DENNIS1963 page 272 states the "Consolidated

Mercury (sic) in Utah," 1891; PEELE1966 page 33-06 states 1891 and "Utah, U.S.";
LESCOHIER1993 page 17; MCQUISTON1986 page 48.

BUTLER1920 page 383 states that the Manning mill was remodeled into a cyanide plant in 1890, yet on page 384 he quotes Peyton as stating that it was in July of 1891 that a carload of ore was shipped to Denver for testing using the cyanide process, and that it wasn't until February 1892 that the new process went online. • The Manning Mill was named for Moses Manning, who remained after the silver bust in 1880. Mercur is so named – as legend would have it, because the Bavarian miner Arie Pinedo, on April 30, 1879, found what he thought was mercury, which in German is *merkur*.

[168] LESCOHIER1993 page 20
[169] HABASHI1967 page 1
[170] PAULING1988 page 545
[171] This order is also a roughly increasing electronegativity.
[172] PEELE1966 page 33-07. The zinc originally used by the developers was "in the form of granules and shavings, and eventually preferences given to the latter…" REUNERT1972 page 211. Millmen soon realized that using zinc powder, it having greater surface area, would enhance precipitation rates. This discovery provided yet another avenue of attack against the patent holders. The courts declared that the MacArthur-Forrest patents were valid for the precipitation of gold by zinc filaments, but not by zinc powder. MILLER1906 page 265.
[173] PAULING1988 page 546, UAPLAMBECK2000. LESCOHIER1993 shows a zinc precipitation equation where H_2 is evolved. If this were true, there would probably be numerous accounts of catastrophic explosions in cyanide processing plants.
[174] UAPLAMBECK2000
[175] MCQUISTON1986 pages 46-47.
[176] MONTANADEQ.50
[177] ALLIS1903 pages 13-15, MILLER1906 pages 229-231, TAGGART1947 page 150, PEELE1966 pages 33-06, 33-07. *Cyanicides* include Fe^{2+}, Zn^{2+}, Cu^{2+}, Ni^{2+}, and Mn^{2+}. Interestingly, Pb^{2+} plays a unique roll: it accelerates the dissolution of gold when present in small quantities, but retards it when the concentration exceeds a certain threshold. HABASHI1967 page 2,26.
[178] $Fe_{1-x}S$ – Iron sulfide with traces of nickel and cobalt.
[179] HABASHI1967 page 25
[180] HABASHI1967 pages 2,26
[181] HABASHI1967 pages 26-27
[182] HABASHI1967 page 11. Au, Ag, and Cu dissolve at nearly the same rates on a gram-atom/time basis.
[183] Only 46% passing through a 4-mesh screen.
[184] HARRIS1987 page 4 and appendix 1.
[185] LESCOHIER1993 page 29
[186] Based on HABASHI1967 page 19 figure 10.
[187] Coconut matting or hessian (hemp fabric) was also used for matting. DENNIS1963 page 272

[188] REUNERT1972 page 211
[189] DENNIS1963 page 273
[190] ALLIS1903 page 132
[191] MILLER1906 page 267
[192] DENNIS1963 page 273, MILLER1906 page 268
[193] ALLIS1903 page 131
[194] TAGGART1954 pages 20-54
[195] VICTOR2000 page 10
[196] MONTANADEQ.126
[197] LESCOHIER1993 page 17, MCQUISTON1986 page 48
[198] LINDGREN1906 pages 139-140
[199] IRVING1904 page 117, FIELDER1970 page 156
[200] MONTANADEQ.51
[201] WELLS2002 page 103
[202] TINGLEY1993 page 21. The first plant in Nevada to treat raw ore was in Delamar "a short time later."
[203] ARBITER1964 page 258
[204] HAMILTON1920 pages 123-124
[205] FIELDER1970 pages 166-170. Merrill reworked – at a substantial profit, the Drumlummon mine tailings in Marysville, Montana during 1896. WOLLE1963 page 198
[206] IRVING1904 page 59, FIELDER1970 page 109
[207] FIELDER1970 page 174
[208] MCQUISTON1986 page 85

SMELTERS AND REFINERIES QUICKSILVER AND ZINC

Figure 1   Dumping Slag
Courtesy Mount Morgan Historical Museum, Inc.

Smelting is a form of *pyrometallurgy* – the chemical reduction of a metal from its ore by a process involving fusion. The fire assay, described in a previous chapter, is a form of smelting. The unwanted impurities form a lighter, fusible *slag* that is readily removed from the reduced metal. Industrial-scale smelting takes place in large *smelters*,[1] where the heat required for fusion is generated inside the *furnace*, as opposed to the fire assay where the heat is provided externally by the muffle furnace. Smelting is used for winning a variety of metals from many different ores, ranging from iron to gold.

Eureka

In Eureka, Nevada, Col. G. C. Robbins demonstrated that the lead-silver ores could be successfully smelted,[2] and Major W. W. McCoy, enlisting the services of Welsh smeltermen Richard P. Jones and John J. Williams Jr., built the first commercially successful lead-silver smelter in the States in July 1869.[3]

The first lead-silver smelter to ship bullion was at Oreana, Nevada, in 1867. See figure 2.[4]

The furnaces used – modifications of the *Piltz furnace*,[5] were well received in the West. The description that follows is based on the Number Four model used by the Eureka Consolidated smelter in Eureka, and as described by Rossiter W. Raymond in *Statistics of Mines and Mining in the States and Territories West of the Rocky Mountains*. See figures 3 and 4. These furnaces cost nearly $14,000 each.[6]

Figure 2   Montezuma Silver Works
Oreana, Nevada ca 1867
Courtesy NARA

At the base of the furnace lies the *hearth*, about four feet in diameter and two feet deep, resting on a substantial stone foundation, and supported by iron bands about its circumference. Above the hearth is the funnel-shaped *shaft* or *bosh* of the furnace, a few feet high, and above that is the cylindrical *chimney*, about six feet in diameter, followed by a brick or iron *smokestack*.

Tapping the hearth on the front side are *spouts* – ports, for discharging the molten slag and *matte* (impure metal that contains sulfides). The slag spout is located about three inches higher than the matte spout. On one side and at the base of the hearth is a tap that is used to drain the hearth after the furnace is *blown out* – described later, and all of the remaining lead and slag are removed.

Arranged about 1-1.5 feet above the hearth, in a horizontal and radial fashion, are ten *tuyeres*,[7] each having a two-inch nozzle inserted into them.[8] They were made of cast iron, conical in shape, and water-cooled. Their function was to admit the air *blast* into the furnace, and also to view the contents of the furnace during operation. The correct location of the tuyeres relative to the hearth was important, as the bulk of the heat generated in smelting was at this level – the source of the air blast. Located too high, and the molten material collecting in the hearth lost too much heat as it descended, and would solidify and clog the furnace. This happened at a furnace in White Pine, Nevada, where the tuyeres

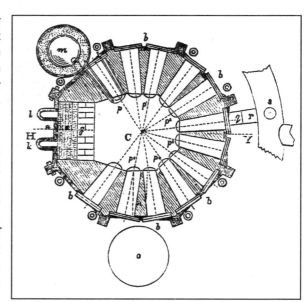

Figure 3   Modified Piltz Furnace, Plan View
Courtesy USGS

were located about three feet above the hearth.[9] Too low – at about six inches, or pointing downwards, and the heat produced was too close to the pool of molten metal in the hearth, which could cause excessive volatilization, especially in the case of lead. The nozzles were connected to a blower by means of a *windbag* – a leather hose.

The shaft rises about ten feet above the tuyeres, which was typical in the West at that time. The shorter shafts were required for ores that contained significant amounts of iron oxide, such as at White Pine. This helped prevent the reduction of the iron oxide to metallic iron and the consequent formation of *sows*. See the box below. Two small doors were located on opposite sides of the chimney. These were used for feeding *charges* into the furnace. The *feeding floor* provided access to these doors.

All parts of the furnace in direct contact with molten materials were lined with firebrick, or local sandstone, if suitable. Sandstone quarried about 25 miles from Eureka, on Pancake Mountain, was often used because it was very resistant and only required replacement every few months. It sold for $20 per ton at the quarry, plus an additional $12 for hauling to Eureka.[10] Those smelter parts that were not in contact with molten material used regular brick. Iron uprights surrounded the shaft, these being secured by iron bands, all of which prevented spreading of the mason work.

For the blast, *Roots blower*, invented by Francis M. and brother P. H. Roots in 1860,[11] was preferred over B. F. Sturtevant's *Sturtevant blower* because of the higher pressure it achieved.[12] See figures 5 and 6, and figure 43 on page 43.

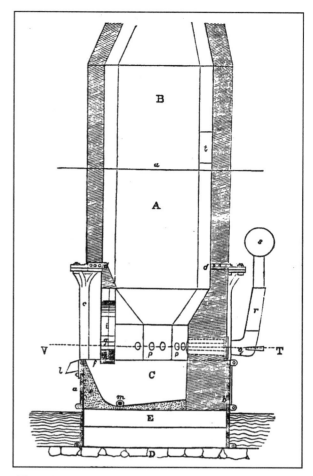

Figure 4   Modified Piltz Furnace, Side View
Courtesy USGS

A Roots blower model No. 8, providing a blast sufficient for three large furnaces, required about 20 HP. Even then, the smelters at Eureka could not generate a blast sufficient to completely combust coke, so charcoal was used instead. The price of charcoal kept rising due to the scarcity of wood, with nut pine being the only wood suitable for charcoaling, and it having been cut for a radius of 10 miles from Eureka. In 1876 about 1,200,000 bushels of charcoal – produced from about 43,000 cords of nut pine, was consumed.[13]

At the Eureka Consolidated, teams brought 120 tons of ore per day from the mines. The ore was dumped in front of the feeding floor. Large pieces were picked out and run through a Blake jaw crusher – described in the next chapter. The fine ore was wheeled directly to the furnaces. A thirty-day supply of charcoal was maintained in an outside storage building. This was transported to the feeding floor by means of track cars, of 20-bushel capacity, running on a trestle connecting the charcoal storage and smelter structures. Each furnace had its own charcoal storage bin.

The Smelting Animal Kingdom

Iron masses that congeal on the floor of the hearth are referred to as *sows*, and are impediments to smelting. These same masses sometimes form in reverberatory furnaces, where they are variously referred to as *bears*, *horses*, and *salamanders*.[14] Lead is cast into *pigs* and *salmons*.[15]

Smelter Operation

Blowing in the furnace started the smelting operation. This involved *charging* – shoveling in, a small amount of charcoal, igniting it, and building up a fire until the charcoal was a glowing, dark-red mass, all the time adding additional charcoal until it reached the throat. This required about 4-5 hours. The men who performed this task are the *feeders*. Most of the tuyeres and accesses were then closed or sealed shut with firebrick and luted with clay. Four nozzles were then inserted into the tuyeres closest to the hearth front, and a blast commenced for about ¾ of an hour. The blast was then cut off, and the remaining nozzles put in place. The blast was again started, and charging commenced.

A pre-measured amount of charcoal was charged, followed by three tons of lead. Up to this point, about 250 bushels of charcoal had been used. The lead melted and formed a molten pool, thus preheating the hearth. The ore was then charged along with additional charcoal. The ore was allowed to build up around the inside circumference of the shaft, all about the tuyeres, leaving a core of charcoal fuel in the center. 270 pounds of ore and 68 pounds of slag were charged in this fashion. The ratio used was about one pound of charcoal for 3.1 pounds of ore and slag. The Eureka Consolidated was fortunate in that the ore from their mines already contained most of the necessary fluxing agents; iron oxide, silica, and lime.[16] Other Eureka smelters had basic ores, as did White Pine, requiring the addition of silica, which is acidic.

The ore melted from the heat of the burning charcoal, and a series of complex chemical reactions took place – see the Appendix for a sampling of the many reactions that take place in a lead smelter. The resulting molten material trickled down through the charge and collected in the hearth. The dense, molten lead – acting as the collector for the silver and gold values, settled to the bottom of this pool, a lower density matte floated on the surface of the lead, and above the matte was a layer of silica-rich slag.

Plugs made of *stubbe* – a mixture of clay and charcoal,[17] were then removed from the spouts, and a *slag cart* was placed underneath the slag spout. See figure 7. The cart consisted of a conical cast-iron pot, 26 inches deep, fifteen inches at the top, and six inches at the base, mounted on a truck. See figure 8.

Figure 5   Sturtevant Blower, Side View
Source: Manufacturer and Builder

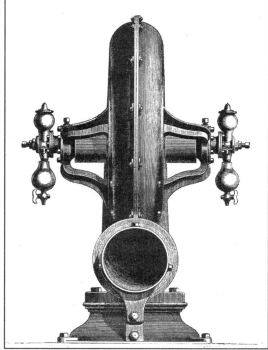

Figure 6   Front View
Source: Manufacturer and Builder

Drills And Mills

About two hours later, the red-hot slag had risen in the hearth to the point where it flowed from the spout and into the slag cart. Initially it was somewhat stiff, partly from its composition, and partly from the furnace having not yet attained the correct temperature. As the smelting continued, the slag became more incandescent and the viscosity dropped. When full, the slag cart was exchanged with an empty cart, and then wheeled to the slag dump where the molten glassy mass was poured over the edge. See figure 9.[18]

After a few hours the blast was stopped, the tuyeres plugged to protect the workers from carbon monoxide, the hearth front removed, and the interior of the hearth and tuyeres cleared of cinders by means of bars and sledges. Additional charcoal was thrown in and the hearth front sealed again. The nozzles were then adjusted and the blast continued. Up until this point, the furnace had been *blazing* at the top, which volatilizes a great deal of lead, and would endanger the feeders. If the depth of the slag was very high, equivalent amounts of ore were added for the slag removed, this being repeated every 4-6 hours. Eventually the blaze disappeared and only black smoke discharged – the *normal charge* had at last been reached; the furnace was blown in and ready for a smelting *campaign* – continuous use.

The Campaign

Every 24 hours 180 charges were run through – one charge every eight minutes. This amounts to 46 tons of fine ore, or 35 tons of coarse ore per day, and about 1260 bushels of charcoal. The feeders certainly had their work cut out. Assuming that it took a few minutes to shovel in a fine-ore charge, this translates to feeding one shovel-full (of ore, slag, or charcoal, weighing from about 5 pounds for charcoal to 16 pounds for slag or ore) every 4 or 5 seconds. This strenuous work was performed adjacent to the brick-lined chimney, in very hot conditions, all the while exposed to hazardous carbon monoxide gas and leaden flue dust that escaped from the feeding doors.[19]

Meanwhile, the slag was tapped until it began to spark, indicating that the pool of molten metal was at the height of the slag spout. The plug on the matte spout was removed, and the matte and lead tapped into a clay-lined cast-iron pot.

Figure 7   Staging Slag Carts
Courtesy Mount Morgan Historical Museum, Inc.

Figure 8   Slag Carts
Courtesy Mount Morgan Historical Museum, Inc.

Figure 9   Dumping Molten Slag
Courtesy Mount Morgan Historical Museum, Inc.

When slag began to issue from the matte spout, it was sealed, and the cycle repeated. Care was taken to avoid having the matte come into contact with any water, as an explosion of molten metal could result. The lead thus collected was poured into bar-shaped molds holding about 120 pounds each. A small ladle was used to sample every fifth bar cast. At the end of the day, all of the samples collected were melted together and assayed, this representing the day's bullion production.

The tuyeres required periodic attention. If on inspection any obstruction was seen, a bar was used to knock it out. If raw ore was visible through the tuyeres, which indicated accretions on the shaft wall, the charge was allowed to descend about halfway down the shaft of the furnace, and wood was added as a fuel to help melt the accretions. Large bars worked through the feedholes were used to knock down any material not melted.

The furnace was operated for weeks or months at a time, or until repairs made it necessary to blow it out. It was costly to blow in a furnace – this expense was distributed over the length of the campaign. One furnace of this description erected at the Eureka Consolidated and blown in on May 31, 1871, made campaigns of 26, 45, and 50 days before requiring any repair. When blown out, the furnace was allowed to cool for about 36 hours. Repairs were made, including replacing firebrick, maintaining the tuyeres, rebuilding the hearth, knocking down accretions, sledging out slag, unclogging ports, and other such activities.

The crew required to operate a furnace of this size were divided into three eight-hour shifts. Each shift had one smelter, two helpers, and two feeders. In addition, for the smelting operation, there were a number of roustabouts, two foremen, two machinists, and one each of chief engineer, blacksmith, outside foreman, metallurgist, and superintendent.

The Arents Tap

A crucial furnace modification, as made (and patented) by Albert Arents[20] and Winfield Scott Keyes in 1870,[21] was the 'sub-surface inverted siphon tap,' later to be known as the *Arents Tap*. This amounted to a pipe connecting the base of the hearth – where the densest metal resides, to a small bowl-like crucible beside the furnace and level with the molten lead in the hearth. As the level of metal rose in the furnace, it rose in the crucible, and was simply ladled out. By avoiding the tapping cycle on conventional designs, the lead bath was kept at a constant depth; the iron that might form sows was kept high enough to be in the hot, highly reactive blast zone near the tuyeres, ultimately leaving the furnace with the slag. The quality of the metal was higher – the lead found at the bottom of the hearth had the least impurities. This invention was rapidly adopted throughout the West, bringing Arents and Keyes a $250 royalty per year from each installation where it was used.[22]

Eureka Production

Eureka ores were, for the most part, self-fluxing.[23] For every 5.6 tons of ore, a ton of bullion was produced, this at a cost of $39 per ton of ore. The ore contained about 25% lead, and assayed $35 in gold and $25 in silver per ton. The smelter could recover up to 93% of the precious metals,[24] the principle loss being in iron matte, and lesser amounts in the flue dust and slag.[25] It was not considered cost effective to recover these values from the matte, so it was dumped with the slag. The loss of lead in the slag varied from between 2-4%. The slag was 80% silica and iron oxide, the remainder being lime, litharge, and alumina. About 10-12% of the slag was reused in the Eureka Consolidated smelters as a flux.

The bullion produced – termed *base bullion* because it was mostly lead, contained from $250-400 in gold and silver per ton. It was cheaper to ship the bullion to San Francisco, then by sea to the Balbach Works in Newark, New Jersey for refining and parting of the precious metals – this at a cost of $69 per ton, than to refine it locally. Some of the Eureka smelters did refine their lead using the *Luce & Rozan* process, which is outlined later in this chapter. In later years the bullion was sent 90 miles by team to Palisade, the nearest railhead, and shipped to Newark for refining. The fees charged were $15 per ton to *desilverize* the lead, and another $7 to part the gold.[26]

Raymond noted why the lead was not cupelled from the base bullion as it is in the fire assay:

"The main reason for not cupelling the lead in the west is not found in the increased rates and risks of freightage for bullion; but the separation of the silver and lead, and the refining of the latter, can be accomplished at much less cost in the eastern centers of trade than in the mining districts."[27]

Very poor business decisions were often made in the ore reduction business. The management of the Geddes and Bertrand property outside of Eureka insisted on building a smelter on their property, which they did, and at great expense. Although the antimonial ore contained up to $200 per ton in values, it contained insufficient lead (6%) for effective smelting. The smelter was a decided failure. The fiasco continued with the erection of a stamp mill, which also failed. The operation would probably have proved profitable had the owners shipped their ore all of eight miles to Eureka for reduction.[28]

From 1873-1906, the Eureka Consolidated had a gross yield of $19,242,012, the largest single producer in the Eureka mining district. See charts 1 and 2.[29]

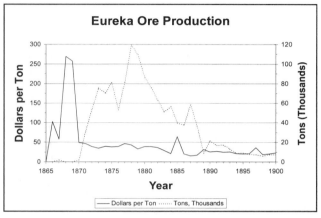

Chart 1

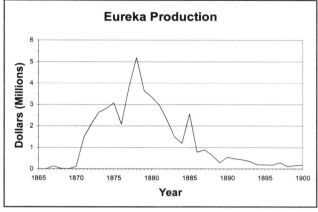

Chart 2

Thieves Won't Play Ball

Senator William Morris Stewart, part owner of the Wyoming and Hemlock mines in Panamint, California, foiled the highwaymen that continually robbed the silver bullion shipments.

The solution? Cast the silver bullion into 750-pound balls and invite them to try and get away with them! [30]

Black Hawk and Denver

A crisis was developing in Colorado in the mid-1860's. Plenty of valuable ore was being found, but investment money to develop the lodes was difficult to come by. Further complicating this was the nature of the ore itself. In the Gilpin County mining districts, the recovery of silver from these complex ores was only about 25%, and the gold was about 50% at best and often considerably lower.[31] Stamp milling was simply not effective, and earlier attempts at smelting had failed. Table 1 shows representative ore values for the Black Hawk – Central City area mining districts from the early 1870's.[32]

In 1868,[33] Professor Nathaniel Peter Hill Jr., of Brown University, organized the Boston and Colorado Smelting Company, and established a reverberatory furnace at Black Hawk, Colorado – the first to successfully smelt the refractory ores.[34] The initial works had a capacity of about 10 TPD. Preliminary heap roasting of up to six weeks was necessary to drive off some of the sulfur.[35] The matte that was produced was shipped at considerable expense to Swansea, Wales for further refining [see also *The Welsh (Swansea) Copper Process* in the appendix].[36]

Mining District	Smelting Ores (First Class)				Milling Ores (Second Class)			
	Gold Oz	Silver Oz	Gold	Silver	Gold Oz	Silver Oz	Gold	Silver
Central City	3.1	18.1	$63.61	$23.44	0.8	8.2	$17.30	$10.60
Gregory	6.7	23.5	$138.98	$30.32	1.2	8.8	$24.10	$11.37
Illinois Central	4.2	31.4	$86.39	$40.57	1.0	10.1	$19.93	$13.12
Nevada	4.4	29.1	$90.30	$37.62	1.1	9.9	$22.51	$12.85
Russell	2.4	47.9	$50.28	$61.90	1.0	13.3	$20.07	$17.14
Average	4.4	33.0	$91.49	$42.60	1.0	10.5	$21.65	$13.62

Table 1   Black Hawk – Central City Mining District First and Second Class Ore Averages

Although the ore was being purchased for about 30% of its value,[37] the operations proved to be a success – the Black Hawk furnaces recovered up to 95% of the values.[38] This led to continued growth, better prices, and a series of expansions: in 1869 a second calciner and reverberatory furnace were added; in 1870 two more calciners were added; in 1871 a third reverberatory furnace was installed; in 1874 the fifth and sixth calciners and a blast furnace for reducing lead-silver ores were installed.[39]

In 1873 Professor Richard Pearce developed the metallurgical methods that produced relatively pure silver bullion. Pearce used the *Ziervogel process* – see below. Gold was still a problem, however. Pearce continued to experiment, and in 1875 developed the methods necessary to part the gold. He found that if the auriferous *bottoms* – a residue, produced by the Ziervogel process were mixed with pyrite and smelted, the copper would preferentially rise to the layer of ferrous sulfide floating above, and a layer of enriched gold would sink to the bottom. The two layers could then be separated. Three successive treatments using this method yielded gold that was 95% pure. This became an unpatented trade secret that was used for the next 33 years.[40]

In 1874 the fifth and sixth calciners and a blast furnace for reducing lead-silver ores were installed.[41] Additional furnaces were added as demand increased, until there were eight. By 1878 the capacity was up to 50 TPD. The value of the bullion produced increased from about $200,000 in 1868 to $2,250,000 in 1878.[42]

Figure 9   Copper Smelting Furnace ca 1882

60 TPD capacity, producing 4 TPD copper

Jerome, Arizona 2002
Author

Fuel availability and the location in Black Hawk were problems. In the winter of 1877, the decision was made to move the operations to Denver.[43] A seven-acre site was located two miles from Denver, and the Argo reduction works were established in late 1878. The former site continued to be used for purchasing and roasting.

In 1878, Pearce's reverberatory furnaces had an area of 145 square feet and smelted 12 TPD, consuming one ton of coal for each 2.4 tons of ore.[44] The plant's capacity and efficiency was steadily increased, taking advantage of the economies of scale: 17 TPD in 1882; 24 TPD in 1887; 35 TPD in 1891; and 50 TPD in 1894.[45] In 1889, the Argo works paid about 85% of the value of the ore.[46] The capacity of the Argo works ultimately reached over 100 TPD, with 30 roasting kilns for desulfurizing the ore, 10 roasting furnaces, 8 smelters, 8 refining furnaces, and 5 melting furnaces.[47] The 50 TPD furnaces were 560 square feet and consumed 1 ton of coal for 3.7 tons of ore – 50% more ore smelted per ton of coal than the 1878 model furnaces.[48] The furnaces became so large that the ordinary method of skimming the slag was no longer practical. Pearce modified them so that the molten slag flowed down an iron trough and to the slagheap.[49]

Drills And Mills

The Ziervogel Process

The Ziervogel process was originally introduced in Hettstadt, Germany in 1841.[50] Argentiferous copper matte produced by reverberatory furnaces was roasted to drive off additional sulfur and to convert the silver into silver sulfate. Silver is converted to silver sulfate by careful roasting at controlled temperatures.

Sulfates decompose into oxides (except for silver) at increasing temperatures in the following order: iron, copper, silver, zinc, lead, and calcium. Thus, if iron or copper sulfates are present, they will decompose into oxides, which produce sulfur oxide gases. The silver subsequently picks up the sulfur trioxide and converts to silver sulfate, as follows:[51]

$$2FeSO_4 \quad \blacktriangleright \quad Fe_2O_3 + SO_2 + SO_3$$

$$CuSO_4 \quad \blacktriangleright \quad CuO + SO_3$$

$$2Ag + 2SO_3 \quad \blacktriangleright \quad Ag_2SO_4 + SO_2$$

The silver sulfate was then dissolved in hot water, leaving behind bottoms containing copper and any gold present. The silver sulfate solution was precipitated onto copper plates, collected, washed, and melted into bullion:

$$Ag_2SO_4 + Cu \quad \blacktriangleright \quad CuSO_4 + 2Ag$$

This process can yield up to 92% of the silver.[52] The bottoms were dissolved with sulfuric acid, which formed copper sulfate and left the gold behind. This was expensive for it consumed significant amounts of high-priced sulfuric acid.[53]

Durango

The Greene smelter in Silverton, Colorado, designed and built by John A. Porter and of 30 TPD capacity, was erected in 1874 to process ore from Arrastra Gulch. This proved to be a failure. It was subsequently remodeled, and incorporated an Arents Tap [54] and a water jacket – the first of its kind to operate successfully in Colorado when it was blown in again in 1875.[55]

In 1880, the San Juan and New York Mining and Smelting Company (SJ&NY) purchased the works. The facility was relocated to Durango in 1881 – where the Denver & Rio Grande established a railroad center in 1880, and on the Animas River where a suitable water supply was available. In addition, the SJ&NY owned a limestone quarry (for flux) and coal deposits in the Animas River valley (for fuel and for manufacturing coke) – everything required but ore, which was available in ever increasing quantities from the growing districts to the north.

The new smelting complex included a blast furnace, two reverberatory furnaces, and eight beehive coke ovens. The capacity was 25 TPD and was blown in April 16, 1881. In 1883 a new 30 TPD blast furnace was added. $1,000,000 in bullion was produced by 1887. During 1892, 12,000 ounces of gold, 1,500,000 ounces of silver, 6,000,000 pounds of lead, and 1,089,552 pounds of copper were produced.

The operations were continually expanded, resulting in six blast and ten reverberatory furnaces with a 300 TPD capacity, and 40 beehive coke ovens by the end of 1893. These basic elements of the plant remained in place until 1930. Due to the drastic drop in the price of silver in 1893, and the attendant depressed mining industry, the smelter closed in 1894. It was leased by the Omaha and Grant Smelting Company in 1895, and was ultimately absorbed by the American Smelting and Refining Company in 1899.[56]

Leadville

Leadville, Colorado became one of the greatest lead-silver camps of all time. Between 1875 and 1879, Leadville experienced a rapid development in the number of smelters that were blown in – see chart 5.[57] In late 1879 and early 1880 these 16 smelters had a total of 34 furnaces – see figure 10. In 1880, 140,623 tons of ore was smelted, producing a stunning 66,658,000 pounds of lead and 9,977,344 ounces of silver worth $14,910,860 – Leadville's greatest year for silver production, and over 22 times the total metal production from just three years before. The following average figures may be made regarding the smelters in Leadville circa 1880.

- The cost of a smelter was $58,000.[58]
- There were 3 furnaces per smelter, each having a capacity of 25 tons per day.
- Motive power was supplied by a 60 HP steam engine.
- Baker's blowers were used almost exclusively. See figure 11.[59]

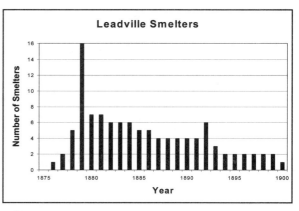

Chart 5

A composite assay made ca 1879-80, based on 1000 tons of *plumbiferous* – lead containing, ore from a variety of Leadville mines, indicated that the average ore contained over 90 ounces of silver per ton, and was 23% lead and 18% iron – easily smelted. Extraction rates were 88% for lead and 96.5% for silver, part of the losses of which could be recovered by smelting the collected fumes.[60] The ratios of ore, fuel, and flux, per ton of ore and per ton of bullion produced, are outlined in table 2.[61]

Smelting Fees

Smelting fees were variable and depended on many factors. This included the current New York price quotations for silver and lead for any payments to be made, plus the cost of fuel (coke and coal for smelting, cordwood for the boilers), flux (dolomite and hematite), bullion freight expenses, refining fees, labor, and profits. The quantity of fuel and flux depended on the character of the ore.

In early 1879, the smelters paid about ½ of the value of the ore. Competition between the smelters was great and reduction costs were lowered. By the end of the year, the mines received about ⅔ of the value of the ore.[62] The average fee was $22.50 per ton, and the actual smelting cost was $15.25.[63] In 1880, the method used was often fairly straightforward, being based on run-of-the-mine ore, as seen in table 3. Precious metals use the troy ounce for their measure. Lead uses a *unit*, which is 1% of a ton, or twenty pounds.[64]

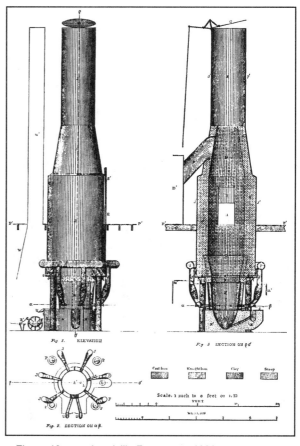

Figure 10   Leadville Furnace ca 1880
Courtesy USGS

By 1885, no less than six different methods of calculating the payment for purchased lots of ore were in effect – one each for lead carbonate, dry (low lead content) oxidized silver, argentiferous iron, sulphurets carrying galena, sulphurets carrying galena and little zinc, and sulphurets with no galena and 10-15% zinc. This was due to the changing nature of the ore bodies, which had a tremendous impact on both the mining and smelting industries.

For example, lead carbonate ore, as was mined from Carbonate Hill, used a schedule as seen in table 4.[65] A more complex method was used for argentiferous iron ores, like that of Tabor's famous Matchless mine. From an assay, the percentages of metallic iron and manganese are added, and from this is subtracted the percentage of silica. This is considered the "base excess" of the ore. The assumption is that it generally equals 40%.

For low-grade ores carrying twelve or less ounces of silver per ton, silver was paid at fifty cents per ounce, and there was no working charge. For each percent of iron or manganese over 40% "base excess," ten cents is added – these metals were very valuable as fluxes. Ten cents was deducted for each percent of iron or manganese under 40% "base excess" – these same fluxes would have to be purchased from other mines and used as a flux to smelt this ore.

For high-grade ores carrying over twelve ounces of silver per ton, silver was paid at 5% less than the New York quotation, and the working charge was $6 per ton. The iron and manganese tariffs were calculated as described above.[66]

Tons of...	Per Ton of Ore	Per Ton of Bullion
Ore		5.69
Dolomite	0.12	0.71
Hematite	0.07	0.37
Charcoal	0.18	1.05
Coke	0.14	0.79
Cordwood	0.10	0.58
Bullion	0.18	
Ounces of...		
Silver	59.2	337
Gold	0.03	0.20

Table 2 Leadville Smelting Charge Ratios

Mine	Deduction for Silver Loss in Smelting, Percent	Smelting Charge per Ton	Price Paid for Lead per Unit
Amie	10	$25.00	$0.25
Carbonate	7.5	$20.00	$0.25
Chrysolite	5	$20.00	$0.25
Dunkin	5	$22.00	$0.25
Evening Star	7.5	$28.00	$0.15
Iron Silver	5	$18.00	$0.30
Morning Star	5	$15.00	$0.30
Tucson	5	$21.00	$0.25

Table 3 Leadville Smelting Fees for Individual Mines, 1880

Ore Beds

One of the reasons for the complicated purchase schedules was due to the varied mineral makeup of Leadville ores.[67] They contained various quantities of carbonate (cerrusite), sulfate, chlorophosphate (pyromorphite), and sulfide of lead; sulfide (pyrite) and oxides of iron; sulfide and oxides of manganese; silver halides;[68] gold; minerals of aluminum, magnesium, zinc, titanium, molybdenum, arsenic, and antimony; numerous silicates; and minor amounts of cobalt and nickel.[69]

Many had compositions making them suitable as fluxes. The Breece Mine, for example, started out as a shallow pit exploiting a deposit of high-grade iron ore, used as a flux in the smelters. While driving exploratory drifts from a decline shaft to determine the extent of the ore body, the miners accidentally struck an ore body of rich lead carbonate. The unusual bonus accompanying the discovery was that the ore body had *increasing* silver values with depth.[70] The Iron Silver mine produced very desirable fluxes that serendipitously contained sufficient silver to offset the purchase price.[71]

Silver	New York quotation less 5 percent
Gold	$19 per ounce if over 0.1 ounce
Lead	45 cents per unit when New York >= 4.25 cents/lb.
	40 cents per unit when New York < 4.25 cents/lb.

Percent Lead	Smelting Charge (dollars)
30	3.00
25	4.00
20	5.00
15	6.00
10	7.00
< 10	8.00

Table 4 Lead Carbonate Smelting Fees

Ores of known composition were dried and layered together in specific proportions, the aim being a mixture having equal parts, by calculation of the mineral constituents, of metallic iron, metallic lead, and silica. The resulting mixture was termed an *ore-bed*. Smelting charges were often composed of a blend of a given ore with a standard ore-bed. This reduced the quantity – and cost, of the flux required for the charge. It also diminished the expensive fuel consumed in the furnace that ultimately went towards evaporating water – the ore bed was dry, while as-received ore contained about 10% moisture.[72]

The use of ore-beds was required to dilute especially rich ores. For example, the Mollie Gibson mine in Aspen had ore assaying 600 ounces of silver per ton. It required mixing with low-grade ore-beds to bring the silver content down to 250 ounces per ton due to difficulties smelting the high-grade ore alone.[73]

Another method used for reducing costs and increasing returns was to substitute slag for a portion of the flux. Experiments indicated that slag could be used in conjunction with the usual fluxes without significantly affecting the extraction rates. Slag was already "saturated" with lead and silver, and carried about two ounces of silver per ton. Compared to using straight fluxes, less of these metals would be lost by adding slag to the charge. Best of all, slag was free – mountains of it were dumped outside the smelters.[74]

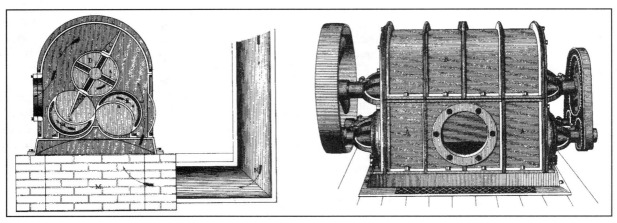

Figure 11   Baker's Blowers   Courtesy USGS

Flue Dust

Smelting lead ores created considerable dust and fumes. If not caught and collected, there was a substantial financial loss, not to mention the effect on the workers, town, and the environment.[75]

In 1885, expensive experiments were performed for capturing the dust. The results were very encouraging. The flue smoke and dust passed into a building composed of dust chambers, each having 28 openings on the ceiling. Above the dust chambers was a wooden structure – the *baghouse*. Suspended from the ceiling, and 30 feet in length, were cloth bags – *Bartlett filters*, one for each opening. The open end of the filter was tied around an iron ring located on the *thimble floor*. The filters removed the majority of the dust and smoke. Wind freely rustled the bags, shaking the collected dust into the dust chambers below.

When a sufficient quantity of dust collected in a chamber, a small fire was built on the pile of dust. This burned the coke and charcoal mixed in with the dust, turning the mass from black to white. It was then shoveled out for further processing – frequently being mixed with lime and sprinkled onto an ore-bed. About 1500 pounds of dust per furnace per day was collected this way. The dust assayed approximately 70% lead and 36 ounces of silver per ton – a value of about $90 per ton in 1885, all going up in smoke until effective filters were introduced.[76] It wasn't until the early 1890's that bag filters came into general use for capturing the dust.[77]

Decline

The beginning of the year 1880 saw the pinnacle of smelting in Leadville. The boom was on, but the smelting industry was seriously overbuilt. As fast as the smelters were blown in, many were blown out just as quickly. Competition was vigorous and obsolescence was rapid, even for technologies only a few years old. This was not the only reason for the decline in the Leadville smelting industry, however. The grade of ore began to diminish as the easily worked and high-grade carbonates were depleted – the ore became *dry*. The real value of the Leadville ore deposits was, at the time, silver. In 1880, the value of the silver produced – at the market price of $1.15 per ounce, was over three times greater than that for lead, yet lead was required to collect the silver. High-grade lead carbonate deposits were becoming scarce and commanded higher prices. The average tenor of the ore contained about 24% lead and 71 ounces of silver to the ton in 1880 – already slipping from the year before.[78]

Then the situation worsened. In 1883, the ore began transitioning to massive deposits of low-grade sulfides.[79] More and more mines reported striking sulfides as the works were sunk ever deeper. In 1884, the average grade of ore had slipped to 20% lead and 31 ounces silver per ton.[80] The price of silver was declining, now at $1.11 per ounce. In 1885, sulfide ores were encountered in the New Pittsburgh group of mines. In September, they were struck in the Silver Cord.[81] Sulfides meant not only lower overall grades, but also smelting problems. Contemporary smelters relied on high-grade carbonates; increasing sulfur and decreasing lead content proved troublesome. Many of the smelting concerns had gone out of business – there were only ⅓ as many smelters operating in Leadville in 1885 than there were five years earlier. Some wisely relocated to the plains – Denver and Pueblo in particular, and were competing with the few remaining smelters high up in Leadville.

The "valley smelters" had distinct advantages over their Leadville counterparts. To name but a few, they were located in major transportation and industrial centers, connected by extensive railroad networks. Ore shipments from Leadville – located at over 10,000 feet elevation, had a *mile descent* in altitude to the plains. Ore (and fuel, such as coke) purchased from other districts – necessary for efficient smelting, was shipped to the valley smelters at lower rates. These differences became more pronounced in the subsequent years, steadily eroding Leadville's grand smelting industry.

The dearth of lead in Leadville ores led to drastic actions. In 1885, the La Plata smelter built a desilverizing plant. The lead thus produced was recycled back into the smelter. While it may have been a technical success, it was not a financial one. The Harrison works, operating since October of 1878, even resorted to resmelting its bullion.[82] Rich lead ore was purchased from mines as far away as the Coeur d'Alene in Idaho and from Mexico.[83] By 1890, Leadville ore had declined to 6.4% lead and 15.5 ounces of silver per ton.[84] Silver was $1.05 per ounce – the Sherman Silver Purchase Act artificially maintained a higher price than the true market value, which was eroding fast. Even so, Leadville produced about $8.1 million in 1890.

Figure 12   Harrison Smelter   Courtesy USGS
Leadville, Colorado 1908

In 1892, the Arkansas Valley smelting works in Leadville had a reduction cost of only $5.87 per ton. As low as this was, it was still higher than smelters located in Denver and Pueblo. By 1897 the cost had been reduced to $3.98 per ton, but still the valley smelters could work for less.[85] The 1893 repeal of the Sherman Silver Purchase act spelled disaster for Leadville, a thriving mining town built from silver. The average price of silver dropped to $0.78 per ounce that year; only three smelters remained operating in Leadville.

Declining metal prices and the shifting composition of the ore bodies led to development of other mineral resources that were not exploited or were overlooked in the past. In 1889, large deposits of copper-bearing sulfide ores were discovered in the Maid of Erin and Henriett properties.[86]

In 1891, John Campion found gold ore in the Little Jonny mine. Gold production in Leadville, spurred by the decline in silver prices following the Panic of '93, reached its peak in 1900. See chart 7.[87]

Leadville's grand lead-silver smelting industry may have passed, having been reduced to a single smelter in 1900, but an assortment of valuable minerals persisted well into the 20th century.

Leadville Production

Leadville minerals worth $225,320,531 were mined, smelted, and sold through 1900. Leadville produced 9,977,344 ounces of silver in 1880, nearly ⅓ of the U.S. silver production for the year. Charts 5 through 8 show the aggregate value and production of silver, lead, gold, and copper for Leadville's big boom.

The silver and lead continued to decline in the 20th century; the former reached its peak in 1880, the latter at 111,575,000 pounds in 1883. In terms of total mineral value, 1882 was the 19th century peak at $15,256,375. This figure would not be exceeded until 1916. Copper peaked in 1892 at over 5,928,863 pounds, and zinc reached its peak in 1912 at 105,945,783 pounds.[88]

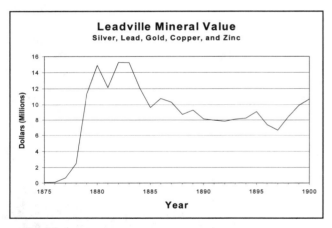

Chart 5

Chart 6

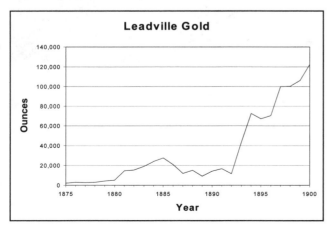

Chart 7

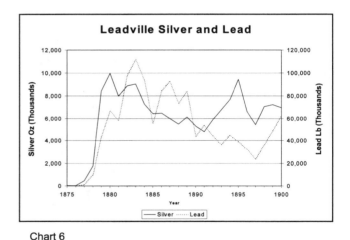

Chart 8

Drills And Mills

Pyritic Smelting

Pyritic smelting sustains the smelting reactions by utilizing the heat generated by the oxidation of iron and sulfur. Coke is generally required to blow in the smelter, but once going, it is self-sustaining. This, of course, assumes that precise ore beds are available.

Semi-pyritic smelting requires the addition of a hot blast (600°-700° F), a small amount of carbonaceous fuel such as coke, or both. Experiments by W. L. Austin, of Denver, lead to the successful semi-pyritic smelting of ores at Leadville and Silverton, where in some cases coke consumption was as little as 3% of the charge.[90]

♦ W. Lawrence Austin set up a pyritic smelter at Toston, Montana, in 1885. This furnace ran for three years, blowing out due to the cost of labor and the arrival of the Northern Pacific railroad providing cheaper access to the smelters in Butte.[91]

♦ A semi-pyritic smelter, operated by the Boston Gold-Copper Smelting Company in Leadville in 1899, ran continuously through 1900, proving that the technology could work.[92] Early attempts at pyritic smelting include the Bi-Metallic smelter in Leadville. This 100 TPD experimental furnace was blown in on July 30, 1892. It proved successful, and two more furnaces were installed. Sadly, the plant was closed – along with a number of mines, when the price of silver crashed in 1893. When the plant re-opened in 1894, procuring the necessary grades of siliceous ores proved problematic.[93]

♦ In 1900, the Kendrick-Gelder semi-pyritic smelter was built in Silverton. In 1901 in nearby Ouray, the Home pyritic smelter failed to work, but semi-pyritic smelters were built in the same year at both Golden and Robinson, Colorado. By 1904, eight semi-pyritic plants were in operation in Colorado.[94]

Refineries

The Germania Separating and Refining Works, erected in 1872 in Sandy, Utah, and managed by the capable leadership of Henry Sieger and Gustav Billing, rapidly dominated the refining industry. No longer was it necessary to ship bullion to New Jersey or to the Pacific coast for refining. Coupled with the reduced freight rates made possible by the transcontinental railway, this was a real boon for the inter-mountain West, and especially the Salt Lake area mining districts and smelting complexes. Initially, the Germania used the Flach Process for desilverizing lead, but in 1878 switched to the Parkes Process, and also added a department to manufacture white lead.[95]

The Flach Process

The *Flach Process* was used at the Germania Works for desilverizing lead. Lynn Bailey's *Shaft Furnaces and Beehive Kilns* includes an interesting and fairly detailed excerpt of the process, as it was originally written in an 1874 edition of the *Utah Mining Gazette*, from which the following description is based.

23 tons of base bullion, containing about 150-200 ounces of silver per ton, was melted in a large pot. Zinc, in the amount of about 1%, was then stirred into the molten bullion for about a half hour. Over the next few hours, the bulk of the silver and gold present would go into solution in the zinc, which itself floated to the surface of the bath as *dross* – scum. The rich dross was skimmed off and put into a different pot, and the process repeated a second time. The second set of skimmings – containing almost the entire amount of remaining silver and gold, was removed, leaving fairly pure lead.

The molten lead was then transferred, by pipe, to a pre-heated reverberatory furnace for additional treatment. As the smelters rabbled the molten lead in the furnace, some of the remaining zinc and antimony was oxidized and found its way out the flue, while a portion became a scum on the surface that was periodically skimmed off. The refined lead – containing less than one-fortieth of an ounce of silver, was then run into a *"market pot,"* from which it was cast into 140-pound pigs for shipment and sale.

The dross from the second zinc skimming was roasted in a calcining furnace, with a temperature sufficient to vaporize the zinc and antimony. The remaining metals were then transferred to a *"flowing"* furnace, where the lead, silver, and gold were separated from a worthless slag. The lead (and contained precious metals) was then added to the next charge processed in the main melting pot. Accumulated rich dross (250 pounds) from the first zinc skimming was refined in a small blast furnace, where hematite (180 pounds) and a small amount of lead slag were used as fluxes, and coke (55 pounds) was used as the fuel. The rich bullion produced was tapped every hour or so and cast into small bars.

The bars were taken to a special cupelling furnace, the operation of which is not unlike a large-scale version of the fire assay's cupellation step. The bars would be introduced into the pre-heated *test* – a large, elliptical crucible made of bone ash supported by an iron frame and placed in the furnace. As the bars melted, additional bars would be added to the test by means of a pipe. A blast from a second pipe would commence, blowing across the surface of the molten metal. The lead oxidized to litharge, of which some was absorbed by the test. The remainder flowed over the edge of a small notch in the rim of the test, carrying impurities and undesired metals with it. The litharge was caught in iron pots made in a fashion similar to truck-mounted slag pots. If the bullion bars being refined contained more copper than the litharge could carry away – as evidenced by small greenish spots on the surface of the bath, additional lead was added to carry it away too.

The bright flash of light variously called *brightening, fulguration,* or *coruscation* [96] indicated that the silver bath was at last free of litharge. The bottom of the test was then bored with a small hole and the molten silver bullion run into a series of molds. These bars were ultimately recast into standard size bullion bars, assayed, and stamped with the fineness. The parting of the gold and silver was left to other refiners – such as the United States Mint, to perform. [97]

The Parkes Process

The *Parkes Process* was used to separate gold and silver from lead. This ingenious method uses from 1-2% of zinc stirred into the molten lead base bullion. Liquid zinc is insoluble in lead, and rises to the surface. The silver and gold dissolve into the zinc – the affinity of silver for zinc is about 3000 times that for lead. This zinc-silver-gold alloy floats to the top of the lead, solidifies, and is skimmed off. The zinc is then distilled from this alloy, leaving the silver and gold. [98] In 1867, Edward Balbach, Jr. patented a graphite retort for the distillation of precious metal-bearing zinc. This became known as the *Balbach* desilverizing zinc process. [99]

The Pattinson Process

The *Pattinson Process,* introduced in 1829,[100] was used to desilverize lead. This process used successive crystallization to effect the separation. A slight modification of this process, called the *Luce & Rozan* process, was utilized in Eureka, Nevada, and is described here.

About 50 tons of base bullion, assaying about 250 ounces of silver per ton, was first roasted in a reverberatory furnace to drive off antimony, arsenic, zinc, and other volatile elements. Other impurities, such as iron, formed a slag on the surface and were skimmed off. The bullion was then cast into four-ton circular blocks. This portion of the process required about 24 hours.

The somewhat improved base bullion was melted down in a large pot. A portion of it (7400 pounds) was transferred into a smaller pot for crystallizing. A stream of water was introduced on the surface of the molten bath to accelerate the chilling of the lead, and steam was introduced through a false bottom in the pot to assist in keeping the bath circulating – this was far simpler than other mechanical contrivances employed in other refineries.

The molten lead began to crystallize as the temperature of the bath fell. As the crystals grew, most of the silver that had been in solution in the lead would be excluded from the crystals and left in the still-molten portions of the bath. Two-thirds[101] of the bath would be crystallized after perhaps an hour. The crystals now contained 100 ounces of silver per ton, whereas the remaining molten bath was enriched to about 460 ounces per ton. The remaining molten and silver-rich lead was drawn off and cast into four-ton blocks.[102]

This rich lead – from the first crystallization, was crystallized separately and upgraded to 500-700 ounces of silver per ton, and at another time when a sufficient amount had been accumulated. It was then specially treated in a bone-ash test, in a manner not unlike the cupellation used in the Flach process described earlier. The litharge produced during cupellation was either re-smelted if rich, or later reduced to marketable lead in a reverberatory furnace if poor in silver, the choice depending on when it was collected from the test.

The silver-poor crystals were then melted with similar batches from other runs, and again crystallized as before. The process was repeated over and over, and by the ninth crystallization, the lead contained only 1.25 ounces of silver, which was marketable. See table 5.[103]

Crystallization Number	Ounces Silver per Ton Lead
Bullion	220
1	100
2	75
3	50
4	30
5	18
6	9
7	5
8	2.5
9	1.25

Table 5   Pattinson Process

Desilverizing Copper

One method of separating silver from copper was not unlike – in principle at least, separating gold from silver in the fire assay.

The argentiferous copper was melted with about five times its weight of lead. Nearly all of the silver dissolved into the lead. The molten metal was then cast into cakes about 18 inches in diameter and 3 inches thick.

The cakes were then very slowly and carefully heated – a temperature high enough to melt the argentiferous lead, but not the copper. The melting lead drained from the cake, carrying with it the silver and leaving behind a sponge of copper.

The copper was then reprocessed a second time and at a slightly higher temperature to remove the last traces of silver.[104]

Carson Mint

The following process outline of the Carson Mint, Carson City, Nevada in January 1881 is based on that described – in fourteen pages of splendid detail, by Albert Williams, Jr., in *Chapter VIII – The Minting of Gold and Silver*, a part of *Statistics and Technology of the Precious Metals*, which is one of the many volumes of the 1880 Census of the United States.[105]

Details about costs, supplies, checks and balances, assaying, the machinery used, boilers and engines, and other such items are omitted in the following outline so that focus may be made on the overall process. This outline is presented in the same order in which the metals moved through the various departments that comprise the mint.

Gold deposits, silver purchases, and retort sponges are received in the *Weighing room*, which uses scales with a range of 0.01 to 6000 ounces. For gold bullion and dust, the mint returns gold coins to the depositor, the service of coinage being free of charge. Silver bullion is purchased at the prevailing market price.

The crude bullion then goes to the *Deposit-melting room*, where it is melted and samples are taken for assay. Three melting furnaces are used. The inside dimensions of each furnace is eighteen inches square. The fuel used is a mixture of Lehigh anthracite (eastern Pennsylvania) and nut-pine charcoal. The graphite crucibles used range from a No. 8 size – having a capacity of about 200 ounces of bullion, up to a No. 150 – having a capacity of 6000 ounces. The life of a crucible varies from about 15-20 melts. Fluxes are added to the charge prior to melting. The crude metal is cast into *shoe-bar* molds, which are designed in such a way as to permit the breaking of the casting into three equal pieces. Each bar weighs from 170 to 220 ounces, depending on the bullion. For gold bullion, diagonal corner chips are taken from the first and last bar for assay. For any other bullion, two samples are taken from the molten bullion in the crucible and granulated.

The shoe-bars are then transferred to the *Melter and Refiner's* departments. 2500 ounces of bullion – in the form of shoe-bars, is boiled in sulfuric acid for five hours and at 650° F, the ratio being 4 parts of 62° Baumé sulfuric acid to each pound of bullion. The kettles are fabricated from cast iron, are three feet in diameter by thirty inches deep, and are heated by yellow pine. The solution produced is allowed to cool for two hours after boiling. The parted gold – which has settled in the kettle during the cooling, is ladled out. The acidic solution of silver sulfate is siphoned off, followed by the collection of any gold left remaining in the kettle. The gold thus collected is boiled in sulfuric acid again, in smaller kettles, for two and a half hours. It is then washed in water – *sweetened*, boiled in sulfuric acid, and washed again. At this point it is dried and sent to the ingot melting room.

The silver sulfate solution is run into lead-lined wooden vats, which are partially filled with cold water, resulting in the desired acid concentration of 18° Baumé. Each vat is two feet deep, and from 6x11 feet up to 9x12 feet in size. The solution is kept at 180° F by coils of leaden steam pipe in the bottom of each vat. Lake Superior copper – of a remarkable 99.97% purity, is cast into plates of 6x12x1 inch in size. Prior to introducing the water and silver solution, 1000 pounds of the plate copper is placed on top of the heating coils and leaned against the inside of the vat.

Precipitation of the silver onto the copper plates, and the formation of cupric sulfate in solution, takes 24 hours. A simple test is used to determine if the precipitation is complete: a small quantity of the solution is drawn off, and brine is added. If silver sulfate is still present, a white precipitate of silver chloride forms. Once precipitation is complete, the silver is scraped from the copper plates with wooden spatulas and collected. The copper plates last about two weeks, new plates being added as older ones are consumed. The remnants of the copper plates are washed free of adhering silver, and are ultimately used in alloying the mint-fine gold and silver to coinage standards. The silver collected is repeatedly sweetened, pressed into cakes, dried in a special drying furnace, and sent to the ingot melting room.

The *Ingot Melting Room* – a part of the Melter and Refiner's department, is used to melt the dried gold and silver into *mint-fine* ingots; prepare standard coinage alloys, melt, and cast these alloys into special ingots; clean the ingots; dress the ingots into the correct shape; and process clippings received from the cutting and adjustment rooms. The melting furnaces and crucibles used are similar to those of the deposit melting room. Ingots of different sizes are cast for each denomination of coin produced by the mint.

The *Coiner's* department receives the prepared ingots from the ingot melting room, and is responsible for the preparation of *planchettes* used for the coins. Rolls are used to reduce the ingots to strips of the correct thickness; the strips are sheared to the correct lengths; the strips are annealed in special furnaces; the strips are then drawn through punching machinery that produces the planchettes. The planchettes represent about 60% of the strip. The remaining 40% – the clippings, are recycled back to the ingot melting room.

The planchettes are then transferred to the *Adjustment room*. An all-female staff operates this room. Their job is to file and make right the planchettes that are overweight, pass on those that are of the correct weight, and reject those that are underweight. At this stage the planchettes having the correct weight are called *blanks*. The filings produced from the overweight planchettes are recycled back to the ingot melting room.

The blanks are then transferred to the *Whitening room*, where they are cleaned in a hot alkaline bath (lye soap; to remove grease), rinsed, heated, immersed in an acidic bath (pickling; a weak nitric acid solution for gold blanks, sulfuric acid for silver blanks; to remove discoloration and oxidation), rinsed, partially dried in basswood sawdust, and finally dried in closed pans. Lastly, the dry blanks are transferred to the *Press room*, where they are pressed into coins (by a female staff) using powerful hydraulic presses. See figure 13.

Figure 13
U.S. Double Eagle
($20) gold coin

Courtesy Smithsonian

Quicksilver

If gold and silver are the *precious* metals, then *quicksilver* – mercury, is the *essential* metal. Without mercury, 19th century precious metal mining would not have been possible in most districts. Nearly all of the gold mining districts relied on amalgamation in arrastras, stamps, and pans for recovery of the values. Amalgamation was very often used as the first stage for precious metals recovery, followed by other processes.

Mercury was used in North Carolina as early as 1809.[106] The supply was from Europe, and it wasn't until about the time of the California Gold Rush that mercury began to be produced in the U.S. in quantities that satisfied demand.

The New Almaden, located in the Coast Range of California near San Jose, was discovered and mined in 1824 by Antonio Sunol and Luis Chabolla, but not recognized as a mercury deposit until 1846. Over a period of four years and as many partial owners, the property became owned by Barron, Forbes Company, an English-owned concern. In 1863, the Supreme Court ordered Barron, Forbes to sell the property to the Quicksilver Mining Company of Pennsylvania for $1,750,000.[107]

Figure 14   New Almaden 1887

Courtesy Library of Congress and
Santa Clara County Parks and Recreation Department

The earliest attempts at quicksilver reduction, in 1846, used gun barrels and whalers' vats with luted iron covers, "but so much salivation[108] of the men resulted from their use that they were soon abandoned." About 26 *flasks* were produced.

Flasks are cylindrical containers made of iron, and hold 76.5 pounds of mercury.[109] See figure 15.

Retorts were tried next, but the process was very expensive and reserved for high-grade ore only. Their use was abandoned by 1860. Furnaces were then used, the mercury vapor being produced, and then condensed, from the roasted cinnabar (HgS) ore and air by the following simple reaction:[110]

$$HgS + O_2 \quad \blacktriangleright \quad Hg + SO_2$$

The first furnaces were poorly constructed, and lost much of the mercury in the foundations. The mercury vapor passing from the furnace to the condenser leaked considerably, causing additional metal losses and "injury to the men." In 1853 it was noted that there was considerable loss from the chimneys – there was a "peculiar gray coating upon their tops." Ten years later, an encyclopedia article mentions the salivation of men and animals around the reduction works, commenting in particular about "the deposit of mercurial soot upon the roofs around."[111]

Figure 15 Mercury Flask   Author

One of the problems at the New Almaden was in processing the finely divided low-grade ore – *tierras,* because it clogged the furnaces. Hand-made sun-dried adobe bricks were made of the tierras, clay, and straw. The adobes were fashioned in wooden frames, each frame making six bricks – made in the same fashion as regular adobe bricks. The bricks were 4.25 x 5.25 x 10.25 inches and weighed about twelve pounds apiece.

In 1875, the cost of making the bricks was 50 cents per ton, and the handling, drying, etc. cost 45 cents per ton, for a total of nearly one dollar per ton. Considering that the tierra ore was low-grade to begin with, the expense of making the bricks significantly reduced the profit from treating the ore. The adobes were interspersed with large pieces of ore in the furnace. There was an estimated 150,000 tons of this ore on the dumps and in the mine, of a grade that could produce 20 pounds of quicksilver to the ton.[112]

Ore running less than 10% cinnabar per ton was dumped in the earlier days, and later conveniently "mined" from the old dumps.[113] The cinnabar ore could also be concentrated. About 1860, Louis Janin devised a system where ore assaying 4% was stamp milled and then washed, the concentrate running 18%.[114] Considerable mercury escaped from the furnaces, saturating the ground below. This became an additional source when old furnaces were periodically removed.

"An old furnace has been taken down, and the soil beneath for twenty-five feet down (no one knows how much deeper) is so saturated with the metallic quicksilver in the minutest state of division, that they are now digging it up and sluicing the dirt, and much quicksilver is obtained in this way. Thousands of pounds have already been taken out, and they are still at work."[115]

The earlier furnaces were intermittent in operation. A firewall separated the fireplace and ore chamber, having holes to conduct the flames. The inside dimensions of the ore chamber were twelve feet long, nine feet wide, and almost 18 feet high. Ore was charged into the furnace by lowering it with baskets. Adobes and large ore pieces were arranged to create "channels" that acted as a continuation of the holes in the firewall. Tierras and soot were used to fill much of the spaces between the larger pieces. About 2-3 feet of ore was then layered above this, and the pattern repeated to the top.

The discharge hole for the vapor was located about six feet above the floor. This helped counteract the tendency of the hot gasses to move upward through the charge. The discharge holes for the burned ore – two on each side, were bricked up. Sheet iron was then placed over the top of the ore, and on this a three-inch layer of straw ma-

Drills And Mills

nure was placed, followed lastly by a three-inch layer of moist clay, this to seal the furnace. A full charge weighed about 90 tons, and took a crew of eight men one day to perform.[116]

The fire was started, and roasting continued for nearly five days. Attendants working back-to-back twelve-hour shifts maintained the fire and looked for leaks, the leaks being filled with ashes. Cooling took about three days. Discharging, which took a day, commenced by first removing the top to create an upward draft through the roasted charge, then the discharge ports were opened and four men raked out the spent ore into carts.

It took about ten days for the entire process to be properly completed. Management, in their never-ending push for increased production, decreased the cooling and roasting time, and "as a consequence, the ore was not always thoroughly roasted, and the men who charged and discharged these furnaces suffered considerably from the heat and the fumes of the mercury." Later management ended the accelerated practice and the "losses and evils formerly connected with their use."

Furnace No. 6 was still in use in 1882. Adobes were not used at that time due to the development of the Scott furnace, described below. 31 runs were made, at a total cost of $1.37 per ton. Had adobes been used, the cost would have risen by 70% to $2.32 per ton.

In 1874, the New Almaden installed a continuous coarse-ore furnace patterned from a furnace introduced at the Idria (Austria) reduction works by Bergrath Adolf Exeli in 1871. This furnace proved so successful that a second was built in 1875. "These furnaces, locally known as Nos. 7 and 9, are also called 'monitors,' an allusion to their shape, and to the fact that they are iron-clad."[117]

The base of the furnace was hexagonal in plan, with fireboxes abutting on alternating sides, each containing the fire, draw, and ash pits. Each firebox had separate iron doors for the fire and ash pits. Above the base was the cylindrical shaft, six feet inside diameter and eleven feet high. Above this was the charging cone, a frustum eight feet high and four feet at the base, then the charging mechanisms, and lastly a flat dome cover. The shaft and fireplaces were made of firebrick surrounded by regular brick, and all iron clad. Near the top of the shaft were three iron pipes, each a foot in diameter, that conducted the gasses to the condensers.

The fireplace ash pits doubled as discharging pits, the burned ore being raked into them and allowed to cool before being carted away. Any vapor emitted while cooling was drawn back into the furnace by the fire. When the spent ore was withdrawn, additional ore would be added from the top of the furnace. A sand or water-sealed cup-and-cone arrangement was used for charging. The top lid would be removed, and a quantity of ore with a small amount of fuel (1.5% of charcoal, coal or coke) would be dumped into the cup. The top was replaced, and the contents of the cup preheated. This prevented condensing of the mercury vapor from the sudden addition of "cold" ore to the furnace. Once heated, a rod connected to the cone was lowered, allowing the ore to fall into the charging cone below and into the furnace. This charging arrangement spared the workers from exposure to mercury vapors – the vapor that did enter between the cup and lid condensed before recharging. Charges were added about every two hours – it took about 52 hours for ore to make its way through the furnace.

Figure 16   New Almaden
Reduction Works ca 1885

Courtesy Library of Congress and
Santa Clara County Parks and Recreation Department

Two men could operate two furnaces, performing both charging and discharging, and working twelve-hour shifts. In 1882, one of the two continuous *granza* (mid-grade ore mixed with rock) furnaces had a total cost of $0.95 per ton (the other $0.96).[118] The problem still remained though – that ⅔ of the New Almaden ore had to be made into adobes.

The Scott Furnace

The furnaces of the time required ten days to charge, burn, and discharge the ore. A continuous process, and one that could handle tierras, would be perfect. Robert Scott, an employee of the mine and a skilled mason, devised the solution with the assistance of H. J. Hüttner, a mechanical engineer. It was based partly on methods used in a cereal mill.[119]

The Scott furnace (No. 1 model) was a large brick structure built with very thick walls, about 36 feet high and 17x25 feet square. Inside were a series of platforms at 45° angles, arranged in a zigzag pattern, and covered with tiles. See figure 17. The aperture between the end of one tile and the next was about three inches, though other models of the Scott furnace had apertures up to eight inches (furnace No. 2, 1879). The fireboxes were located on the sides, and the condensers on the end. The ore was loaded into a hopper on the top, feeding the furnace by means of stuffing boxes equipped with lever-activated slide valves.[120] It took from 7-10 days for the furnace to reach a temperature high enough to produce mercury vapor from the ore.[121]

The ore slowly made its way towards the bottom – mostly by gravity, as the workers withdrew burned ore from the bottom. A ton of spent ore was withdrawn from alternating sides of the furnace every forty minutes. Nearby Alamitos creek was used as the tailings dump. Peepholes with iron plugs were placed on the furnace to permit inspection and to dislodge clogged ore.

The firebox drew in its air supply through a 16-inch diameter earthenware pipe running through the condensers; thus cooling the condensers and preheating the air. Air was also drawn through airways built into the walls of the fireplace and ore chambers, cooling them as well. The flames were conducted through *pigeon holes* and across the ore resting on the tiles at that level, this being repeated at successively higher levels of ore. After passing over the highest level of ore – that had just been admitted to the furnace, the temperature of the furnace gasses was just hot enough to keep the mercury vaporized. This method of preheating the furnace air supply and zigzagging the resulting mercury-laden furnace gasses over the roasting ore economized fuel consumption.

Figure 17   Scott Furnace During Repair

Courtesy Library of Congress and
Santa Clara County Parks and Recreation Department

The mercury vapor was conducted through a series of 8-10 condensers, each connected to the next by a large iron pipe. Inside of each condenser was a brick partition with an archway at the base, its purpose to force the mercury vapor to travel along a longer, "folded" path. The vapor would enter at the top of a condenser through the pipe, flow to the bottom and beneath the arch, and then up through the adjacent compartment to the pipe leading to the next condenser. After the last condenser was a flue leading to a stack. The bulk of the condensation occurred in the third and fourth condensers.

The base of each condenser was built at a slight slope, and protruding through the walls were small iron pipes of about ¼ inch diameter. These iron pipes ran to a central collection box, and from there the mercury from each box flowed to a common iron vat, one vat per furnace, where it was weighed and bottled.[122] The smoke leaving the condensers was conducted to a brick stack, which had a fireplace in case there was an insufficient draft in the flues that connected the tower and chimney.

Furnace No. 1 roasted 36 tons per day, a single charge taking 36 hours to work its way through the furnace. In eight months of 1882, this furnace roasted 7591.25 tons of ore at a cost of $0.64 per ton. Furnace No. 3, which processed tierras, was of similar design, and cost $0.72 per ton to operate.

In 1876 the first Scott furnace at New Almaden was patented and built at a cost of $50,000. The tiles used were shipped around the Horn, the freight costing twice what the tiles did. The new furnace reduced handling costs by 70%, and the mercury losses were only 3%. Concerning the success of the furnace, Scott remarked that,

> "The ore gets cooked, couldn't do a better job of it anywhere this side of hell, and the quicksilver comes out of the condensers, not the stack." [123]

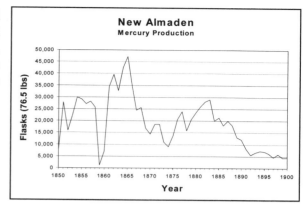

Chart 9

Table 6 outlines production and cost comparisons between the different model furnaces used at the New Almaden mines in 1882.[124] Furnace No. 1, a Scott furnace processing granza and *granzita* (small pieces of lower-grade granza) ore, had the lowest cost of the four furnaces – $0.64 per ton.

Through 1900, imports of mercury amounted to about 5% of the domestic production. Much of this may have been mercury originally exported from the U.S. for sale abroad.[125] See chart 9 for New Almaden production figures. The lack of significant production for the years 1859-60 is due to an 1858 court injunction that stopped mining, which wasn't resumed until 1861 when the decision was reversed on appeal.

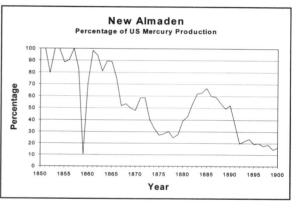

Chart 10

Through 1893 the New Almaden produced nearly 57% of the total U.S. mercury production. See chart 10. The nearest competitor, the New Idria mine, had produced about 8% of the total U.S. production through 1893.[126]

Furnace No.	Type	Granza	Granzita	Tons of Ore Terrero	Tierra	Total
6	Intermittent	2259		298	184	2741
9	Continuous	3296				3296
1	Scott	426	7166			7591
3	Scott				12022	12022
	Length of Run (Months)		Percentage of Ore			Ore Grade
6	12	82.4		10.9	6.7	7.16%
9	11+	100.0				6.95%
1	9	5.6	94.4			1.57%
3	11				100.0	1.39%
	Flasks (76.5 lbs)	Fuel Cords	Coal, lbs	Costs Fuel	Labor	Total
6	5132	414		$2,425.87	$1,324.50	$3,750.37
9	5986	212	98880	$1,800.73	$1,317.50	$3,118.23
1	3107	345	149040	$2,669.71	$2,186.78	$4,856.49
3	4379	524	326000	$4,493.23	$4,175.00	$8,668.23
	Per Ton of Ore					
6	1.87	0.151	0.0	$0.89	$0.48	$1.37
9	1.82	0.064	30.0	$0.55	$0.40	$0.95
1	0.41	0.045	19.6	$0.35	$0.29	$0.64
3	0.36	0.044	27.1	$0.37	$0.35	$0.72

Table 6   Comparisons of Four Furnaces used at New Almaden

Zinc

Up until about 1915, zinc was produced by distillation of the calcined (roasted) ore in retorts. Roasting converted sphalerite (ZnS) and smithsonite ($ZnCO_3$) to zinc oxide (ZnO):[127]

$$2ZnS + 3O_2 \quad \blacktriangleright \quad 2ZnO + 2SO_2$$

$$ZnCO_3 \quad \blacktriangleright \quad ZnO + CO_2$$

The Hegler furnace, developed about 1880, was used for this purpose. It was seven hearths high and mechanically raked. Charged from the top, the ore was raked from top to bottom and side-to-side over the hearths, and discharged at the base.

Coal or natural gas was used to provide the required heat, it being burned in an outside firebox. Because a dead roast was required, a substantial amount of fuel was consumed.

The gas created during roasting of sphalerite was suitable for making sulfuric acid, the sale of which partially offset this cost.

The retorts were clay cylinders about 8 inches diameter and four feet long, charged with about fifty pounds of roasted ore mixed with fine coal. The charge was heated to a bright red, the zinc oxide reduced to zinc vapor by the carbon[128]

$$ZnO + C \quad \blacktriangleright \quad Zn + CO$$

and the vapor condensed in clay condensers. This distillation cycle took about 24 hours.[129]

Initially, the condensers were cool and a combination of zinc, zinc oxide, and some impurities (cadmium, iron, lead, and arsenic) condensed as part of the zinc dust. As the condenser heated, the zinc vapor condensed to a liquid form, this being drawn off and cast in ingots called *spelter*. Careful redistillation was required to remove the impurities.[130]

1885 Zinc was first intentionally recovered from Colorado ores. Up until this time, and for a long time afterwards, it was considered a nuisance at the very least.

Bartlett began experimenting with treating lead-zinc sulfides in Portland Maine. These experiments resulted in establishing the American Zinc-Lead Company zinc oxide plant in Cañon City, Colorado in 1891.

1888 A Belgian retort zinc furnace was built in Denver but failed.

1899 Smelters in Kansas received small shipments of zinc blende (ZnS) concentrates from Creede. Zinc ore was shipped from Georgetown, and large shipments made from Leadville to Belgium between 1899-1903 helped to start the zinc industry in the Rocky Mountains.

1900 Domestic smelters finally succeeded in treating zinc-lead ores and concentrates, driving the Europeans from the market.

1902 Zinc concentrating mills were built at Leadville.[131]

1905 Zinc ore produced in the Coeur d'Alene district.[132]

Endnotes

1 A *galemador* is a small furnace used for roasting galena ores. RAYMOND1873 page 393.

2 TINGLEY1993 page 16

3 MOLINELLI1997 page 16, SLOANE1970 page 135, BAILEY2002 page 65. The smelter in Argenta, Montana was the first to smelt lead-silver ores. Samuel Thomas Hauser of the St. Louis and Montana Mining Company erected this smelter. 200 tons of Legal Tender ore were smelted, though imperfectly. When manager August Steitz became sick, Phillip Deidsheimer of square-set timbering fame replaced him. The St. Louis and Montana Mining Company failed in 1872, and when it reorganized as the Hope Mining Company, the smelter was shut down and operations were focused on the Philipsburg area instead. In the later 1880's it was discovered that the original smelting processes allowed silver values to boil over the cupel and into the ground, where nearly $8,000 worth of silver was recovered; thus, it was not very *successful*. MONTANADEQ.2

4 TINGLEY1993 page 16

5 Circular or octagonal shaft, usually for lead smelting.

6 RAYMOND1873 pages 174,380-399

7 Molinelli used both *twyer* and *tweer* in the same sentence. MOLINELLI1997 page 30

8 One tuyere with a 2" diameter nozzle was required for every 1.5 square feet of hearth area.

9 At the peak of the White Pine frenzy, at least 40 different smelting furnaces were in operation. An improperly cured hearth at a White Pine smelter exploded, blowing the smelter walls apart. BAILEY2002 pages 53, 55.

10 Bricks produced by the Utah Fire-Brick Manufacturing Company, and used to line Salt Lake valley furnaces, cost from $80-$100 per thousand. BAILEY2002 pages 122-123

11 Manufactured in Connersville, IN. BAILEY2002 page 56

12 In 1855-56, Phillip Wallace McKenzie patented the McKenzie blower for use in smelting. BAILEY2002 page 14. Sturtevant fans came in about a dozen sizes, and ranged in price form $25-$1000. His first patent was awarded in 1867. About 12,000 were in use by 1874. MAB.1873-2, MAB.1874-3

13 BAILEY2002 page 86

14 RAYMOND1873 page 394

15 HUTCHISON2003.2

16 MOLINELLI1997 page 26 mentions that the district's ores were self-fluxing.

17 BAILEY2002 page 68

18 Slag dumps are about all that remains of 19th century smelting operations. The dump on the north side of Eureka has been cut for that very lonely Highway 50, and provides a visual clue to the vast number of slag carts that were individually dumped.

19 The Eureka Sentinel stated, "the work is rather unhealthy – the most exposed to the fumes being subject to lead paralysis; but of late the attention paid to ventilation has remedied this in a great degree." BAILEY2002 page 82 – this quote from the *Sentinel* is itself a quote from the *Mining and Scientific Press* in 1877.

20 TINGLEY1993 page 16 spells his last name as *Arentz*. MOLINELLI1997 page 31 spells it *Arnst*. Albert Arents was born in Clausthal, Germany, March 14, 1840.

21 TINGLEY1993 page 16

22 BAILEY2002 page 79.

23 MOLINELLI1997 page 26

24 About 85% of the silver was saved. MOLINELLI1997 page 26

25 The breakdown was about ⅔ in dust, ¼ in *speiss* (a type of matte of metallic arsenides and sulfides), and the remainder in slag. MOLINELLI1997 page 32

26 BAILEY2002 page 69. The Sierra Nevada mine in the Coeur d'Alene district shipped their rich lead carbonate ore to Portland for treatment. The cost of mining, freight, and treatment of $96 ore was $48.85. By 1892, smelting charges for ore shipped to Denver or Omaha ranged from $9 to $12 per ton. RANSOME1908 page 155

27 RAYMOND1873 page 380

28 MOLINELLI1997 page 81

29 COUCH1943 page 62

30 TAYLORJ1964 page 146, DOUGHTY1989 page 20, WOLLE1963 page 140. The Silver King mill in Pinal, Arizona, experienced similar robberies. They too foiled the thieves by casting the silver bullion into bars that were too big for a mule to carry. WOLLE1963 page 85.

31 RAYMOND1873 page 345

32 RAYMOND1873 pages 343-344

33 MORSE2000 page 18 gives 1868, as does MANRY1999 page 53. BANCROFT1890 page 486 gives 1866. HENDERSON1926 pages 9-10 gives June, 1867 as the date for the Hill smelter being erected in Black Hawk, and commencing operation in January, 1868.

34 In Empire, Colorado, the Swansea smelter, built by Richard Pearce, *may* have been the first in Colorado to treat complex ores, pre-dating the efforts to be made in Black Hawk. WOLLE1977 page 39. John Collom may have been the first person in Colorado to build and operate a blast furnace in 1869. FELL1979 pages 57-58

35 FELL1979 page 29

36 BANCROFT1890 page 486, MANRY1999 pages 53-54

37 FELL1979 page 161

38 FELL1979 page 30

39 FELL1979 page 35

40 FELL1979 pages 44-46

41 FELL1979 page 48

42 MANRY1999 page 54 gives $193,490 for 1868, BANCROFT1890 page 486 gives $300,000. FELL1979 page 54 gives $271,00 in 1868 and $2,260,000 in 1878.

43 FELL1979 page 53

44 1911ENC.Copper

45 FELL1979 page 160

46 FELL1979 page 161

47 BANCROFT1890 page 486, MANRY1999 pages 53-54. The Argo works were blown out on March 17, 1910. HENDERSON1926 page 15

48 1911ENC.Copper

49 FELL1979 page 160

50 1911ENC.Silver

51 HUTCHISON2003.1

52 1911ENC.Silver

53 The French Smelting Works in Golden, Colorado, headed by J. Guillardon and completed in 1879, treated matte and specialty ores. The methods used were similar to those used at the Argo works: heap roasting to burn off excess sulfur; roasting the ore in a reverberatory furnace to produce a copper matte; crushing the mate and then roasting it to produce silver sulfate; dissolving the silver sulfate with hot water; precipitating the silver onto copper-lined wooden tanks; collect the precipitate, dry it, press it into cakes, and melt it into silver bullion. The copper sulfate solution was then run into tanks containing scrap iron, where iron sulfate would form and precipitate the copper for recovery and reuse. MANRY1999 pages 49-52

54 SLOAN1975 page 19

55 RANSOME1901 page 20. Nathaniel Haskell developed the first water-jacket smelting furnace to be used in America in 1866. BAILEY2002 pages 18-19

56 HAER02. This report states that the Greene smelter was of 10 TPD capacity, which is likely. The American Smelting and Refining Company charged from $2-$12 per ton, the higher rate for dry ores. An additional charge of $0.50 per unit was made for ores running more than 10% zinc. RANSOME1901 page 41

57 EMMONS1886 page 626. HENDERSON1926 pages 10-13, EMMONS1927 page 135. FELL1979 pages 80, 83, 87, 88, 93, 94, 97, 98, 101, 103-104, 105, 113, 125, 147, 206, 210, 212, 213, 231. Emmons (1927) states that construction on the Malta started in 1875, completed 1876. Henderson states 1875 for completion.

58 In 1875, Greene and Company had finished building their first smelter in Silverton, Colorado. Each brick was imported and cost $1.15 each! BIRD1986 page 15.

59 Manufactured by Wilbraham Brothers, Philadelphia, PA.

60 EMMONS1886 pages 620, 639

61 EMMONS1886 pages 626,637-639,662,697. Table based on 7 of the 9 smelters for which there was complete data.

62 FELL1979 pages 101-102

63 EMMONS1886 page 628

64 EMMONS1886 page 628

65 USGS1886 pages 251-252

66 USGS1886 pages 251-253. One wonders if the minds that devised such a fee schedule found rewarding employment developing income tax forms.

67 EMMONS1886 pages 648-649

68 approximately 89% chlorine, 10.5% bromine, and ½% iodine – EMMONS1886 page 620

69 EMMONS1886 page 732

70 VOYNICK1984 page 75

71 FELL1979 page 102

72 EMMONS1886 page 732

73 ROHRBOUGH1986 page 186

[74] EMMONS1886 pages 639,658

[75] A fume chamber – the first to be used in Utah, caught over a ton of leaden dust a day at the Chicago Company's furnace in Stockton, Utah. BAILEY2002 page 130

[76] EMMONS1886 pages 636,673,674,711,717, EMMONS1885 page 292

[77] TAGGART1947 page 144

[78] EMMONS1927 page 112

[79] FELL1979 pages 116, 118

[80] EMMONS1927 page 112. This includes copper ore tonnage as part of the estimation.

[81] EMMONS1927 page 135

[82] FELL1979 pages 124, 126

[83] FELL1979 page 207

[84] EMMONS1927 page 112

[85] FELL1979 pages 131, 208

[86] EMMONS1927 page 136

[87] EMMONS1927 page 136

[88] EMMONS1927 page 112

[89] WELLS2002 pages 133-135

[90] 1911ENC.Copper. Successful experiments in the pyritic smelting of copper ores was conducted by John Hollway of London about 1879. MAB1879-8

[91] MONTANADEQ.36

[92] HENDERSON1926 page 13, EMMONS1927 page 136

[93] FELL1979 pages 210-211

[94] HENDERSON1926 page 13, EMMONS1927 page 136

[95] BAILEY2002 pages 110-112, 118

[96] HUTCHISON2003.2

[97] BAILEY2002 pages 112-116. Standard English tests were made in an iron frame, which was elliptical, about five feet long, three feet wide, and made of ribs of flat iron. Pounded into this, in layers, was the moistened bone ash. The sides were about two inches thick at the top and thickened to three at the base, and the bottom was about 1.5 inches thick. The test was allowed to dry for a few days before use. It was then placed on a truck, rolled beneath the furnace, lifted into place, and supported by bars and wedges. HUTCHISON2003.1

[98] TAGGART1947 page 145, PAULING1988 page 545

[99] BAILEY2002 page 59

[100] HUTCHISON2003.2

[101] The *law system* crystallized ⅞ of the contents of the pan, and was generally used for lead that was poor in silver. The *high system* removed ⅔ of the crystals, and was used for silver-rich lead. In the high system, as many as fifteen pans were used, where the essence of the operation was to move the crystals into the pan to the right, and the rich lead into the pan to the left, no matter which pan was being worked. Thus richer lead moved to the left end and silver-poor crystals moved towards the right. HUTCHISON2003.2. It is interesting to note that gaseous diffusion of uranium isotopes was worked out in a similar fashion, but using sintered nickel instead of a large ladle.

[102] In English installations, the crystallized lead was fished out of the melting pot with a giant ladle. HUTCHISON2003.2

[103] CURTIS1884 pages 162-164, MOLINELLI1997 pages 105-107. Both sources provide substantially similar descriptions.

[104] HUTCHISON2003.1

[105] EMMONS1885 pages 383-392

[106] PAUL1965 page 59

[107] JACKSOND2001

[108] Excessive salivation is one of the first signs of mercury poisoning, accompanied by inflammation of the gums and mouth, loosening of the teeth, tremors and spasms, kidney damage, behavioral changes, etc.

[109] Up through June of 1904 flasks contained 76.5 pounds of mercury. After that they contained 75.

[110] PAULING1988 page 547

[111] USGS1885 pages 507,510, MONAHAN2001

[112] USGS1885 pages 507-508, SCHNEIDER1992 pages 63-64

[113] SCHNEIDER1992 page 25

[114] SCHNEIDER1992 page 34

[115] FARQUHAR1966

[116] USGS1885 pages 512-514

[117] USGS1885 page 508, MONAHAN2001. The Idria furnace was itself patterned off of an 1830's design by Count Rumford (Berlin) for burning lime. USGS1885 page 508.

[118] USGS1885 pages 514-518

[119] SCHNEIDER1992 pages 63-64

[120] A worker quickly opened up doors at the top of the furnace, added additional ore, and quickly closed them again, this operation being repeated about once an hour, as practiced by the Chisos Mining Company in Terlingua, Texas, in the early 20th century. No doubt these unfortunate individuals were exposed to considerable mercury vapor.

[121] It took 2-3 weeks of continuous firing to bring the Chisos furnace up to temperature.

[122] The condensed mercury was tapped directly into iron flasks, ready for sale, in Terlingua.

[123] RAGSDALE1976 Appendix C, SCHNEIDER1992 page 64, USGS1885 pages 508-511, 519-534. The Chisos Mining Company, operating a mercury mining and refining complex in Terlingua, Texas in the early 1900's, had losses of mercury in fumes as great as 30%. When the Scott furnace was installed, these losses dropped to 10%. Plans were made to build an ice-house for enhancing the condensing of the mercury vapor. RAGSDALE1976 page 71.

[124] USGS1885 pages 513,514,518,523,527

[125] USGS1904 page 256

[126] USGS1894 page 112

[127] PAULING1988 page 546

[128] PAULING1988 page 546

[129] TAGGART1947 pages 146-148

[130] PAULING1988 page 546

[131] HENDERSON1926 pages 11-13, EMMONS1927 page 135, 136

[132] RANSOME1908 page 83

MILL MACHINERY

Figure 1   Stamp mill batteries and amalgamation plates   Source: Hatch, 1895

To be sure, there were hundreds of different machines that were used – and as many variations on the more popular types, in the mills in the West. Some were rather unique, possibly being a one-of-a-kind invention by the owner. In the Clear Creek area of Colorado, "a miner named Red fixed a trip hammer, pivoted on a stump, the hammer pounding quartz in a trough. His invention was called the Woodpecker Mill."[1] Another mill, shown in figure 2, may have been better at hammering a dulcimer. Patents were issued for 54 different ore concentrators in 1892.[2] In 1893, *The Mineral Industry* reported that there were improvements or new designs for milling equipment numbering: Crushers and granulators, 7; roller and ball mills, 3; and concentrators, separators, and tables, 10.[3]

Other types of machinery were destined to become fixtures in most every milling operation. Some may have been developed in the 19th century, but didn't take hold until the 20th century. A good example is the *ball mill*, invented by Brückner in 1876. It wasn't used on precious metal-bearing ore in the U.S. until about 1905, when it was adopted from the cement industry. At about this time, sizing by sedimentation using mechanical classifiers of various forms (drag, spiral, and rake) were being adopted.[4] The equipment outlined in this chapter is a selection of types that were widely used in the 19th century mills.

Grinding and Crushing

To liberate the desired metals and minerals from ore, it must first be ground or crushed to varying degrees of fineness. The most primitive forms used by prospectors would include a *sapling stamp*, which amounts to a rock or pestle hung from a sapling and taking advantage of its spring to make the job of crushing easier; hammering at the piece until it was pulverized; using one rock to grind another; and using a hand mortar and pestle for fine grinding. The quantity of rock crushed in this manner was sorely limited, but it was sufficient for proving the value of the ore. Machinery of greater capacity would then be required to profitably work the ore.

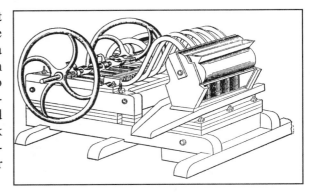

Figure 2   Crusher
Source: Raymond, 1873

The Arrastra

The *arrastra* [5] is an inexpensive, simple, reliable, and effective means of crushing ore. It has been used for millennia; evidence indicates its use as far back as the fifth century B.C.[6] See figure 3.

Paving for an arrastra was typically one-foot thick pieces of very hard rock, such as granite or basalt. *Drags* – drag stones, ranged from two to twelve per arrastra; typically four were used, each weighing about 300 pounds. The drags were fastened to a horizontal pole by chains. The horizontal pole rested on a vertical pillar in the center of the arrastra. Men, mules, waterpower, and steam were all used to power arrastras.

A charge of ore is fed into the arrastra, water added to control the pulp consistency, and grinding commenced. Lye or ashes might be added to the ore to help *saponify* – convert to soap, any grease present. Grease has the undesirable property of coating the freed flakes and grains of valuable metals and preventing their subsequent amalgamation.[7]

Figure 3   Arrastra ca 1865

Courtesy Library of Congress

After a few hours of grinding the quicksilver is introduced. If gold ores were being worked, only enough quicksilver was added to produce a pasty amalgam. Silver ores, on the other hand, required an excess of quicksilver, often amounting to one pound for each ounce of silver present. These ores frequently had bluestone (copper sulfate) and salt added to assist in the chemical reactions that liberate silver.[8]

The total time of working a given charge was ten to twelve hours. Towards the end of this time, water was added to thin the pulp, and the speed of the drags (typically 200-300 feet per minute if powered by water or steam, much slower if powered by a mule) was reduced to allow the amalgam to collect and settle on and in the cracks of the pavement blocks. Plugs were pulled, or a gate opened, to carefully wash the tailings from the arrastra. If the work were custom, a cleanup of the amalgam would be made. If the owner's ores were being worked, cleanups were made less often. The amalgam was collected and strained through a chamois or canvas bag, and then retorted.

Smaller arrastras could be worked by a single mule or horse, or by waterpower when available. The capacity of an arrastra varies depending on its size, the type of ore, and the motive power used. During the 1880 Census year, the arrastra mills surveyed ground an average of about 170 tons of ore annually. It is doubtful that these mills operated full-time. A mule-powered arrastra at the Birdie mine in Montana worked one ton of ore per day.[9]

A very simple mule-powered arrastra could be built for about $150. More complete milling operations using arrastras cost in the neighborhood of $5,300 for an entire mill with multiple arrastras, or about $1,500 for each arrastra and its associated works.

Figure 4   Wolverton Mill, 2002   Author

The Wolverton Mill, built by Edwin Thatcher Wolverton in 1921, serves as a suitable example for a small arrastra mill. See figure 4. The sixty-year-old Wolverton built this mill with the help of his sons, on Mt. Pennell, in the Henry Mountains of Utah. It was designed to crush auriferous ore. The primary crushing was by a *Chilean wheel*, also called a *Chile mill*. See figure 5. An arrastra was used for final grinding and gold recovery. See figure 6. The mill was powered by a 20-foot overshot water wheel, which powered the ore crushing machinery and also a sixty-inch straight saw.[10]

Arrastras were sometimes preferred to other methods of ore crushing and metal recovery. Gold ore in the Piños Altos district of New Mexico was discovered in 1860, and by 1869 two mills, a 5- and a 15-stamp, were in operation. Interestingly, by the 1890's, most of the district's gold ore was milled in as many as 75 arrastras.[11] In inaccessible areas like the South Boise mines, arrastras were extensively used. By the end of summer 1864, the number in service jumped from 10 to 80, some of which had a capacity of over a ton per day.

Figure 5   Chilean Wheel   Author

The recovery was sometimes low, however, as Henry Thomas Paige Comstock (for which the great Comstock Lode in Nevada was named) discovered when tailings panned 100 feet downstream from his arrastras carried $10 to the pan.[12] The Rough and Ready mine, Montana, used an arrastra to recover about 60% of the values from the gold ore.[13]

Some arrastra mills had surprisingly good recoveries. For example, W. A. Norton, operating two water-powered arrastras in the Yankee Fork district of Idaho, recovered over $70,000 from Charles Dickens ore during 1878 and 1879. Norton's arrastras were said to have recovered about 70% of the values.[14] The Scales & Wagner Mill in Idaho could recover up to 90% of the gold, and from 75-80% of the silver. The milling cost per ton was about $9, the charge per ton was $15 if over 100 tons, $16 for 50-100 tons, and higher for smaller lots.[15]

Figure 6   Arrastra   Author

Stamps

A *stamp* is a pestle that is raised by some form of power – typically water or steam, but sometimes by men or animals. Gravity causes the stamp to drop, crushing ore placed between the stamp's *shoe* and the *die* below. Stamps are very old devices, used since the middle ages. See figure 7.

The first stamp mill used in the U.S. was in Georgia in 1829.[16] Possibly the first stamp mill erected in California was in 1850 at Coulterville, Mariposa County. James Rickard brought it in sections for testing the ores of the Mother Lode.[17] New Mexico's first stamp mills were built at Piños Altos in 1867.[18] The Golden Chest Mining Company built the first gold quartz mill in the Coeur D'Alene, Idaho area in early 1885. It was a 5-stamp model with a single amalgamating plate.[19]

One of the earliest stamp mills used in the west was near the Cosumnes River, California in the summer of 1851. The mill was purchased from Tennesseans, and was of the pattern used in the east. The *mortar* – the box containing the dies and on which the ore is placed, and the *stems* – the long shaft which is lifted and dropped and on which the shoe is fastened at the bottom, were made of wood, and the stamps were square. The *heads* – primitive shoes, were made of soft iron.

The group quickly discovered that they spent more time repairing than running it. One of the group realized that the difficulties would be greatly reduced by substituting iron for the wooden stems, and to make the stems and stamp heads round to reduce chipping of the corners. A "Yankee mechanic" hired to effect some of these changes suggested that if the stems and heads were to rotate, the wear would be much smoother.

Figure 7   Medieval Stamp Battery
Source: Georgius Agricola's
De Re Metallica

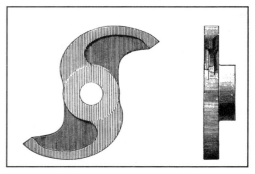

Figure 8   Stamp Cam
Source: Allis-Chalmers, 1902

The design changes proved to be very successful, and were rapidly adopted throughout the region. Additional innovations followed, notably cast iron shoes used in place of the soft iron heads, the wooden mortar box was replaced by one made of cast iron, and curved tangential *cams* were exchanged for the straight ones. See figure 8. In but a few short years the *California Stamp* was born.

The rapid development of the stamp mill, frequently called a *quartz mill* because much of the gold-bearing ore was found associated with quartz, did not translate to increased recovery of the gold from the quartz. The percentage recovered was sometimes appalling: contemporary accounts indicate as little as 20% to as much as ⅓ – only the richest ores could be worked at a profit. Experience showed that the stamps did not pulverize the ore sufficiently. The tailings from the stamps were generally run through arrastras or blanket sluices to enhance the overall recovery. Finer crushing was not always the answer either.

One problem was poor construction of the stamp batteries, and inexperienced millmen operating them. Concerning the construction of the stamp battery of the Gregory mill in Aurora, Nevada, Wasson said,

"The battery-mortar was a wooden trough with an iron bottom, with nothing much to prevent both the quicksilver and gold from running around the country at pleasure. The rock was so rich, however, that much money was obtained nevertheless."[20]

Part of the problem was the ore itself. As the mines went deeper, the ore transitioned from being highly oxidized near the surface to containing significant amounts of sulphurets (sulfide minerals). Gold was frequently found associated with these sulfides, sometimes locked within. Where the fire assay revealed their presence, the stamps could not free the particles, and the quicksilver refused to help. The solution to this problem was roasting and the chlorination process – and later the cyanide process, as described earlier.

Towards the later 50's the growth of the California quartz industry grew rapidly. See chart 1. By 1858 the price of a mill averaged around $12,000.[21]

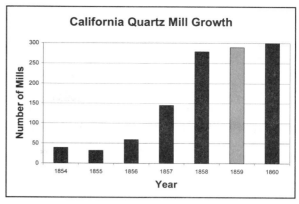

Chart 1

Stamp Battery

A typical stamp arrangement is illustrated in figure 9. A common pattern in stamp mill design was to use five stamps in a *battery*. *Guides* kept each stamp's stem aligned on the wooden framework. A *tappet* was fixed to the stem near the top. The stamp was lifted and dropped by the revolving cam engaging the underside of the tappet. On the bottom of the stem was a *bosshead*, and press-fit into it was the shoe. Fixed to the bottom of the battery frame is the iron mortar, and within it the dies are held in place by lead.

The entire stamp assembly – stem, tappet, bosshead and shoe, weighed from about 500-1300 pounds, 750-1000 being typical.[22] The weight of all the iron work, guides, and the wood pulley – but less the timber frame, generally weighed a little more than three times the combined weight of the stamps in the battery. That is, for a 5-stamp battery where each stamp weighed 750 pounds, the weight of the battery (less the frame) would be about 12,000 pounds.[23]

A worker called a *feeder* shoveled ore into the mortar. A stream of water was also directed in. Water consumption in a stamp battery could be significant – from 150-200 gallons per hour per stamp.[24] This was a serious issue in desert regions, and led to dry crushing of the ore.[25] The stamps pulverized the rock, which when mixed with water, is called *pulp*.[26] The fine particles splashed against and were discharged through a *screen* fixed to the front of the mortar. The screens were either steel or brass wire, or slotted or needle-punched plate.[27]

Copper amalgamation plates were often used to line the interior of the mortar, this affording the first chance of collecting the gold. As the pulp then splashed through the screen it passed over a large, sloping amalgamation plate for a second chance at gold recovery. From that point onward the pulp might wind up as tailings, or it might be processed by additional machinery.

Figure 9   5-Stamp Battery   Author

The order that the stamps dropped, numbered from left to right, was typically the *Homestake Sequence* of 1-3-5-2-4. Millmen in California preferred the *California Sequence* of 1-4-2-3-5, claiming that the pulp distribution in the mortar was more even and that the swash of the pulp passed through the screen better. A 10-stamp battery would use a drop sequence of 1-7-3-9-5-2-8-4-10-6. See figure 10.[28]

The rate at which the stamps were dropped was variable, depending on the stamp weight, the height from which it was dropped, the type of ore, screen mesh size, etc. 30 drops per minute was used in the Gilpin County, Colorado mills, 85 in the Black Hills, and 90-105 in the Mother Lode region of California.[29]

If the stamps were run too fast, *camming* occurred. This is when the stamp is still falling when the cam engages the tappet. The stamp must be allowed to fall and come to rest before being lifted again. Excessive wear was the least that might be expected from camming; parts breaking and failure of the battery was more likely. The *pulley* that drove the camshaft was usually made of wood; the shock of the cam engaging the tappet caused too much strain on cast iron pulleys and they were shaken apart.[30]

Stamps should make about one and a quarter revolutions about the axis of the stem per drop, depending on the condition of the tappet and cam. The friction of the revolving cam on the tappet caused this motion, which evens out the wear on the shoe and die below.[31] Common bar soap was recommended for lubricating the stems, as it does not interfere with amalgamation like oil or grease does.[32]

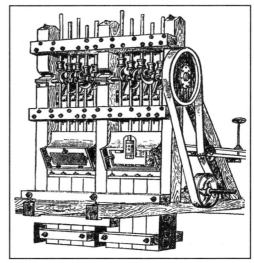

Figure 10   10-Stamp Battery
Source: Eissler, 1889

The disadvantage of the stamp was that of over-crushing the ore. Just because the ore had been crushed to a size small enough to pass through the screen did not mean that it immediately did so. The pulp was continuously splashed around in the mortar as the stamps dropped, all the while subject to additional crushing. This excessive crushing reduced a stamp's overall capacity, but it could also be helpful in some situations, especially where the gold was very finely divided in the ore. Stamps, unlike most other crushing equipment of the time, could easily crush two-inch size pieces of ore to fine sand.

Stamps were often times more effective than other methods of crushing. The Eureka Mill attempted to use Cornish Rolls, invented in England in 1806 and introduced to the U.S. in 1832 – see figure 11,[33] but they failed to perform effectively and were replaced by stamps in 1900.

Figure 11   Crushing Rolls
Source: Allis-Chalmers, 1903

The *Silverton Standard* commented:

"After a thorough trial on the unusually hard quartz from the Sunnyside Mine, it is found that satisfaction is in no way given. These new fandangle experiments are costly and while in some cases they prove to be better adapted for some ores than the old fashioned stamp, yet the old fashioned stamp has always been adapted for all ores and in many cases, as in this instant (sic), better than any other process."[34]

Screens were subjected to the splashing of the abrasive pulp. Their lifespan varied greatly due to the type of screen and nature of the ore being crushed. For slotted screens, it ranged from as little as seven days in the Black Hills of South Dakota (25 mesh), to as long as 60 days in the mills of Gilpin County, Colorado (50 mesh).[35]

Some ore was particularly difficult to stamp. In 1914 the rhodonite found in the 4th of July vein of the Sunnyside Mine near Eureka, Colorado was so tough, stamps could not crush it and instead ejected the pieces through the screen, necessitating a shut-down for repairs. Later this same material was used in the place of steel balls in the ball mills for fine grinding.[36]

When the battery was ready for a cleanup or repair, *finger pieces* [37] were used to support the stamps. These pieces of wood were hinged to the battery frame or placed into a socket. As the cam revolved, but before it engaged the tappet, a spacing tool – made from a stack of leather strips an inch or two thick and affixed to the end of a wooden handle, was slipped over the cam by the operator. As the cam engaged the tappet and lifted the stamp to its peak height, which was made another inch or so higher due to the leather strips in between, the finger piece was quickly slipped beneath the tappet, and the tool pulled clear of the revolving cam. This disengaged the stamp, and kept the tappet a safe distance above the revolving cam. Each stamp was thus disengaged in turn. Figure 1 on page 191 shows all of the stamps disengaged and supported by finger pieces.

Wear on stamp shoes and dies depended not only on the ore being crushed, but also on the material from which they were made. In Gilpin County cast iron shoes wore out nearly twice as fast as chrome steel, and dies wore out 50% faster. But, chrome steel cost about twice that of cast iron. Factoring in the rate of wear and the cost of the metal, the chrome steel shoe and die pair ended up costing 20% more per ton of ore crushed than did cast iron.[38] The lifespan of the various parts that make up a stamp battery as practiced at the Homestake mills in South Dakota is outlined in table 1.[39]

Part	Iron	Weight pounds	Life months
Camshaft	wrought	1060	48
Cam	cast	250	24
Tappet	cast	132	20
Stem	wrought	385	4
Bosshead	cast	236	96
Shoe	cast	145	2.5
Die	cast	110	1
Mortar	cast	5500	36

Table 1   Homestake Stamp Battery Part Lifespan

The design of the stamp battery lent itself to simplified disassembly, transportation, and setup. All that was required was a foundation robust enough to endure the incessant pounding of the stamps.

Automatic Ore Feeders

Ore feeders were developed to automate the feeding of ore into the mortar. In regards to using automatic feeders, Raymond states,

"Some of the most experienced millmen in California prefer feeding the batteries by hand to any form of automatic apparatus. The self-feeders, they say, may be superior to careless or unfaithful workmen; but a skillful feeder can, if he chooses, by giving to each stamp at exactly the right instant exactly the amount of rock it requires, increase the capacity of the battery to an extent which more than compensates for the extra outlay in wages."[40]

One disadvantage to using automatic feeders was that pieces of drill steels, tools, and other such implements could wind up in the mortar, causing considerable wear or even damage. This could be reduced somewhat by the use of magnets.[41]

In 1880, of the 233 surveyed western precious metal mills using automatic feeders, of the Hendy, Tulloch – see figure 12, Stanford, and Victor types, almost half were using automatic feeders, the rest still hand-feeding the stamps.[42]

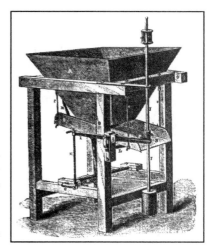

Figure 12
Tulloch Ore Feeder
Source: Eissler, 1889

Many of the ore feeders were designed on a similar plan, where a hopper discharged ore to the mortar by a lever activated by the center stamp. As long as there was sufficient ore beneath the center stamp, it would not drop far enough to activate the lever. As the ore was crushed and passed through the screen the center stamp would drop far enough to activate the lever, which opened a gate on the feeder momentarily, or shook an apron, thus allowing a dribble of ore to be fed into the mortar.

The Challenge Ore Feeder was a design favored by millmen. By 1880 about 600 were in use.[43] It consisted of 43 parts, and had left- and right-handed versions. The Improved Challenge Feeder could be used either way. See figure 13. It weighed about 850 pounds, and fed ore by means of a plate mounted beneath the hopper. The plate was automatically rotated by beveled gears driven by a clutch-like friction device, this device's motion being controlled by the blow received from the stamp's tappet engaging the forked lever.[44]

Figure 13 Challenge
Ore Feeder
Source: Allis-Chalmers, 1903

Stamp Summary

The daily tonnage of ore crushed and gold values won was highly variable, and depended greatly on the character of the ore, the weight and drop of the stamps, and the size of the screen. A ton per day per stamp was a typical figure.

♦ In the early days of the Reese River excitement, many miners were making from $5-$10 per day as "millmen" by purchasing small amounts of high-grade ore, and milling it by hand with crude mortar and pestles. Some of the more industrious millers developed one- and two-stamp hand-cranked mills. The success of these experiments led to four- and five-stamp mills powered by hand and by horse.[45] Figure 14 shows a three-stamp, hand-cranked mill designed and built by Billy Birkhead in Marysville, Montana ca 1880.

♦ A one-stamp mill in Roubaix, Dakota, pounded out $50,000 in gold in a single year.[46]

♦ A water-powered 6-stamp mill, fabricated from discarded wagon parts, proved very effective, stamping $1500 worth of gold a week from the Dakota claim at Bannack, Montana, in 1863.[47]

Figure 14 Author
Hand-Cranked
3-Stamp Mill ca 1880

♦ Early Colorado stamp mills saved only 15-40% of the gold, but by the late 1870's this rose to 50-70%.[48]

♦ The Maginnis[49] mine, Montana, sent its ore to a tiny two-stamp mill nearby. The owners of the mine made a profit even though the mill only recovered 40% of the values from the lead carbonate ores.[50]

♦ The Christy 5-stamp mill crushed 45 tons of Silver Reef sandstone daily – 9 tons per stamp per day.[51]

♦ In a six-week period during the summer of 1878, the Bodie mine in Bodie, California, produced $600,000 in gold and silver, the ore "so heavy with gold and silver that the metal caked under the stamps."[52]

♦ About 1880, the 80-stamp Homestake and the 120-stamp Golden Star mills in South Dakota extracted 88% of the gold, valued at $131 per ton, at a cost of $11.69 per ton.[53]

♦ In 1896, Cripple Creek had five plate-amalgamation stamp mills in operation that saved perhaps 55% of the gold values.[54]

- At the North Star mill in 1892, 72% of the gold saved was by amalgamation. Amalgamation plates were both in and outside of the battery. 47% came from the inside plates, 25% from the outside plates. Mercury losses were about eight-tenths of an ounce per ton of ore crushed.[55]

- In 1914 the Buster Mine's 10-stamp mill in Jarbidge, Nevada won only 35% of the values.[56]

- Tonopah, Nevada's first local stamp mill was built in 1903. The capacity was 8 TPD, with up to 75% recovery of gold & silver using stamps, concentrating tables, and amalgamation.[57]

Figure 15   Author
Circular Stamp Mill

Dust Buster

The Reese River process used dry crushing before roasting the ore. The dust produced could be significant. Louis Bailey, of the Bi-metallic mill in the Philipsburg area of Montana, devised a collection scheme to avert this problem. A V-shaped trough, closed at the top, ran above the length of the stamp batteries. Each battery was enclosed in a box, and the box connected to the trough by an iron pipe. Fans drew a current of air through the trough, which collected the fine dust that otherwise would have escaped the batteries. Dust that was not caught in the trough collected in dust chambers in the roasting furnace's stack.[58]

Pans

Pans – essentially mechanized arrastras, were used extensively in the Washoe and Reese River processes. Guido Küstel, in his 1868 publication *A Treatise On Concentration Of All Kinds Of Ores*, described a number of pans that use rotating mullers. Included in his book are such models as the Bartolo, Knox, Union Grinder and Amalgamator, H. Moore's Quartz Grinder and Amalgamator, Gaston's Grinder and Amalgamator, Hepburn & Peterson's Pan, Belden's Pan, Baux & Guiod's Grinder and Amalgamator, Excelsior Pan, Varney's Pan and Wheeler's Pan. The last two are outlined here, and were used for run-of-the-mine ore or concentrates that had not been roasted.[59]

Varney and Wheeler Pans

The bottom of *Varney's Pan* was formed of four dies made of cast iron. The rotating muller, which was raised and lowered by means of a lever, has twelve shoes. The muller framework was sometimes called a *spider*. The mullers were raised, and water sufficient to make the proper consistency of pulp was poured into the pan. The mullers were then set in motion, revolving at from 80-100 RPM. 600-800 pounds of ore was then introduced. Steam was admitted directly into the ore. The muller was gradually lowered, grinding the largest pieces first. The motion of the muller forces the pulp to the sides of the pan, where curved plates fixed to the top of the muller serve to redirect the pulp back towards the center of the pan. This creates a circulation of the pulp. About four hours were required to grind a coarse charge, two hours for a fine charge. Three to five HP were required to operate each pan. Shoes and dies lasted 40-60 days when operated 24 hours a day.

Wheeler's Pan is illustrated in figure 16. Seen on the left of the illustration is the hand wheel-lever arrangement that raises and lowers the mullers. The steam chamber is located beneath the muller shoes and pan dies. A series of inclined ledges on the periphery of the pan assist the pulp in rising and circulating. These are the curved objects, drawn with a solid line, in the plan (lower) view.[60]

Pans used for roasted ores were constructed differently. They had a cast iron base, but a wooden stave side and lid rather than ones made of iron. The die was cast whole rather than in sections, and the muller and shoes were also cast as one piece. Where grinding of the ore was not important but motion in the pan was, wooden shoes were sometimes used.

Heating the pans was accomplished by injecting steam into the pulp through a pipe. The disadvantage of this method was the slow dilution of the pulp and the abrasive effect of the circulating pulp on the iron steam pipe. The other method was by heating the pan from beneath with steam chests or jackets, the steam used being engine exhaust that was otherwise wasted. The temperature at which the pulp was kept was also variable, being in the range 100°-200° F. Roasted ores were kept on the high side, while ores containing lead carbonates were kept on the low side.

The length of time for working a charge ranged from 5-8 hours. Economics played a part, as seen in chart 2 on page 139. With increased time there were diminishing returns, and a point was reached where the processing cost would exceed the values recovered.

Typical pan capacity was 1500-4000 pounds, the mullers rotating at from 60 to 90 RPM. Not less than 100 pounds of quicksilver was added per ton of ore, the ratio of quicksilver to silver never being less than about one pound to the ounce. When working free-milling ores, the quicksilver was added about half way through the process. On roasted ores the quicksilver was introduced with the ore charge. The mullers were raised to prevent flouring of the mercury, yet still maintain agitation and circulation of the pulp.

Pans had just as much experimentation and development on their designs as did any other mechanical contrivance of importance. The 1880 Census takers report that,

> "in a certain mill in Arizona glass shoes and dies and a wooden muller are used. The muller has copper and iron plates fastened to it (said to be for the purpose of furnishing electricity), but the whole affair is reported to be a failure, and is cited merely to show what extraordinary pans are sometimes constructed."[61]

Clean-up pans may be used for recovering considerable values from around a large plant, in the form of stamp battery mortar scrapings, scrap battery ironwork that has been completely rusted, ashes from burned straining cloths and brooms, and floor sweepings, drain muck, and dust. A revolving spider in the pan has attached to it hardwood blocks. Some pans substitute a pair of arms and drag stones for the

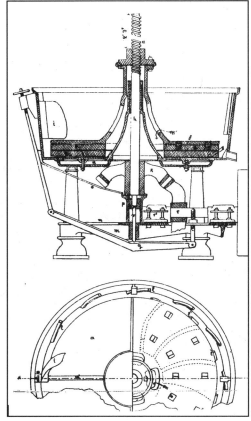

Figure 16   Wheeler's Pan
Source: Küstel, 1868

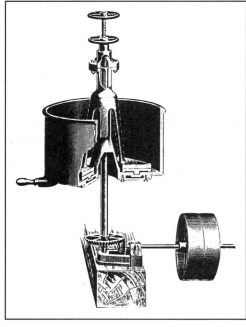

Figure 17   Cleanup Pan
Source: Allis-Chalmers, 1903

Drills And Mills

spider and blocks. See figures 17 and 18. The pan subjects amalgam to a gentle grinding action, which is not severe enough to flour the mercury. This action can separate the gold particles from the iron, charcoal, magnetite, and other matter present in the charge.[62]

Blake Jaw Crusher

Eli Whitney Blake patented his *jaw crusher* in 1858, and it was first used in 1861. See figure 19. When observing a jaw crusher for the first time, one might say that, "When watching this device work one seems to witness a mastodon consuming its forage."[63] In 1871, the Eureka Consolidated in Eureka, Nevada purchased a large model Blake jaw crusher for $1866.50.[64]

A Blake jaw crusher's action consists of two crushing surfaces, one fixed and one movable, set at an angle relative to each other. See figure 20. The movable surface – the *swing jaw*, pivots from the top, thus the area where the rock is admitted – the *mouth*, between the two crushing surfaces has a fixed width and gape.[65]

Power is applied to turn an *eccentric shaft* at about 275 RPM, this moving a *pitman* – connecting rod, up and down. The pitman transmits this power through two *toggles*, one attached to the frame of the crusher (rear), the other attached to the lower end of the swing jaw (front) near the *throat* – the discharge end. As the pitman falls, the toggles pull the swing jaw away from the fixed surface. The gap between the jaws is progressively widened from mouth to throat. When rising, the pitman and toggles push the swing jaw towards the fixed surface. The distance between the two surfaces at the throat, when at the minimum gape in the crushing cycle, is the *set*, which can be adjusted by means of movable blocks.

The two crushing surfaces are lined with replaceable *crushing plates* made of chilled or white iron, or chrome steel. Wear is mostly at the throat. When that portion of the plate is somewhat worn, the plate may be removed and turned upside-down, doubling its life. Wear is variable, a typical range being 0.02 to 0.2 pounds per ton of rock crushed. *Cheek plates* cover the sides of the crushing area, and are made of the same materials as the crushing plates.

The rock to be crushed is screened to a size no larger than about 80% of the mouth's gape, this by means of a grizzly. The rock falls into the mouth to the lowest point that it can – either on rock being crushed, or wedging itself directly between the jaws. As the jaws pull apart slightly, the rock slips and falls a little towards the throat, wedging itself between the crushing plates and other rocks. The crushing half of the cycle then begins, applying tremendous compressive force against the rocks, and they are crushed into smaller fragments. The cycle is repeated, and a steady stream of crushed rock drops through the jaws and from the throat.

Figure 18   Hand-cranked   Author
                   Cleanup Pan

Figure 19   Blake Jaw Crusher
              Source: Allis-Chalmers, 1903

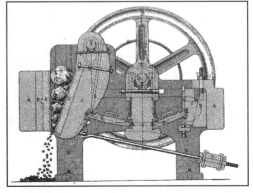

Figure 20   Blake Jaw Crusher
              Courtesy USGS

As the rock is crushed into ever-smaller fragments, the volume required for containing all of the pieces increases. This is sometimes referred to as *rock swelling*.[66] Because of the cyclic increase of the gape from mouth to throat (due to the swing jaw being fixed at the mouth), additional volume is made available for the newly crushed fragments to fall into. The Blake jaw crusher is seldom clogged, and sorting out the undersized rock from the crusher feed further enhances this virtue.[67] On occasion, a stubborn rock will wedge itself and refuse to break, the crusher jams, and operator intervention is required. This is also an infrequent occurrence on a properly fed machine of the correct capacity, settings, and power. To protect the crusher, the rear toggle is sometimes designed to shear in this situation.

It is worthwhile to note that this style crusher uses compressive forces on most of the components while crushing. This action lends itself to reliability and reduced parts breakage. The machine cycle is split between two phases, one requiring the great force required to crush rock, the other requiring very little force in simply opening the swing jaw. This cyclic imbalance of forces would normally shake the crusher, driving motor, and belts to pieces were it not for the dampening effect of a substantial flywheel.

Figure 21   Author
Dodge style Jaw Crusher
(McFarlane and Eggars, ca 1889)

Another popular crusher was the *Dodge* jaw crusher. See figure 21. It differed from the Blake principally in that the swing jaw pivoted at the throat instead of the mouth. It was less efficient at crushing than the Blake due to the relatively small motion at the throat.[68] It was made in sizes smaller than the Blake, finding use in smaller mills. Figure 22 shows a *Challenge* jaw crusher that used a wooden frame.[69] Table 2 compares Blake and Dodge style crushers.

Figure 22
Challenge Jaw Crusher
Courtesy USGS

Another jaw-like crusher was the *Alden*, patented in 1874. It was available in sizes ranging from a 30-pound hand cranked model to an 18,000-pound model that pulverized a ton per hour. What made the Alden novel was that it used a rubbing-like motion – the jaws remained a fixed distance apart, with a wider gape at the mouth than at the throat, but the actuating mechanism moved the throat of both hinged jaws at the same time in a sliding fashion. This produced an effect more like our mastodon friend grinding his forage between molars. See figure 23.[70]

Taggart reports that about 1871, a 20-stamp mill had a production of about 30 TPD on sledged rock, and 33 TPD on that crushed by a Blake jaw crusher. Some millmen asserted that the sledged product was better because of the concomitant manual feeding and attending of the battery by a skilled worker.[71]

Figure 23   Alden Crusher
Source: Manufacturer and Builder

Mouth Sq. In.	HP	Weight Tons	Tons Per Hour
Blake			
70	7.5	3.4	2.5
135	12.5	6.1	8.2
200	17.0	7.8	16.0
360	30.0	12.0	18.0
432	35.0	21.7	30.0
720	57.5	31.5	45.0
864	70.0	39.0	55.0
Dodge			
24	3.0	0.6	0.5
54	5.0	1.6	2.0
96	10.0	3.0	4.0
165	15.0	7.0	7.0

Table 2   Blake-Dodge Comparison

Concentrating

Many mills *concentrated* their ore in a *concentration mill*. Ore of, say, ½ ounce of gold and 12 ounces of silver per ton might be concentrated to 2.5 ounces of gold and 60 ounces of silver per ton of concentrates – the value increased, per ton, by a factor of five. A very good reason for doing this was to save money in freight expenses; why ship five tons of lower grade ore when it could be concentrated and only one ton needed to be shipped? Low-grade ore could be concentrated to a much higher grade, and once freight and milling or smelting fees were factored in, the ore could be worked for a profit, but only if it was concentrated.

The simplest form of concentration is hand sorting. This was practiced at many mines. The ore would be visually inspected and cobbed, with higher-grade going one direction, lower grade another, and gangue to the waste dump. This was practiced, for example, at the New Almaden quicksilver mine's *planilla*, and at the Amethyst mine in Creede.

Cripple Creek ores were somewhat unique in that the gold was frequently found in combination with tellurium, and located in the minerals that cemented larger masses together – the fines were the most valuable part. Blasting would pulverize much of these cementing fines, but a significant portion was left adhering to the larger low-grade or worthless pieces of rock. Ordinary concentration methods that utilized differences in specific gravity could not be effectively employed; rather, a considerable amount of hand sorting, washing, and screening using a *trommel* – see figure 24, was required to separate the valuable fines from the waste.[72]

Hand sorting was very labor intensive. Concentrating machines were developed to automate this task. The arrival of concentrating machinery or concentration mills took time to reach many mining districts. New Mexico's first mill with a mechanical concentrator was built at Piños Altos in 1883.[73] In 1894, the decision was made at the Revenue Mill to eliminate costly hand sorting, and to replace it with jigs. This reduced concentration costs from $10 to a few cents per ton.[74]

Blankets were commonly used in sluices to capture and concentrate fine sulphurets and amalgam present in the tailings that escape the mill machinery and settlers. See figure 11 on page 136. The blankets were about 13-20 inches wide, made of wool, and manufactured in San Francisco. At the California mill on the Comstock, concentrates collected from the blanket sluices were allowed to weather for 1-6 months, and were then reworked in pans.[75]

Mechanical concentrators of the 19th century generally took advantage of the differing densities of the gangue and the desired mineral. For example, the specific gravity of quartz (SiO_2) is 2.65, that of galena (PbS) about 7.6, that of silver about 10.5, and that of gold about 17.5.

Figure 24   Trommel, Victor Colorado, 2002
Courtesy Dan Wilson

The Buddle

The *buddle* is a concentrating device that consists of a convex, conic surface made of wood or concrete, with dimensions of about 16-22 feet in diameter and one foot high at the apex. See figure 25. Resting on top of this shallow-sloping cone is a smaller cone, of about eighteen inches in diameter and height. Just above the smaller cone is a funnel-shaped cone that receives, from a feed launder, the sands to be concentrated. A centrally mounted vertical drive shaft is connected to a horizontal shaft by beveled gears. Attached to the vertical drive shaft are two (or more) arms that nearly span the diameter of the buddle. Combs are suspended from each arm, the teeth coming within a few inches of the bottom surface. The arms revolve at a rate of 2.5-4 revolutions per minute.

Sand to be concentrated is transferred to the feed funnel by means of the launder. From there it passes through perforations in the base of the funnel and onto the surface of the cone beneath. This cone serves to dispense the sand to the intersection of the smaller cone with the bottom surface, where the combs then distribute the sand onto the sloping surface.

The sand moves slowly down slope and towards the circumference, sorted by the agitating action of the combs. The heavier sands tend to deposit first, nearest the intersection of the two cones, the lighter sands moving towards the perimeter. Three roughly defined concentric rings form, and are, from inner to outer edge, concentrates, *middlings*, and tailings. The middlings contained a mix of the desired mineral and gangue, and were often reworked.

Buddles can treat up to about two tons per hour, but require frequent stopping so that the concentrates and middlings may be shoveled out. A buddle of 18 feet in diameter can work approximately 30 TPD.[76]

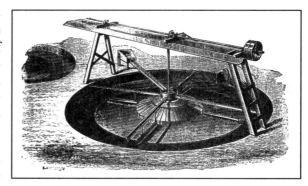

Figure 25   Buddle
Source: Mannix, 1913

Hendy's Concentrator

Hendy's Concentrator was "the one most employed in California" at one time.[77] This concentrator consisted of a shallow pan about six feet in diameter, with the center sloping upwards nearly to the height of the rim, as seen in the left half of the cutaway illustration of figure 26. Ore that had already been subject to crushing and amalgamation was sent to the concentrator, feeding (from the upper right of the illustration) into a centrally located hopper. The sands then flowed through a pipe protruding from the hopper and emerged over the middle of the pan.

This hopper-pipe assembly was affixed to a cylindrical shaft (with a second and separate shaft enclosed within) that slowly revolved by means of a ratchet and pawl mechanism, the rim of the pan being lined with the teeth of the ratchet. This mechanism, though a bit complicated, ensured that the sand would be evenly distributed in the pan. The downward slope of the pan towards the rim encouraged the motion of the sands in that direction.

Borrowing from the buddle, arms with rakes revolved at a lively 210 RPM within the pan. These arms were mounted to a second shaft concentric with the first. Like the buddle, the rake-like combs attached to the revolving arms stirred the sands and effected a separation. Unlike the buddle, the concentration was not in concentric circles; instead the lighter gangue moved upward as the heavier concentrates sank downwards, the whole mass gradually moving towards the rim with the addition of more sand. The lighter gangue discharged from the side of rim. The concentrates and amalgam collected in the small semi-circular depression located on the periphery of the rim, discharging from the underside edge of the rim.[78]

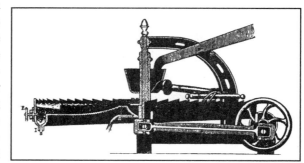

Figure 26   Hendy's Concentrator
Source: Eissler, 1889

The Gilpin County Concentrator and the Rittinger Table

The *Gilpin County Concentrator*,[79] see figure 27, was a fine-sand concentrator using a continuous, smooth table. It was *bumped* about 1.5-3 inches, and from 120-180 times per minute, at the *end* of the table by means of a spring, cam, and bumping post. The bump causes the ore to move up the slope and stratify, lighter particles moving above the dense ones below. Water would then wash the lighter particles down slope, as the heavier particles continued on their journey. The table could treat 4-5 tons per day.

End-bumping tables can only separate gangue from a single concentrate. If there were more than one mineral present, say, galena and sphalerite in a quartz gangue, then two tables would be required. The first table would concentrate one mineral – perhaps the galena, and the tailings from it would go to the second table. The second table would then concentrate the sphalerite from the quartz. Altogether, this is not as effective as a single table, like the Wilfley (description follows).

The *Rittinger Table* is a continuous, smooth table of the *side-bumping* type, using a cam and spring mechanism for the bumping action. The *classified* pulp – pulp that has been sorted by particle size, is fed to a corner of the high end of the table, where the bumping action separates the heavier and lighter materials, moving the grains in a fan-like shape across the table surface. Wash water propels the particles down slope. By the time the particles reach the end of the table, the particles have spread apart into bands.

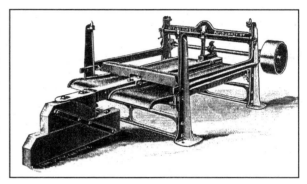

Figure 27   Gilpin County Bumping Table
Source: Rickard, 1897

Dividing fingers are placed at the foot of the table in positions that create the desired separation of concentrate, middlings, and tailings. This table may be considered the father of the jerking table, of which the Wilfley was notable.[80]

Tables that used a bumping post lost favor in the mills "chiefly because of the disintegrating effect of the bump upon the mill building."[81]

The Wilfley Table

Arthur Redman Wilfley invented the *Wilfley table* in 1895 and received his patent in April 1897.[82] See figure 28. After numerous experimental table designs – including the use of a sheet of glass for the table surface, which was rejected in favor of linoleum, Wilfley began production of his No. 1 concentration table in July 1896. This model, selling for about $450, featured seven riffles on a table 5.5x16 feet in size, and used a King-Darragh shaking mechanism. According to Wilfley, the size of the table was "simply the biggest that would go into a narrow-gauge railroad box car."[83] By 1925, 22,000 Wilfley tables were in use.[84]

The speed of the motor and the length of the stroke of the crankshaft controlled the table's head motion. Less than ¾ horsepower was required to run the table. The crankshaft engaged a pitman with two toggles, one toggle attached to the foundation sill, the other attached to the tabletop by a *thrust rod*.

The side-to-side velocity of the tabletop is a function of the angle that the toggles take in relation to the pitman. When approaching a straight line, the velocity is lowest, but as the pitman rises and the angles increase, the velocity

Figure 28 Wilfley Table   Author

increases. In this way, a sudden reversing motion of the table – a *jerk*, was made at one end of the stroke, and a gentle reversing motion made at the other end of the stroke. This is a key feature of this type table. This motion encouraged the pulp to move from one side of the table towards the other. A hand-wheel adjustment controlled the range of motion of the toggles, effecting an overall increase or decrease in the strength of the jerking motion.

The tabletop is made of strips of redwood, with a linoleum surface. Attached to this were tapered *riffle cleats* made of sugar pine, ending in a diagonal line, and fastened to the tabletop by means of small brads.[85] The cleats are ½ inch tall by ¼ inch wide at the *mechanism side*, and taper to a point towards the *tailing side* (description follows). They are spaced about 1-⅛ inches apart. Coarse pulp required taller riffles. The riffles and linoleum last about 2-4 years. The table required a stout support, often in the form of 12" by 16" pine beams.

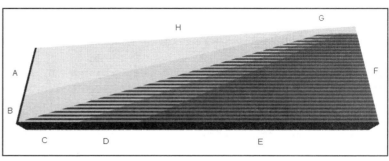

Figure 29   Wilfley Table Concentration Zones   Author

The Wilfley table may be divided into four sides – see figure 29: The upper side is the *feed* side (G and H), the lower side is the tailing side (C, D, and E), the side where the concentrates discharge is the *concentrate* side (A and B), and the remaining side is the mechanism side (F). The entire machine is about 17.5 feet long and 6 feet wide. The pulp is introduced into the *feed box* (G), which is about four feet long and located along the feed side at the corner shared with the mechanism side. Next to this is the *wash water distributor* (H), which occupies the remaining length of the feed side. Optimum pulp is a little less than a pound of solids per gallon of water. Better results are obtained from carefully classified pulp rather than from the natural product.

Figure 30   Wilfley Tables
Courtesy Mount Morgan Historical Museum, Inc.

The jerking motion, pulp consistency, and riffles combine to form a fluidized bed of grains, the pulp filling the gaps between the riffles. This stratifies the lighter gangue from the concentrate, the former rising above the latter, between the riffles. The bed is also stratified according to the particle sizes. The wash water carries the gangue over and to the next riffle down slope and ultimately towards the tailing side (D). The riffles provide support for the heavier grains under the crossflow of the lighter gangue. The concentrates slowly advance towards the concentrate side (B) by virtue of their contact with the table surface, riffles, and the resulting friction and uneven motion caused by the table's jerk.[86] Slimes are generally caught in suspension and washed directly down the slope of the table (E), carrying whatever values they might contain. Mineral losses in the slimes can be appreciably high.[87]

As the height of the riffles diminishes, progressively heavier sands begin to wash over the tops of the riffles towards the tailing side, forming a zone of middlings. The heaviest concentrates make their way to the tips of the riffles, where they are then washed down to the end of the next lower riffle, forming a narrow fan moving across the tips of the riffles and the plane area of the table (B). The plane area (A) serves to wash the concentrates a final time, but reduces the overall capacity of the table somewhat.

Fingers placed on the edge of the table simplified dividing the slimes (E) from tailings (D) from middlings (C) from concentrates (B). This alleviated excessive adjustments to the tilt of the tabletop to ensure that the correct product went to the proper destination, concentrate or tailing. The tabletop could be tilted by means of a hand-wheel adjustment. The downward slope varies, from the feed side to the tailing side, between zero and three degrees with one degree being typical. A very slight upward slope of about ½ inch across the length of the table is set from the mechanism to the concentrate side.[88]

The Wilfley tables, when fine-tuned for the pulp that they were to concentrate, required very little supervision – one man could attend to about 30 tables.[89] Table 3 outlines typical settings for fine, normal, and coarse feed.[90]

In 1897, the Gilpin County bumping table was pitted against the new Wilfley table at the Bobtail mill in Black Hawk and the California mine in nearby Nevadaville. Much to Wilfley's consternation, his device did not prove superior in handling the unique ores of the district.[91]

Wilfley Table	Minimum Fine	Typical Normal	Maximum Coarse
Table jerk, inches	0.25	0.75	1.25
Vibrations, strokes per minute	290	240	150
Feed Water, gals per minute	10		22
Wash Water, gals per minute	3	8	12
Capacity, tons per 24 hours	5	25	50

Table 3   Wilfley Table Typical Operating Parameters

In 1900, S. I. Hallett, the general manager of the Smuggler properties in Aspen, devised a shaking table – the *Hallett table*, which was more or less a copy of a Wilfley table, except that the riffles were set diagonally instead of down the length of the table. The drive mechanism – which the Hallett Company conveniently controlled, was formerly used on the King-Darragh table. In the Smuggler setup, a single table treated the middlings from four tables.[92]

Other similar table designs came later. Most have riffles across their entire surface, such as the *Deister* – see figure 31, *Butchart*, and the *Card*.[93] Emil Deister patented the Deister table in 1906.[94]

The Frue Vanner

To *van* is to wash a small amount of ore in a flat, circular shovel.[95] William Frue adapted this motion in developing his concentrator, the *Frue Vanner*. See figure 33. The Frue vanner is something of an adaptation of a concentrating apparatus used in China and India, which consisted of an endless cloth belt running over two rollers, one of which was hand-cranked, and with a stream of water running on its surface. The man turning the crank also pulled a rope tied to one side, which provided lateral motion, while a second man fed the finely crushed ore onto the belt. Chinese miners in Australia apparently used these devices during the 1860's, with fair results.[96] Frue patented his vanner Dec 22, 1874. Within four years about 250 were in use.[97]

The Frue Vanner is a *continuous belt, side-shaking* concentrator. See figures 34-36. A heavy frame of six and eight inch ash timbers supports the belt and its associated drive mecha-

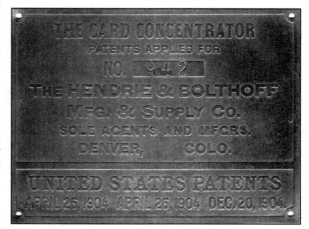

Figure 31   Deister Table   Author

Figure 32   Card Concentrator Plate   Author

nism. The entire machine is about fourteen feet long, nine feet wide, and five feet high. Less than one horsepower was required for operation. Wedges or jackscrews adjusted the slope of the belt. The belt was about four feet wide.[98] The top surface was about twelve feet long (from center to center of the *head* and *tail rollers*), a little less than ¼ inch thick, made of two-ply rubber with flanged edges to retain the pulp, and lasted from three to five years.

The top of the belt – the concentrating and cleaning surface, is supported by twelve iron rollers 50" long, eight spaced a foot apart at the tail end of the belt, and the remaining four placed closer together to form a smoother *cleaning surface*. There are two rollers on the underside of the framework. The first – the *dipping roller*, is located about five feet behind and a foot below the head roller. The belt travels on the underside of this roller and through the *cleaning tank*, which washes the adhering concentrate from the belt.

As the belt rises out of the cleaning tank, jets of water are sprayed for a final cleaning of any stubborn concentrate. The belt then passes over the *tensioning roller*, two and a half feet aft from the dipping roller, on its return to the tail roller, ready to begin the next revolution. The tensioning roller is shorter than the rest, and had rounded edges, due to the flanges of the belt passing over it.

The wash water is introduced from a cast-iron distributor about one foot from the axis of the roller at the head (top) end of the belt. It has brass spouts 1-½ inches apart. The pulp is fed through a distributor a foot farther down slope. The distributor has a built-in copper box, used to recover amalgam when the feed is from amalgamation plates. Vanners require very small particle sizes, typically about 0.75 mm. The pulp is optimum at about two pounds solids per gallon of water.

The shaking motion is about one inch, and has the effect of separating the desired mineral from the gangue, the latter being lighter and rising to the top of the layer of pulp. The belt travels about three feet per minute. The wash water helps flush the gangue down slope and into a waste trough. The water present in the feed pulp is nearly enough for concentration – only a small addition of wash water is required to effect good separation. It was usually preferred to have about 5% gangue make its way into the concentrate rather than 5% of the valuable mineral make its way to the tailings.

A fairly complicated set of variables were involved in setting up the vanner for optimum performance. Chiefly, pulp size and consistency, feed water rate, belt slope, and belt rate were the major parameters, but also subtle effects like standing waves in the belt's lateral motion, which could create longitudinal ridges and troughs. It took skilled millmen to master the machine. Table 4 outlines typical operating parameters for the Frue vanner.

Figure 33   Frue Vanner
Source: Aaron, 1881

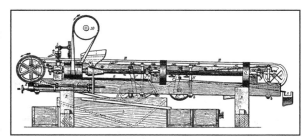

Figure 34   Frue Vanner, Side View

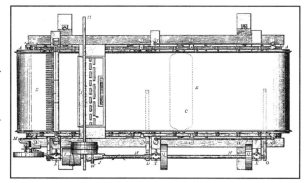

Figure 35   Frue Vanner, Top View

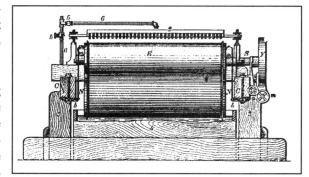

Figure 36   Frue Vanner, End View

Figures 34-36 Source: Eissler, 1889

The greater the difference between the densities of the gangue and mineral to be concentrated, the more effective the Frue vanner was.

It could only make a single concentration, however. If the pulp contained two desired minerals, one of which having a density intermediate to the other and the gangue, then two vanners were required, each separating one mineral.[99]

Desliming – removing the slimes from the feed, could improve the concentration over a natural pulp feed. At the Bunker Hill & Sullivan West mill in the Coeur d'Alene Mining District of Idaho, lead ore resulted in a 45% loss in tailings for natural feed, but only a 9.5% loss in deslimed feed.

The cleaning tank required the hoeing of the accumulated concentrates. A clever device, the *Shackelford Patent Cleaning Box*, alleviated this. It utilized the side-to-side shaking motion of the vanner and what amounted to a board with saw tooth-shaped teeth cut into it. As the board went one direction, the perpendicular side of the teeth caught the concentrate and inched it towards a drain, but when it went the other direction, the angled side of the teeth passed over the concentrate for the most part. Each tooth acted, in effect, as a miniature shovel, advancing the concentrate an inch at a time. It was claimed that this apparatus allowed one man to operate 92 vanners at the Consolidated Mining Company in Utah![100]

The *McKim concentrator*, developed in Park City, Utah, and patented February 15, 1876, was patterned on the Frue vanner. A 15x5 foot frame enclosed an endless canvas belt, which passed over rollers at each end. Pulp and wash water were administered in a fashion similar to the Frue. After additional experiments, these machines were put to use in 1878 working tailings from the Ontario mill, and also tailings from the Marsac mill (which itself reprocessed tailings from the Ontario mill) for two years. A concentrate of 17:1 – valued from between $85-$140, was produced, and the waste sands carried $5-$6.[101]

The North Star Mill, in Grass Valley, California, used sixteen *Triumph concentrators* rather than Frue vanners. The Triumphs were of the end-shake, end-slope style. The Triumphs were perhaps not triumphant, inasmuch as "they give more trouble than the Frues."[102] See figure 37.

Frue Vanner	Minimum	Typical	Maximum
Grain Size, mm	0.41	0.75	1.13
Depth of Pulp, inches	0.10	0.21	0.43
Jerk, inches	0.5	1.0	2.0
Vibrations, strokes per minute	120	190	280
Belt Slope, inches	2.25	3.42	6.00
Belt Rate, inches per minute	22	40	72
Feed Water, gals per minute	1.5	4.25	7.5
Cleaning Water, gals per minute	1.0	1.35	2.8
Capacity, tons per 24 hours	4	7.5	12

Table 4   Frue Vanner Typical Operating Parameters

Figure 37   Vanner Room, North Star Mill
Grass Valley, California 1887

Courtesy North Star Mining Museum, Grass Valley, California

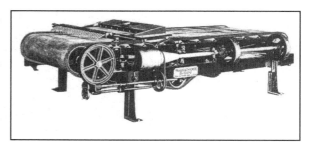

Figure 38   Improved Frue Vanner
Source: Allis-Chalmers, 1902

Roasting Furnaces

Brückner Cylinder

The *Brückner Cylinder* furnace was of an uncomplicated design – essentially, a brick lined iron shell about nine feet in diameter and 18 feet long, and requiring few repairs. See figures 39 and 40. Brückner first experimented with his roasting furnace in Georgetown, Colorado during the winter of 1867-68.[103]

The furnace was charged and emptied from a brick lined door on the side. A firebox was at one end, and a flue at the other. They were not very economical with fuel. A considerable amount of labor was required in charging and discharging, and while discharging a lot of smoke and dust escaped into the building.[104]

The cylinder was made of boiler iron. Three bands were bolted to the outside, one being a *spur gear* used for revolving the cylinder. Within the cylinder were six pipes, parallel to each other, with perforated plates held between them by longitudinal grooves on the pipes. This formed a plane at a 15° angle to the axis of the cylinder. Its purpose was to prevent the formation of clumps of ore, agitate the ore, and to reduce the amount of flue dust produced by the furnace. See figure 33.

The inside of the cylinder was lined with brick, built up at either end so that the lining was conical in form. Four rollers supported the cylinder, and a pinion engaged the spur gear. The flange at one end of the cylinder projected into the firebox, while the other projected into the dust chamber and flue.[105]

One man could easily attend two Brückner furnaces. The Brückner required about 900 pounds of cordwood per ton of ore roasted, and was one of the least efficient designs of its day. This was due to its large surface area and the need to reheat the furnace for every charge-discharge cycle.[106]

The *Improved Brückner Roasting Cylinder* was developed to alleviate some of the difficulties associated with the original version. See figure 41. The charge was loaded from the hopper above. The movable firebox – on the left side of the figure, was used to start the charge burning, and once started was removed and used at the next furnace. The furnace revolved, exhausting combustion gasses and dust into the dust chamber seen on the right of the figure. When the sulfur content of the ore was almost consumed (which sustained combustion), the firebox was brought back to finish the roast.

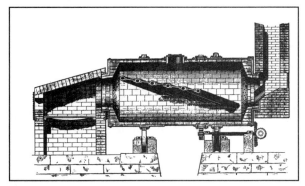

Figure 39   Brückner Furnace
Cutaway View
Source: Eissler, 1889

Figure 40   Brückner Furnace
Source: Allis-Chalmers, 1903

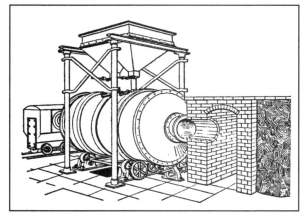

Figure 41   Improved Brückner Furnace
Source: Wilson, 1907

A furnace of this type roasted nine tons of concentrates in 24 hours and brought the sulfur content down from 30% to 5%. The roasting cylinder, as shown, was 8.5 feet in diameter and 18.5 feet in length, weighed 45,000 pounds, and required about 3400 firebricks and 8500 red bricks in its construction.[107]

White-Howell Furnace

The *White-Howell Roasting Furnace*, see figure 42, required a substantial foundation – skilled masons were required for installation.[108] The cylinder alone weighs about 28,000 pounds, excluding bricks. The furnace is made of separate segments, bolted together as it is assembled. A furnace 5 feet in diameter and 30 feet long requires over 30,000 bricks in its construction. See table 5.[109]

About 7-12 HP is required to revolve the furnace. Longitudinal shelves made of firebrick run the length of the furnace, and are responsible for the creation of a lot of dust. The ore is fed from the top, and gradually moves down the incline of the furnace as it is rotated, discharging into a pit at the lower end.[110] White-Howell furnaces required only about 300 pounds of cordwood to roast a ton of ore.[111]

About 1888, the Deloro mine in Ontario, Canada contributed significant innovations in roasting:

"The air which feeds the No. 1 furnace (drier) is preheated by the escaping gases of the second cylinder (roaster), by passing through an air space between the two arches which form the top of the second roaster dust chamber.

The two roasting cylinders are jacketed, first with an air space, and then with a covering of mineral wool, and paper over that. The whole arrangement of the roasting cylinders, their jacketing, and the plan of utilizing the escaping gases to heat the feed air for the first cylinder, are believed to be new, and are found very economical and efficient in practice."[112]

Figure 42 Thompson's Improved White-Howell Furnace Source: Aaron, 1881

Capacity Tons	Weight of Iron Work	Fire Brick	Common Brick
15-20	25,500	1,900	22,000
30-40	48,500	2,700	28,000
50-60	54,000	2,700	28,000
60-70	59,000	3,000	31,000

Table 5 White-Howell Furnace Brick Usage

Figure 43 Revolving Dryer Source: Allis-Chalmers, 1903

Endnotes

[1] BANCROFT1890 page 611

[2] NIEBUR1982 page 72

[3] ROTHWELL1893 pages 825-831

[4] ARBITER1964 page 7, TAGGART1947 pages 93,95

[5] Other spellings the author has seen: *arrasts*, JOHNSON1898.6; *erastra* and *Spanish rass*, seen on an information sign at Little Pinto (Old Irontown), Utah.

[6] YOUNGO1972 page 69

[7] And that is an interesting point. Millmen were rather fastidious in regards to using lubricants on mill machinery for this reason. Oils, as it would turn out, would form the basis of the first flotation methods.

[8] *See* the Patio Process in a preceding chapter.

[9] MONTANADEQ.117B

[10] WOLVERTON1988

[11] ACKERLY1997

[12] WELLS2002 page 20

[13] MONTANADEQ.130

[14] WELLS2002 page 120

[15] EMMONS1885 pages 282-285

[16] MCQUISTON1986 page 12

[17] MCKINNEY1995 page 56. T. A. Rickard's grandfather.

[18] NORTHROP1975 page 22

[19] SMITHR1932 page 92

[20] WASSON1878 page 9

[21] PAUL1965 pages 136-143. 1859 estimated.

[22] ALLIS1902 page 33. The Argo mill in Idaho Springs, Colorado, had 20 stamps weighing 1050 pounds each. ARGO2000 page 4.

[23] ALLIS1902 page 33

[24] JOHNSON1898.6

[25] The consequences of dry crushing – and the attendant clouds of siliceous dust, was often devastating on the workers' health. Delamar, Nevada was notorious for this.

[26] Dry crushing battery output is sometimes called pulp.

[27] EMMONS1885 page 254

[28] TAGGART1954 page 4-90

[29] RICKARD1897 page 222, MILLER1906 page 187. Every millman had his own ideas about stamp weight, drop height and rate, screen height, angle, and sieve size, etc.

[30] TAGGART1954 page 4-91. Repeated shocks slowly crystallize the iron, and would eventually lead to failure of the part.

[31] MILLER1906 page 189

[32] ROTHWELL1896 page 717

[33] ARBITER1964 page 7

[34] BIRD1986 pages 67-68

[35] RICKARD1897 page 224

[36] WOLLE1977 page 291

[37] ALLIS1902 page 68. Also called a *finger bar* or a *cam stick*.

[38] RICKARD1897 pages 209,222,225

[39] ALLEN1920 page 112

[40] RAYMOND1873 page 34

[41] JOHNSON1898.6

[42] EMMONS1885 page 254

[43] AARON1881 (advertisement cut in back of book)

[44] ALLIS1903 page 71, ALLIS1902

[45] ABBE1985 page 21

[46] WOLLE1963 page 450

[47] MONTANADEQ.4

[48] MANRY1999 page 40

[49] or McGinnis

[50] MONTANADEQ.51

[51] PROCTOR1991 page 176

[52] SMITHG1998 page 215

[53] EMMONS1885 page 279

[54] ROTHWELL1896 page 245

[55] MILLER1906 page 196

[56] HALL1998 page 113

[57] By 1910 the Tonopah Extension Mining Company mill, using 30-stamps, tube-mills, and Deister tables, recovered 90% of the values. This figure rose to 92% in 1916 when processing over 5 TPD per stamp.[57] In 1907 the Tonopah Belmont Development Company constructed a 60-stamp mill – the Miller plant. The milling cost per ton was $7.82, partly due to the purchase of steam-generated electricity, and partly to hiring a large labor pool for shoveling sand from leaching tanks. By 1910, mill improvements, reduced electric costs, and a reduction of the mill labor force from 72 to 48 men brought the cost down to about $4 per ton. By 1911 the mill extraction was 89.2%. A new 500 TPD mill was built in 1912, the milling costing $3.44 per ton. By 1913 extraction reached 93.2%. At this time the Miller plant cost $4.16 per ton, duty was 8.66 tons per stamp, and recovery reached 94.45%. CARPENTER1953 page 62-3,82-3

[58] EMMONSW1913 page 197

[59] KUSTEL1868 pages 115-123

[60] KUSTEL1868 pages 116-119

[61] EMMONS1885 pages 262-264

[62] RICHARDS1925 pages 62,63

[63] ARBITER1964 pages 4,7

[64] RAYMOND1873 page 174

[65] The gape is the shorter of the two dimensions – how far the jaw opens.

[66] Imagine having a piece of granite, cut as a perfect cube, one foot on a side. Imagine having a box that exactly holds this rock – one cubic foot, with an open top. Now sledge the rock into, say, 10-20 large chunks. Toss them into the box. No longer will the original mass of the rock fit in the box – it has *swelled*. Break these pieces into still smaller pieces. It still won't fit into the box. If this concept is taken to an ideal limit of very tiny spheres, only about 74% of the rock will fit into the box.

[67] Modern Blake-style crushers used a convex swing jaw that enhances this effect.

[68] The Dodge produced a more uniformly sized product than the Blake because of the fixed discharge opening, at the expense of more frequent jams.

[69] TAGGART1954 pages 4-02 to 4-09

[70] MAB.1878-11

[71] TAGGART1947 page 87

[72] LINDGREN1906 pages 136-137

[73] NORTHROP1975 page 29, ACKERLY1997

[74] GREGORYD1996 page 139

[75] EMMONS1885 page 267

[76] EISSLER1889 pages 134,135, STANIER1998 pages 43, 47. This book has *excellent* photographs of buddles and other milling equipment.

[77] EMMONS1885 page 267

[78] EISSLER1889 pages 144,145

[79] A McFarlane Bumping Table, as used in Gilpin County, Colorado, was patented in 1887. RICKARD1897 page 30

[80] RICHARDS1925 pages 207,219

[81] RICHARDS1925 pages 206,207

[82] NIEBUR1982 page 80. Patent application submitted October 1896, issued April 1897. HENDERSON1926 page 12. Wilfley tested his table at his mill in Kokomo, Colorado. It is interesting to note that many maps still show *Kokomo*, but it is *No Mo*. It is buried under a *zillion* tons of tailings from the nearby Climax molybdenum mine.

[83] NIEBUR1982 pages 73, 75, 78. Quote from page 78.

[84] RICHARDS1925 page 207

[85] The cleats lasted about 5000 tons. Later models had 46 cleats. TAGGART1954 page 11-63. There were fourteen numbered models of Wilfley tables, plus a special design used for washing coal. NIEBUR1982 Appendix F.

[86] RICHARDS1925 pages 208-215.

[87] The Morning lead-silver mill of 1000 TPD capacity, during 1904, and located in the Coeur d'Alene district, had coarsely crushed ore that averaged about 15 ounces of silver per ton, whereas the slimes carried about 19. RANSOME1908 pages 87, 88

[88] It is interesting to note that the advancing concentrates climb a very slight grade on their journey, the tabletop being sloped slightly upwards. This is also due partly to the diminishing height of the riffles, and partly from the jerking motion of the stroke.

[89] TAGGART1954 pages 11-61,11-65,11-66

[90] TAGGART1954 page 11-69, RICHARDS1925 pages 208-215

[91] NIEBUR1982 page 83

[92] HENDERSON1926 page 199

[93] TAGGART1954 pages 11-69 11-70 11-74. The Butchart riffles have a bend in them along the line where the concentrates move. RICHARDS1925 page 216. The Card table has riffles of a sawtooth-triangular cross section *cut into* the surface of the table. TAGGART1954 page 11-74.

[94] DEISTER2001

[95] YOUNGO1972 page 302

[96] JOHNSON1898.7

[97] AARON1881 (from an advertisement cut in the back of the book). MCQUISTON1986 page 29 states that the Frue Vanner was developed in 1867. He developed his vanner while at Silver Islet (in Lake Superior), which was between 1870-1875, so the patent date of 1874 is probably correct.

[98] Some were six feet wide. TAGGART1954 page 11-91

[99] RICHARDS1925 pages 220-227, EISSLER1889 pages 147-162

[100] TAGGART1954 page 11-94

[101] BOUTWELL1912 page 29

[102] RICKARD1897 page 49, TAGGART1954 page 11-90

[103] FELL1979 page 59

[104] TAGGART1947 page 133

[105] EISSLER1889 pages 183-187

[106] EMMONS1885 page 274. The White and Howell each required 300, reverbs 600, and the Stetefeldt 200.

[107] WILSON1907 page 49

[108] ALLIS1903 page 96

[109] A furnace of 25 feet length and 4' 4" diameter weighs on the order of 90-100 tons. JOHNSON1898.8

[110] WILSON1907 page 54

[111] EMMONS1885 page 274. The Stetefeldt furnace was the most economical in terms of fuel, requiring only about 200 pounds of cordwood to roast a ton of ore. It was built of solid brick; thus retaining its heat better.

[112] EISSLER1889 page 217

MINES AND MILLS
OCCUPATIONAL HAZARDS

Figure 1   Silver King Mill, Park City, Utah ca 1902   Courtesy USGS

Arthur F. Taggart, the "Dean of Ore Dressing," described a typical, small mill located in the mountains in the early 1870's as resembling "a timber maze through which pulp, operators, and superintendent seem to pursue each other in an endless chase."[1]

Mills ranged in size from the simple arrastra to expansive industrial complexes filled with thundering machinery and occupying many acres of land. The Silver King Mill pictured in figure 1 falls into the latter category. Mills were generally located on a fairly steep slope, this giving a characteristic multi-level appearance. Gravity was leveraged to advantage wherever possible, moving the pulp from process to process in a step-like fashion. 19th century mills did not have the automation like that which is used in 20th century mills. One of the few exceptions was the use of automatic ore feeders on stamp batteries, described in the preceding chapter.

Many mining camps followed similar trends in their growth and development, both in numbers and sophistication of the mines and the mills. At the great Comstock Lode in 1859, horse-powered arrastras were initially used, followed by water-powered arrastras, a horse-powered 4-stamp battery, and then in 1860 by two steam-powered stamp mills.[2] In the Radersburg district of Montana, the free-milling and oxidized gold ore was originally worked by arrastras. Soon after another arrastra, plus 15, 12, 6, 5, and 2-stamp mills joined in. Unfortunately, the oxidized ores played out at about 100 feet depth – a sad but recurring theme in the mining West.[3]

After John Hamilton Gregory located the famous gulch named in his honor, mills began to be erected in what was to become Central City and Black Hawk, Colorado. In July of 1859, there was an arrastra at the mouth of the gulch, soon followed by a steam-powered stamp mill in September. By October an additional five arrastras and two stamp mills, all water-powered, were operating on North Clear Creek. By the close of 1860 there were 71 steam-powered stamp mills (dropping 609 stamps), 38 water-powered mills (dropping 230 stamps), and 50 arrastras in the Clear Creek region. These mills generally only saved from ⅓ to ½ of the gold present, at best, and none of the base metals.[4]

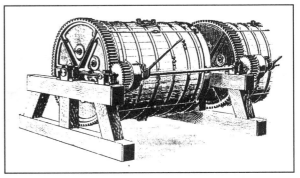

Figure 2   Amalgamation Barrels
Source: Allis-Chalmers, 1902

The White Pine district in Nevada showed a similar pattern of growth that was then followed by disasters and a rapid decline. Early in the summer of 1869 ten mills were operating with 120 stamps. By fall, 15 mills were dropping 181 stamps, and 5 mills were under construction with an additional 80 stamps, the largest being the Stanford with 30 stamps. During 1870-71 some mills moved out, and "two or three others" burned.[5] By 1871, there were 13 mills with a total of 232 stamps. As the district declined, 5, 8, 10, and 15-stamp mills were dismantled and relocated to other districts.[6]

Mills frequently changed ownership. In the early 1860's, the What Cheer stamp mill was established at Georgetown, Colorado. It was discovered that no free-milling ores were available locally, so the mill was leased to Garrett, Martine & Co. for five years. They added Brückner cylinders for roasting and revolving barrels for amalgamating the silver ores. See figure 2. This process saved between 80 and 85% of the silver treated, and produced the district's first silver bar. In 1867 they sold to Huepeden & Co. The superintendent embezzled the firm's funds. Next came Palmer & Nichols, who failed. In 1873, the Pelican Company purchased the property, and after renovating the mill produced silver bullion from the Pelican mine. In 1877 the mill was leased to Ballou, Napheys & Co., who operated it for 10 months at a loss. Then the Boston & Colorado Smelting Company acquired the mill, and used it for sampling and assaying.[7]

Figure 3   Caledonia No. 1, Deadwood Terra
No. 2, and Terra No.3 Gold Stamp Mills
Terraville, Dakota 1888
Courtesy Library of Congress

The famous Homestake mine was located on April 9, 1876, by Hank Harney, Moses Manuel, and brother Fred Manuel. George Beemer had his 20-stamp Racine mill in production on April 15, 1877. July 12, 1878 saw the Homestake mill dropping 80 stamps. The 120-stamp Golden Star mill was in operation September 1, 1879. By 1882, 620 stamps were working in the Deadwood area; in 1901 that number rose to a deafening 900; and by 1904 it reached 1000 stamps. The 4.5 acres of the Manuel brothers had grown to Homestake holdings of over 2600 acres in 1905.[8] The Homestake mine, from its beginning to June 1, 1900, recovered $30,931,543 in gold and silver, and paid $8,668,750 in dividends. See chart 1.[9]

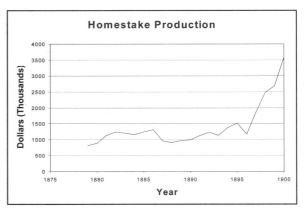

Chart 1

Mills

The Allis-Chalmers Prospecting Mill was a portable 3-stamp mill. Each stamp weighed 250 pounds. Mercury coated copper plates, which were electroplated with one ounce of silver per square foot, were used for amalgamation. The mill was available complete with all necessary parts and pieces, including a boiler and three-horsepower engine.[10] See figure 4.

For what might be considered a "typical 10 stamp gold mill," the mill building would require about 75,000 board feet of lumber, 5,300 square feet of corrugated iron and tar paper for the roof, and about 1300 pounds of miscellaneous fasteners, nuts, bolts, and other hardware. See figure 5.

This mill would include a 4x10 foot grizzly – see figure 6, a 7x10 inch Blake jaw crusher, an ore bin, two ore gates – see figure 7, two Challenge automatic ore feeders, two complete 5-stamp battery assemblies, amalgamating plates for the inside and outside of the mortars, two tailings sluices feeding two concentrating tables, a melting and retorting furnace, a 30 HP steam engine and boiler, a wood or coal bunker, a one-ton capacity overhead crawl and block, and all mounting hardware, plumbing, a water tank, belts, pulleys, lighting, etc.[11] The horsepower requirements for small mills are outlined in table 1.[12]

Figure 4   3-Stamp
Prospect Mill
Source: Allis-Chalmers, 1902

Figure 6   Grizzlies   Author

Figure 7   Ore Bin Gate   Author

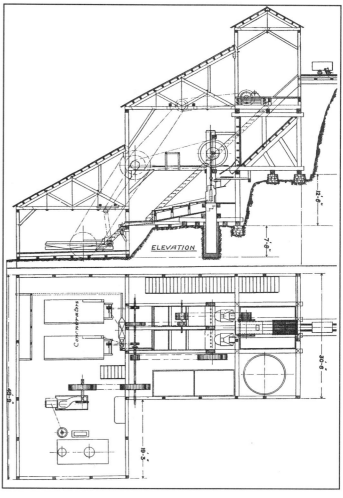

Figure 5   10-Stamp Mill Plan
Source: Miller, 1906

The cost of building a mill could be quite high, especially when located in remote areas that commanded higher prices for both freight and lumber. A selection of mill costs follows.

- In 1866, the Excelsior Company in Meadow Lake, California invested $100,000 in a 20-stamp, 40 TPD mill, where some $20,000 of the price represented shipping.[13]

- The 80-stamp Homestake Mill in South Dakota, powered by a 190 HP engine, was completed July 1878 at a cost of $164,500.[14]

- The 120-stamp Golden Star Mill in South Dakota, powered by a 300 HP engine, was completed September 1879 at a cost of $251,500.[15]

- In 1904 the Old Hundred Mining Company in Silverton, Colorado, erected a 40-stamp mill with a capacity of 125-200 TPD. The American Bridge Company built it for $450,000.[16]

- The 20-stamp Standard Mill in Bodie, built at a cost of $86,000, began operations on July 10, 1877. This mill used a pan process similar to the Washoe process. After 13 months it produced nearly $1.3 million in bullion, where the average yield per ton during 1878 was $59 in gold and $2.68 in silver, at a milling cost of $6.78. See chart 2.[17] In 1899 the mill burned down, and was immediately rebuilt using corrugated steel. It survives to this day.[18] See figure 8. Between 1892-1903, recovery varied between a low of 62% and a high of 79% of the values. When a cyanide circuit was added in 1904, the recovery jumped to 88-91%.[19]

- The 40-stamp Ontario mill in Park City, Utah, ca 1877, cost $325,000.[20] It used 2 Blake jaw crushers, 2 rotary driers, 8 self-feeders, 40 850-pound stamps (dry crushing), 2 Stetefeldt and 1 Howell roasting furnace with dust chambers, 24 combination pans, 12 settlers, 1 agitator, 2 cleanup pans, 4 retorts, and 2 melting furnaces. An additional stamp battery, having five 400-pound stamps, was used *just to crush salt*, where from 15-18% salt was added to the dried ore prior to stamping. Recovery was 92.7% of the silver, the bullion averaging 750-fine silver and the remainder being mostly copper. Milling cost $15 per ton.[21] Between 1875-1900, the Ontario produced 55% of Park City's silver – $33,454,249, and paid $15,112,500 in dividends.[22] See chart 3.

Machinery	HP	10-Stamp Qty.	10-Stamp HP	20-Stamp Qty.	20-Stamp HP
No. 2 Blake Jaw Crusher	6	1	6	1	6
Ore Feeder	0	2	0	4	0
Stamps (five @ 750 lbs)	12	2	24	4	48
Frue Vanner	0.5	4	2	8	4
Grinding Pan	3	1	3	1	3
Settler	3	1	3	1	3
Friction			4		7
Total			42		71

Table 1   Stamp Mill Horsepower Requirements

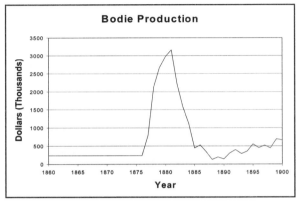

Chart 2

Figure 8   Standard Mill, Bodie, California 2002   Author

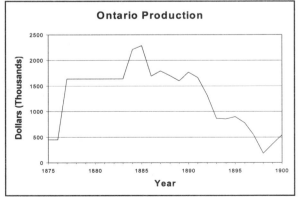

Chart 3

Drills And Mills

Disasters

Disasters struck many of the mills, causing considerable damage or a total loss of the works. Fire was the chief villain, burning down mills with the same regularity as it did mining camps and towns. Note the enormous stack of wood behind the white building in figure 3.

- On October 26, 1875 Virginia City was destroyed by fire. The new 60-stamp Consolidated Virginia mill, which cost $300,000 and went into operation in January 1875, was destroyed. The hoisting works, assay office, 1,250,000 board feet of lumber and timber, and 800 cords were also destroyed in addition to the stamp battery works of the California, and the hoisting works of the Ophir, for a total loss of $1,461,000.[23]

- White Pine had its share of disasters, some of which were preventable.

  o In 1869 a mill and a dozen buildings were destroyed by a tornado.
  o Water pipes had not been laid at the International Mill so that it could be flooded in the event of a fire. It burned to the ground on August 31, 1872.[24]

- The Enterprise mill collapsed from snow in the winter of 1866-67 at Meadow Lake, California.[25]

- In 1902 at Pandora, Colorado three snow slides at the Liberty Bell Mine took 16 lives and injured 12 others, destroying the boarding house, part of a bunk house, the crusher house, the tram house, and ore bins.[26]

Mines and Mining Districts

The following mines, mills, and mining districts have been selected to exemplify some of the successes and problems encountered during their operational histories. It is the author's hope that these historical vignettes provide context to the mining methods and milling processes that have been discussed.

The Elkhorn

The Elkhorn Mine, Montana, originally the A. M. Holter mine in 1875, is typical of many silver mines that transitioned from easily worked surface ores to complex refractory ores at depth, necessitating costly changes in milling. The early history showed great promise as the free-milling oxidized surface ores were worked in a small, 5-stamp wet crushing mill, but as the mine reached depth, the simple recovery methods lost half the values present in the ore. By 1881 it became obvious to the management that a new mill, using a chlorodizing roast and pan amalgamation – the Reese River process, would be required.

Figure 9   Ghost Buildings   Author
Elkhorn, Montana 2002

In 1883 – and under new management, a new 10-stamp mill was erected, complete with roasting furnaces and amalgamating pans. Eleven TPD were milled, using dry stamping, where the salt – 5% in the earlier years and 16% in later years, was added to the ore in the battery. The battery sands were then roasted in Brückner cylinders. After cooling, the sand was transferred to amalgamating pans, and then settlers. Overall recovery using this process was a very high 90-92% of the ore values. Mill capacity was increased to 20, then 25, stamps.

Sand and slimes leaving the mill were captured by a series of dams, as the water downstream was used for irrigation. The unique feature of the dams was that they were made of sandbags – the bags were those that the salt was delivered in.

At the 800-level lean ore was encountered. In 1888 the mine again changed hands. By 1896 the ore in sight was mostly exhausted, but a program of exploration revealed new ore bodies. Treatment costs were high due to the price of salt and other mine supplies. In 1896, the cost of salt per ton of ore milled was $1.88, $2.14 in 1897, and $2.22 in 1898. For these same years, fuel cost $1.05, $1.10, and $1.40 per ton milled. About ⅔ of the ore was milled, the remainder being sent to smelters. The bullion produced was about 900-fine silver, a trace of gold (less than 001 fine), and the rest copper.

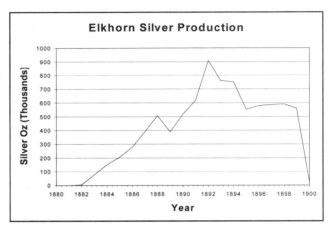

Chart 4

In 1899 the expense of pumping, coupled with the low grade of ore and increasing milling expenses, made mining unprofitable, and the Elkhorn closed down after having produced 8,300,000 ounces of silver. See chart 4.[27]

Mercur

Mercur, Utah deserves special mention. Mercur was the first mining camp to use the cyanide process in the States. Mercur also demonstrated that low-grade and finely disseminated gold ores could be worked at a substantial profit.

John Dern, E. H. Airis, G. S. Peyton, and Hal W. Brown incorporated the Mercur Gold Mining & Milling Company (MGMMC) in Utah in 1890. They expended $25,000 in building an amalgamation mill at Manning. About 1500 tons of ore, assaying $17-$18 per ton, was run through the mill. The tailings from the mill assayed 20% of the ore value. The owners fully expected to clean up the other 80%, or about $21,000. Instead, they got less than $5,000.

The attempts to amalgamate the auriferous Mercur ores failed miserably. This was primarily due to the gold being disseminated in a microscopic state in the ore (micron-size particles). The fire assay could collect the gold by fusion, but simple amalgamation could not. Another part of the problem was that potassium cyanide had been used to clean the mercury in the amalgamation process – a portion of the gold that did amalgamate may have unknowingly been dissolved away by the cyanide.

Once the cyanide process had been tested in Denver – with favorable results, the situation changed. Cyanidation was adopted, and by February of 1892 the recovery reached 86% on ore assaying $12 per ton. The mill was quickly enlarged to 100 TPD in 1893, 200 in 1896, and again to 350 the same year. In 1896, the MGMMC produced 25,283 ounces of gold, all by cyanidation, and paid $225,000 in dividends, or about 43% of the gross revenue, on an average extraction of ½ ounce per ton – a surprisingly high return to the stockholders for any mining concern, let alone one working low-grade ore.

In 1895, Captain J. L. De La Mar bought out the Golden Gate group of claims. Two years of research in practical recovery methods followed. A suitable source of power for the project was required. In 1897, L. L. Nunn contracted with De La Mar to provide 500 HP of electricity to the planned mill. The power was generated at the Olmstead Generating Plant on the Provo River, and transmitted 32 miles – and at 40,000 volts. This was the first long-distance high-voltage project in the world.

The enormous Golden Gate Mill, built by Daniel C. Jackling for De La Mar, became operational in 1898. See figure 10. The process used included roasting and crushing the sulfide ore, and then recovering the gold by cyanidation. This mill – the largest in North America at the time, could treat 1000 TPD. In 1899 the MGMMC became the Consolidated Mercur Gold Mines Company after merging with the De La Mar group.

Figure 10   Golden Gate Mill
Mercur, Utah 1902

(portion of figure 43, page 117)
Utah State Historical Society

On June 26, 1902, Mercur burned to the ground. See figures 43 and 44 on page 117. The town was immediately rebuilt, but the ore grade was declining. By 1912 the tenor of the ore decreased to an extraction of only ⅛ ounce per ton, which proved unprofitable to work with the existing technologies. The enterprise closed shortly after, and by 1917, Mercur was a ghost, having produced an estimated 4,336,621 tons of ore, $16,500,000 in gold, of which $3,500,000 was paid in dividends. [28]

Philipsburg

Hector Horton discovered the Hope mine in 1864. In 1866, the St. Louis & Montana Mining Company acquired the Hope and Comanche lodes. In 1867, a $75,000 mill was financed to process these ores. The camp that grew up around the James Stuart mill, named after a partner in the enterprise, was named Philipsburg after mill superintendent Philip Deidsheimer of Comstock square-set timbering fame.[29] The Stuart mill has the distinction of being the first silver mill in Montana. This same year, the company reorganized as the Hope Mining Company, and the mill became known as the Hope mill.

This mill used the Washoe process, crushing with 10 stamps, and amalgamating in six one-ton Wheeler pans and three settlers. The mill was then converted to the Reese River process. Even switching to this process proved unsatisfactory, as it was not wholly effective. The cost of the salt – initially $120 per ton delivered from Salt Lake City, eroded profits. When the cost of salt hit $320 per ton in 1869, profits vanished and the mill was closed. The mill and mine were operated sporadically afterwards, with production surging in 1881 upon discovery of a large, high-grade ore body.

Other mines in the area – notably the Granite Mountain, Bimetallic, and Cable, helped transform Philipsburg into one of the premier silver producers in the country.[30] For the week ending January 9, 1889, the Granite Mountain produced 35 bars of bullion containing 56,207 ounces of silver and 36 ounces of gold. By April of that year, increased mill capacity led some to estimate a weekly production of 125,000 ounces of silver. While that estimate was a bit lofty, the Granite Mountain was still producing prodigious amounts of silver later that year – for the week ending November 7, 56 bars of bullion containing 88,563 ounces of silver and 177 ounces of gold were produced.[31]

At its peak, the district had five silver mills dropping 320 stamps that utilized the Reese River process, two mills dropping 15 stamps that used the Washoe process, and a 20-stamp mill that used a combination of the two processes. This mill – appropriately named the Combination, used twelve Frue vanners for concentrating only the sulfides for roasting. After roasting, all of the ore went to the pans. This substantially reduced the expense associated with the chlorodizing roast.

There were also 14 gold mills dropping 176 stamps, two using rolls, and two using *Huntington mills*. All used amalgamation, and early in the 20th century, some utilized cyanidation.[32]

The district declined after the massive silver deposits were worked out, the bonanza years being 1881-1893. Exact figures are unavailable, but estimates place the production of the mines and mills of the Philipsburg quadrangle at $50,000,000, of which about $20,000,000 came from the Granite Mountain mine alone.[33]

Butte

Butte, Montana deserves special mention and a brief sketch of it's mining history, when one considers that gold, silver, and copper were mined, the latter metal making an immeasurable contribution to the economy and prosperity of Montana and the nation. The Butte mines and mineral deposits are as fascinating as the history of the great city and its people. Although this is not a book about geology, visualizing the structure of the veins and ore bodies helps one better appreciate the dynamic and changing metals industries of the district.

The Butte gold, silver, and copper-bearing ore bodies may be viewed in a simplistic manner as buried domes or blunted cones, where the point of the cone has either been partially eroded away, or is at or near the surface of the present landscape. A horizontal cross section of this idealized ore body would reveal a series of concentric rings – *zones*, not unlike the layers of a sliced onion: the innermost – and by far the zone with the greatest volume, is predominantly copper minerals; the next zone outward has less copper and greater concentrations of zinc minerals; this is followed by a third zone[34] comprised of veins containing silver, zinc, and manganese in quartz, and is often *gossan* – decomposed, above the water table; and lastly an outer gold-bearing skin. All of the zones contain some silver and small amounts of gold.

Erosion and weathering assisted in the accumulation of the electrum as placer deposits, and created vertical zones of enriched and oxidized minerals concentrated on the level of the local water table.[35] Minerals are preferentially dissolved, carried downward, and redeposited in this zone of enrichment; thus silver- and copper-bearing ores often increase with depth as the water table is reached. Below the water table sulfides predominate.

The area of Montana destined to become Butte began with the discovery of placer gold in the summer of 1864. The placers had a value of only $11-$14 per ounce due to the significant amount of silver alloyed with the gold – fairly low by any standards. The town of Butte (City) was platted in 1866, and over the next three years about $1,500,000 was mined.

During this period of placer mining some effort was made towards mining and milling the oxidized gold ores found at very shallow depths. The milling generally relied on simple methods such as grinding in arrastras or crushing under stamps, followed by amalgamation. This proved to be somewhat ineffective due to the amount of silver present in the gold. When the placers were mostly worked out, Butte slumped, and was almost deserted by 1875.

Figure 10a (left half of panorama)   Butte Mines ca 1914   Courtesy Library of Congress

Early in this period of gold mining, numerous black manganese-stained outcrops of silver veins were noted, but were mostly ignored. Late in 1864, William L. Farlin located the Asteroid claim, which was later relocated as the famous Travona silver mine. It caused some excitement, but early silver milling attempts failed for a variety of reasons, both technical and financial, and very little silver was produced.

In 1875 Farlin erected the 10-stamp Dexter mill and furnace, utilizing a chlorodizing roast followed by amalgamation. This was a significant step forward, but even so, very little bullion was produced. Farlin's note was due, and unable to pay, agreed to have William Andrew Clark – from whom he borrowed the money, manage the properties. Clark invested more capital, tinkered with things, and fine-tuned the process by 1876. A practical method of silver recovery was made available, and at the tolerable rate of about $30 per ton. Mining and milling began to take off. Butte's placer-gold-mining epoch had faded away, supplanted by silver mining.

In 1875, the owners of the Acquisition claim sent silver ore to the Walker Brothers, Salt Lake City, for assaying. The Walkers were so impressed that they sent young Marcus Daly to Butte to investigate the district. Daly bought the Alice in 1876. In 1877, the Alice shaft was down 200 feet, and a 20-stamp mill was brought up from Ophir Canyon, Utah. By 1879 the dry-crushing mill was equipped with a White-Howell roaster; thus permitting sulfide ores to be processed using the Reese River process.

Figure 11   Parrot Operations
Butte, Montana ca 1906
Courtesy NARA

The district continued growing, and by 1887, five major mills were dropping a total of 290 stamps on 400 tons of ore per day, with an additional 100 tons of ore per day being shipped to smelters, yielding about $25 per ton in gold and silver.

Right from the start, the massive copper deposits that would make Butte world famous did not go unnoticed. Claims along the Parrot lode were filed in October of 1864. The Parrot claim, worked by William Parks, has the distinction of being the first copper mine in Butte, and also Butte's only copper mine having ore above the 200-foot level. The Parrot was also blessed with ore averaging 12% copper and 8 ounces of silver per ton above the water table at 800 feet.

Early attempts at smelting the copper ores failed. In 1872, Clark became interested in developing the copper veins in the district. The copper ore was hauled 400 miles by wagon to the railhead in Corinne, Utah, where it was then shipped to ore buyers. This was not profitable, but did help promote the district. For example, a high-grade shipment of ore to a buyer in Maryland, carrying 35% copper (worth $130) and about $50 per ton in gold and silver, netted *nothing* after deductions for mining, shipping, and smelting fees. What was needed was a local smelter that could process the copper ores at reasonable costs.

Figure 10b (right half of panorama)   Butte Mines ca 1914   Courtesy Library of Congress

One of Clark's buyers was the Boston & Colorado Smelting Company (B&CSC) in Black Hawk, Colorado. The B&CSC required high-grade copper ores for efficiently smelting the low-grade Gilpin County copper ore that contained appreciable gold [see also *The Welsh (Swansea) Copper Process* in the Appendix]. Clark, in 1878, suggested to Nathaniel P. Hill of the B&CSC that they consider building a smelter in Butte; Henry Williams was sent to evaluate the situation, and his reports were favorable. On June 1, 1879, the Colorado & Montana Smelting Company was formed, and by August of that year their 12 TPD smelter went into operation. Copper ores were smelted with manganese-silver ores being used as a flux; the *regulus* produced being shipped to the B&CSC for further refining.

In 1881, Daly, representing the new Anaconda Silver Mining Company, leased the Dexter mill to process silver ore from the Anaconda vein. Interestingly, the silver ore contained just the right amount of copper to make it unnecessary to add copper sulfate during milling. The ore carried about 30 ounces of silver per ton, but the bullion produced was very base, sometimes only running 400-fine silver. At 100 feet depth in the mine, a seam of chalcocite a few inches wide was discovered. At 300 feet, this vein was five feet wide – copper was found increasing with depth. In 1883, construction began on a new smelting works about 27 miles west of Butte, in what was to become one of the largest copper smelting complexes in the world – Anaconda. Butte's copper-mining period was well underway, one that would last another 100 years.

Figure 12   Colorado Smelting And
              Refining Company
              Butte, Montana ca 1906
              Courtesy NARA

The drastic 1893 decline in the price of silver crippled the silver-mining industry. Silver and gold were still important co-products of copper mining, though: each ton of copper produced contained about 75 ounces of silver and ¼ ounce of gold. As an aside, the Travona would become one of Butte's leading manganese producers in the second decade of the 20th century. Of the national manganese production, Butte produced 50% in 1919.

Very few production facts and figures are available from the gold mining and early silver mining epochs of Butte's history. Company production records, kept as closely guarded secrets, confound this. During a fourteen-year period (1884-1898), the Anaconda – the largest single producer in Butte, mined 9,575,793 tons of ore yielding 1,068,922,000 pounds of copper. This is equivalent to 5.5% copper, and 4.5 ounces of silver, and 0.017 ounces of gold per ton, most of which came from bonanza-grade ore bodies. Charts 5 and 6 illustrate the facts that have been compiled concerning Butte's historic production from 1882-1900.[36]

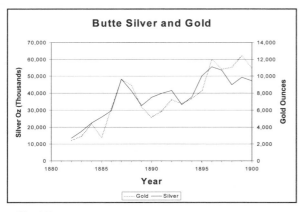

Chart 5

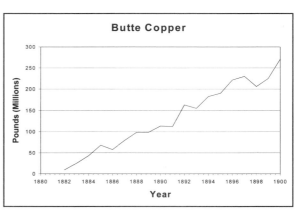

Chart 6

The Horn Silver

James Ryan and Samuel Hawkes discovered the Horn Silver Mine, in the San Francisco mining district near Frisco, Utah, on September 24, 1875. After sinking a 40-foot shaft, of which 30 feet was in ore, they felt that the ore might fail, and sold the claim for $25,000 on February 17, 1876. The new purchasers developed the mine, sold ore, and built a smelter. By early 1879 they sold most of their interests in the mine for $5,000,000.

The Horn Silver Mining Company was organized, and worked the property in addition to owning a smelter, refining works in Chicago, nearby iron mines for smelting flux, charcoal kilns, two stores in Frisco, a 40-mile telegraph line, and other mining properties.

The argentiferous lead ore was roasted prior to smelting, where one cord of wood ($2.50) was required for three tons of ore. A pile of cedar cordwood four feet high, thirty feet wide, and 140 feet long was laid down. Twenty inches of ore was spread on top of this, then another foot of wood, and lastly a final foot of ore. It was ignited and allowed to burn for two or three weeks. The roasting was incomplete, however: about one ton of matte was produced for every fifteen tons of bullion. The matte was roasted in heaps, crushed, and re-smelted.

In January 1879, 723 tons of ore – mined at a cost of $3.05 per ton, 329 tons of local iron ore (flux; 55-64% iron; $8 per ton), and 33,286 bushels of "an inferior quality of charcoal" (18 cents per bushel) were smelted, producing 202 tons of bullion that averaged 150 ounces of silver per ton. Dust chambers attached to the flues of the three furnaces caught from 1200-1500 pounds of flue dust daily. The cost per ton of ore was $18.31.

The Horn Silver Company found it more economical to build a smelter in Francklyn – six miles south of Salt Lake City, once the Utah Southern Railroad extended its line to Frisco in 1880. The decision to extend the line was spurred greatly by the fantastic developments of the Horn Silver mine. The new smelter began operations in June 1881, and by June 1882 smelting ceased in Frisco.

The new smelter's life would be short-lived, however; the famous caving-in of the Horn Silver on February 12, 1885 interrupted ore production, thus starving the smelter, which closed permanently in March 1885. A 20-stamp concentrating mill with 12 Frue vanners was built and put into operation early in 1894. In April of that year it burned to the ground. A larger plant was immediately built, with 30 stamps, 18 vanners, and a 200 TPD capacity, and operated into the 20th century.

From 1880 to 1884, the Horn Silver was a leading producer of silver and lead in Utah – see charts 7 and 8. Prominent in these figures are the effects of the 1885 cave-in on ore production. Through 1900, the Horn Silver produced, from 376,304 tons of ore, 12,801,728 ounces of silver, 277,998,000 pounds of lead, and 3,424,751 pounds of copper, with a value of $18,939,094, and from this $6,520,000 in dividends.[37]

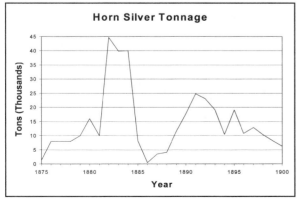

Chart 7

Chart 8

Are Stamp Mills Extinct?

Almost. The author is unaware of any commercially operating stamp mills in the U.S. There are a number of operating stamp mills at museums, parks, and tourist sites, however.

In the Pilbara Gold Fields near Marble Bar, Australia, there is at least one operational 10-stamp amalgamation mill. Garry and Monika Mullan operated their mines and this mill from 1990 until June 2001. It is hoped that this mill will continue to drop its stamps for years to come. The following facts and figures are provided courtesy of Mr. Mullan.[38]

The Western Australian Government built the original 5-stamp battery in 1910. See figure 13. It was privatized in 1987. During that period 70,897 ounces of gold was won from 115,234 tonnes[39] of ore crushed for the public.

The ore is mined using a jackleg drill, drilling holes 1.8 meters deep. ANFO is used to break the rock, and about 20-25 tonnes of muck are produced in 4-6 hours. Mucking is by a diesel-powered Eimco 911LHD mucking machine. The ore is trammed to the surface along an inclined adit that is about 9x9 feet, and inclined one foot in seven. The ore is then transported by truck to the mill, nearly 20 miles away.

The ore is dumped into an ore bin, and if oversized it is crushed by a jaw crusher before going to the automatic feeders. The ore is mostly quartz, and the schist that is present also contains gold, so it is crushed too. The schist is very soft and is readily crushed, so extra attention is required to ensure that the mortar is kept properly filled. The feed is sufficient for running one of the two 5-stamp batteries, crushing between 0.8 and 1.2 tonnes per hour, and powered by a 50 HP electric motor. The shoes and dies require replacing after about 1000 tonnes have been crushed.

The gold is saved using amalgamation both in the mortar box and on copper plates. Rubber riffle mats catch and save the heavier sands and amalgam that escapes the plates. The mats are emptied every two hours while the battery is running. Recovery is about 65%. The concentrate collected assays about ten ounces of gold per ton.[40] The concentrates are presently stored in drums, and the tailings are impounded behind a dam for possible future cyanidation.

The bullion produced varies according to the composition of the ore being mined. It typically assays 730 fine gold and 100 fine silver from the first ore body, and 840 gold and 100 silver from a second ore body a hundred feet from the first. A nearby lease has a 23,000 tonne ore reserve assaying 12 grams gold per tonne.[41]

Figure 13   Stamp Mill ca 1910
Courtesy Garry Mullan

Figure 14   Stamp Mill in 2000
Courtesy Garry Mullan

Figure 15   Jaw Crusher
Courtesy Garry Mullan

Figure 16   Riffle Mats

Figure 19   Crucibles

Figure 17   Stamp Batteries

Figure 20   Retorting Gold

Figure 18   Automatic Ore Feeder

Figure 21
Pouring Bullion

Figure 22
A Bullion Bar

All figures courtesy Garry Mullan

Occupational Hazards

"There is no trouble getting men to work in the mines on account of danger at present, where one gets killed 50 stand by to take his place." [42]

Homestake mine manager Harry M. Gregg, to a stockholder in November 1883

"Hard-rock stiffs drilled single or double jack, and they drilled a round and shot it before tally, on every shift. ... There were few air blowers, or suction fans, in use, and the stiffs worked in lung-choking, eye-smarting powder gas for an hour or two after their shift went on. There was little, and, sometimes, no, timbering – men were cheaper and expendable. There were scores of stiffs waiting for a job. ... If a stiff didn't like the job and it was 'deep enough,' or if he did not 'put in a shift,' he went down the hill, with his time, talking to himself, and some other stiff, in just as hard luck, took over the job." [43]

Frank Crampton, in *Deep Enough*

Working in a mine or a mill was a hazardous occupation, as will be seen. Statistical summaries are included after the sampling of events, facts, and figures that follow. The reader is cautioned that much of what follows is both startling and somewhat sobering.

Diseases & Sanitation

Miners working in very low illumination could suffer from *miner's eyes - nystagmus*. The eyes oscillate back and forth, and balance could be affected. The remedy is better illumination.[44] Nystagmus seems to have been more prevalent in coalmines than in metal mines, and in Europe as compared to the U.S. Perhaps the combination of poor illumination and the near zero reflectance of coal tended to exacerbate this effect in the coalmines.

De Quille described a station in one of the Comstock mines, mentioning "there is also a large cask containing ice water, with a tin dipper hanging on a nail near at hand."[45] This would be a quick way to get the latest flu bug or many other contagious diseases.

Hookworm (*Ancylostoma duodenale* or *Necator americanus*), also called *bunches, ground itch*, or *miners' anemia,* had its first attention-getting epidemic during the driving of the St. Gothard Tunnel through the Alps in 1879. Hookworm was found predominantly in the coalmines of Europe and the eastern U.S., but outbreaks were also reported in gold mines in California and Nevada.[46] In 1916, over 30% of 1440 gold miners in the Mother Lode region of California were infected by hookworm.[47]

Hookworms begin as eggs hatching in excrement, where the temperature and humidity are favorable. While conditions are favorable, they can live for up to a year. Within a week or two the larvae are fully developed, and can then penetrate skin anywhere, but usually between the toes or fingers, causing itching. The larvae are then passed to the lungs via the lymph or circulatory systems. There they penetrate the lung tissue and crawl up to the throat where they are swallowed, and once in the intestines bite into the tissue, sucking blood. It is there that they grow into a worm, reaching between ¼ to ½ inch in length. Once mature, they are ready to lay eggs. Thousands of these worms may be present in a severe infection.[48]

For this and many other reasons, sewage control is of prime importance in mines to help prevent sickness and disease.

Ver ist der *Krappen Hausen?* [49]

Author Stephen Voynick, in *Leadville: A Miner's Epic*, describes the contribution of a variety of pungent sources to the overall atmosphere in a mine:

> "The mules' abundant droppings enhanced the already distinctive fragrance of the mines. Mingled with the oil mist from drills, the fumes and smoke from giant powder, the rotting, mildewed timbers, and the human waste of the miners themselves which, in the 1880s, was deposited alongside that of the mules, it created an aromatic essence of noteworthy and lasting character."[50]

Figure 23   Latrine Car   Author

It is hard to believe that a miner, working in a confined area with poor ventilation, would not construct some form of makeshift latrine.

At least two contemporary and differing opinions existed during the heyday of the Comstock. Concerning the sensitivity of the miners' noses, De Quille states, "even a dead rat in any close or heated part of the mine annoys the men and is speedily scented out and sent above. So with everything else from which there can arise the slightest effluvium."[51] Lord states, "the stenches of decaying vegetable matter, hot foul water, and human excretions intensify the effects of the heat."[52]

Which was it? Both statements are true. Crampton makes no mention of the smell of human waste as he learned to hand drill in Cripple Creek in 1905. He said, "It was harder getting used to the smell of dead powder smoke and the reeking, water-soaked timber, but I did."[53]

It is difficult to imagine that the miners would tolerate more than they had to underground. A lengthy trip to the surface to use the privy was probably out of the question. Makeshift privies were no doubt constructed. Crampton mentions that *thundermugs* were made of empty powder boxes.[54] Sand-filled powder or candle boxes were often used. Peele mentions just such a "destructible latrine." [55] Lime could also be used for a covering. It had the virtue of being cheap and somewhat effective.[56]

The more sophisticated mines might use a *latrine car*, also called a *honey wagon*.[57] They were made either of converted ore cars, or built from scratch using ore-car trucks. See figure 23. Figure 24 shows the author *posing* for the sake of an amusing photograph. Figure 25 lends new meaning to a *mine dump*. And the lucky man that gets to collect the filled thundermugs? His title? Why, he's the *honey dipper*.

Figure 24 ▲   Author
Honey Wagon

Figure 25 ▼   Author
180° panorama of a mine dump track shed with an affixed *2-seater* privy

Drug Abuse

Drug abuse was a problem in the Old West, just as it is today. Some things never change. Many miners and mill-men probably went to work with a hangover from a night out drinking *Ho Joe* with the boys. The consumption of whisky and beer by miners in the boomtowns is legendary. A hangover, lack of sleep, and fatigue could easily conspire against the miner's attention and better judgment – one careless step descending a ladder could mean certain death hundreds of feet below.

Voynick is of the opinion that, "Alcohol and drugs, especially morphine and opium, were used in quantities that might make today's ideas of abuse seem mild."[58] This is probably true. *Laudanum* – opium usually packaged in a liquid form, was readily available from doctors and druggists. This potent narcotic was both intoxicating and highly addictive. Opium dens in many mining camps' Chinatown catered to numerous clients.

Bennett describes a situation where the changing of rotating shifts at the Amethyst mine was timed with a popular dance held in town, the consequence being fatigue and lack of sleep. He states,

"Some of the ore house force weren't in too good shape to get through the third day of work, but they had a little something to ward off fatigue and that something was a mixture of bourbon and absinthe."[59] The shift boss "was a strict teetotaler and the mine had a rule against drinking on the job, but they needed it and had it and got away with it so no harm ever came of it."[60]

Figure 26   19th Century Opium Pipes   Author

Exactly the reasoning management did not want in their operations, as it was probably responsible for numerous accidents.

Poisoning

There were many ways in which miners and millmen could be poisoned. For the miners, there were poisonous gasses in the mines, both natural and man-made (from explosives), toxic mineral dust, and contaminated water supplies. For the millmen, the very nature of their employment revolved around hazardous materials. This included chlorine, hydrogen sulfide, sulfur dioxide, and carbon monoxide gases; acids; cyanide; mercury, arsenic, lead, and their vapors; and other toxic dusts and gases. According to the 1880 census, *leading* – lead poisoning from inhaling lead carbonate dust in dry lead mines or lead fumes from metallurgical processes, accounted for 11% of the reported non-fatal accidents. The Census compilers note that this was certainly an understated figure.[61] Lead poisoning could lead to gastritis, Bright's disease, and cirrhosis of the liver.

♦   In 1867, two miners working at the New Almaden mine died from suffocation when they ventured into workings filled with carbon dioxide.[62]

"Big George" Sample, co-owner of the Jupiter claim southeast of Butte, Montana, nearly passed out in the sump of the 40 foot shaft in 1878. While climbing out – and probably still dizzy from the bad air, he lost his grip near the top and fell to his death.[63]

In 1878, James Doyle, a young Bodie miner, died of suffocation in the Bodie drift when he became curious as to the progress of the planned connection of the Bodie and Standard workings. Earlier, a massive Giant powder round was fired in the hopes of breaking through the workings, and had filled the workings with deadly fumes.[64] The detonation of a powder magazine and the spread of the toxic fumes killed 34 men on July 16, 1902, at the Daly-West and Ontario mines in Park City, Utah.[65]

♦ According to the 1880 Census, the Salt Lake area of Utah reported over 500 cases per year of leading. The treatment was usually large doses of magnesium chloride, which eliminated the lead as a soluble chloride.[66] In Park City, Utah, between 1872-1903, more than seven thousand miners sought medical attention for lead poisoning – on average over two hundred cases a year.[67]

The Horn Silver Mine, near Frisco, Utah, was a dry lead-silver mine, producing ore containing about 30% lead. This resulted in lead poisoning of the miners, and an attendant high turnover rate. According to the *Mining and Scientific Press*, many miners left work partially paralyzed from leading.[68]

In the winter of 1886-87 at the Terrible Mine near Ouray, Colorado, some of the miners showed symptoms of lead poisoning after drinking the water flowing from the mine. Superintendent David Reed ordered the men to melt snow for their cooking and drinking water.[69]

♦ Early smelters at Cerro Gordo, California – near Owens Lake, had no flues, and consequently large quantities of leaden flue dust settled all around the workings.[70] At least one Leadville smelter had inadequate flues and condensing chambers for the smelters. The works were "perpetually enveloped in a thick atmosphere of smoke and lead fumes, and 'leading' is of frequent occurrence."[71]

George Backus, working for the Tomboy near Telluride, Colorado, developed lead poisoning from supervising a lead-zinc concentrating mill, where the ore was roasted and sacked.[72]

In January 1889, the *Madisonian* reported, "The men of the Butte police force complain terribly of the effect which the smelter fog has upon them, producing severe hoarseness and sickness of the stomach."[73]

In 1912 – over 30 years after the published 1880 census figures, approximately *twenty-five percent* of workers in U.S. lead smelters suffered from lead poisoning.[74]

♦ Even animals were poisoned. On February 5, 1914, 1095 sheep were killed after drinking cyanide solution near the tailings pond of the Tonopah Mining Company's Desert Mill in Millers, Nevada.[75]

♦ On the Comstock, thieves were retorting stolen amalgam or high-graded silver ore in open pots, causing "a large number of children, and other persons" to be poisoned by mercury vapor.[76]

The practice of hot straining lead-silver amalgam – at temperatures near the boiling point of water - was used for a while, but was abandoned due to the "ruinous effect that it had upon the health of the men."[77]

The bursting of retorts, or their leaking from imperfect luting, caused a few cases of salivation. Cleanup of hot pans was also a cause.[78]

Regarding cinnabar reduction at the New Idria quicksilver mine in California, Brewer states:

"The work at the furnaces is much more unhealthy and commands the higher wages. Sulphurous acids, arsenic, vapors of mercury, etc., make a horrible atmosphere, which tells fearfully on the health of the workmen, but the wages always command men and there is no want of hands. The ore is roasted in furnaces and the vapors are condensed in great brick chambers, or 'condensers.' These have to be cleaned every year by workmen going into them, and many have their health ruined forever by the three or four days' labor, and all are injured; but the wages, twenty dollars a day, always brings victims."[79]

Silicosis

The advent of the noisy, buzzing machine drills – the ones that produced huge clouds of rock dust, had a very serious side effect. Miners had a variety of names for the condition that quickly developed from inhaling the dust: *rock in the box*, *rocked up*, *dusted*, and the *jack-hammer laugh*.[80]

Inhaling microscopic particles of silica dust for many years causes *silicosis*. This would lead first to nodular lesions in the lungs, and then to fibrotic scarring of the lungs – silicosis, an irreversible disorder. Slight shortness of breath marked the first stage. This was followed by the second stage – moderate shortness of breath, frequent episodes of coughing, and impaired performance. Body wracking coughing fits, near-total disability, and being bed-ridden marked the third and final stage. This generally led quickly to death. Many miners clung to their occupation even in the final stages.

Miners with silicosis had a predisposition for pneumonia and tuberculosis. A survey of silicotic miners in Joplin, Missouri revealed that 8 of 128 miners in the first stage had tuberculosis, whereas those in the third stage numbered 73 of 141. The mean age at death for silicotic Joplin miners was less than 37 years.[81]

Other data indicate that hardrock miners with silicosis died in their late forties, shortening their expected lifespan by perhaps fifteen years. Altogether, silicosis was in all probability a greater hazard than all other safety hazards combined. Alan Derickson, author of *Workers' Health Workers' Democracy*, feels it is not unreasonable to conclude that perhaps as many as twenty percent of North American metal miners suffered from silicosis. See table 2.[82]

Between 1880 and 1902, the number of rock drills used for precious metal mining in the U.S. increased from less than a few hundred to more than three thousand – a ten-fold increase. Rock dust in mines using rock drills could be so dense that "it was impossible to see the strong light of a carbide lamp fifty feet away." Butte miners referred to the stoper as "Larry Dugan's friend." Larry Dugan was an undertaker.[83] Although Leyner-style machine drills – ones that use water to suppress dust, were available from about the turn of the century, many mine owners and managers did not immediately adopt them. It was very expensive to buy all new drills when those being used worked fine. The miners paid with their health, and with their lives.

Silicosis was not limited to mines. Taggart described the dust in an 1870's vintage dry-crushing mill: "... the murk grows in intensity as one moves up through the mill until finally is entered a region of perpetual gloom." It was "made dangerous by unseen belts, pulleys, steps, and other pitfalls" by poor lighting and dust.[84]

Dry crushing found extensive use throughout the west, especially when preliminary chlorodizing-roasting was required before pan treatment (Reese River process), as in Georgetown, Caribou, and Silver Cliff, Colorado. It was also used in White Pine and Delamar, Nevada.[85] See figure 27. Mr. Parsons, Tonopah Mining Company's mill superintendent, died in 1915 as a result of inhaling silica dust while working at a dry-crushing mill in Delamar.[86] Dr. William Betts reported that the dry-crushing gold mills of Delamar produced so much dust that "one can not be recognized a few feet away." Employees at the mill referred to the conveyer room as "the death trap." Dr. Betts found that the mean duration at the mill for thirty deceased employees was just fourteen months, surviving on average only *eight months* after leaving the mill. The mean age at death was but thirty years.[87]

Figure 27   Delamar, Nevada ca 1900
Courtesy Lincoln County Historical Museum
Pioche, Nevada

Miner Joe Duffy, of Butte, Montana, apparently recognized his condition before it was too late:[88]

Study	Location	Miners		
		Examined	Silicosis	Percentage
BOM-PHS	Joplin, MS	720	433	60
Lanza	Butte, MT	1018	432	42
BOM	Tonopah, NV	303	244	81
US Gov	California	181	45	25
US Gov	Oatman, AZ	112	33	29

Table 2   Silicosis Occurrence in Miners

Explosions & Explosives

In the ten-year period 1893-1902, there were approximately 728 deaths in Colorado metal mines. The leading cause, accounting for 192 deaths, or 26% of the total, was explosions.[89]

♦ An explosion killed Frank Crampton's mentor and best friend, Michael "Sully" Sullivan. The metal miner's cleaning spoon that he used to tamp the charge touched it off and was driven through his chest.[90] John Coley, a miner in Empire, Colorado, was luckier than Michael Sullivan. He was blinded when he used an iron bar to tamp black powder in a drill hole, and a spark touched off the powder.[91]

In 1891, miners Jerry Downey at the Bimetallic mine, and Samuel Lavin at the Granite mine in Philipsburg, Montana, were killed by blasts. In 1892, explosions killed H. B. Smith at the Bimetallic, and Hank Shifler and Thomas Rogers were killed at the Granite. 1893 saw John C. Darby lose his life from a blast at the Granite.[92]

♦ In 1874 at the Sutro Tunnel, John Delaney, shift foreman, and Samuel Richards, "boss blaster" of the shift, [93] were killed when a spark from the blasting battery ignited giant powder that was allowed to collect near it. Four others were injured by the blast.[94]

One Comstock miner was seriously injured by rock from a blast at the bottom of a shaft being worked on. After the fuses had been lift, the bell cord was pulled once, signaling to the engineer 1700 feet above to begin hoisting the cage. The miners were not hoisted because the bell cord was stuck on a timber. They quickly scrambled to pull out the burning fuses, and managed to get all but two. Panic ensued, and three of the four managed to escape injury. The injured miner made a full recovery after having the rocks – and part of his skull, removed by a surgeon.[95]

Reverend Gibbons was called to an accident at the Revenue Tunnel near Ouray, Colorado. "It appeared that three men, Robinson, Maloney, and Big Paddy Burns were loading holes, before retiring from their shift, when an explosion occurred. The two former were over the holes and Paddy had just put down a box of dynamite at the breast of the tunnel, when without a moment's warnings, the dynamite went off" blowing Robinson apart. A rock projectile penetrating the skull killed Maloney. "Big Paddy Burns, who was standing at Maloney's side, was knocked down, receiving a rock canister in the side of the head." Burns survived, spending six months in a hospital "during which time a splinter now and then worked its way out of the skull to the great amusement of the boys and the dismay of Paddy."[96]

♦ Unexploded charges might be left in the face or in the muck pile. Picking into a missed hole at the Silver King mine in Park City, miner Alonzo Mason was "instantly blown to eternity." Miner Eric Cook drilled into an unexploded charge and was killed by the blast.[97]

White Pine miner John Murphy attempted to drill out an unexploded charge that had been soaked with water. It exploded and severely lacerated his hands and face.[98]

- On July 8, 1879, the Giant Powder Company's magazine in Bodie – containing two tons of Giant powder and black powder, detonated. The cause of the explosion was never determined, but the effects were pronounced: At least six people were killed in the blast, and a couple of dozen others suffered injuries ranging from cuts and bruises to broken bones to the loss of an eye. $50,000 worth of damage was caused to nearby mine headframes and surface structures, boarding houses, and residences.[99]

- In February 1891, miner Billy Mahar practiced a very dangerous custom of the times: he put four sticks of frozen giant powder into his oven to thaw. When he went to remove them, the dynamite exploded, seriously injuring him. His partner was not injured by the blast, and immediately sought help. It took him seven hours to travel one mile through the snow and reach the Terrible mine. Four men from the mine immediately left to aid Billy. A relief party from the nearby Virginius mine was requested. When they arrived, they fabricated a makeshift sled, and left to take Billy back to the Terrible. When they arrived at the mine, the relief party from the Virginius mine hadn't arrived, so the men left to take Billy to Porter's, the nearest town, where a doctor took him to Ouray for medical attention. The relief party never made it – all four were later found dead, killed by an avalanche.[100]

Falls

Of the 728 deaths in Colorado metal mines, 176 deaths, or 24%, were caused by falls down shafts and related accidents.[101] De Quille attributed many accidents to "old timers" rather than to "greenhorns," especially when it came to following ore cars down into shafts:

"The old miner sometimes forgets where he is, while 'where he is' is just what the greenhorn is all the time thinking about… a man who has worked in the mines for years will walk into a winze or chute in a musing mood, or run a car into the main shaft and be pulled in after it, which is a thing a green hand has never been known to do." [102]

In Aspen during the late 1880's and early 1890's there were occasional reports of luckless – or careless, miners following an ore car into a shaft.[103]

- A worker at the Eureka Mill fell from a platform and died from skull injuries.[104]

  During the dredging of the Swan River in Colorado, one man leaned too far on the bow, fell and struck a bucket, and drowned; another man fell from the gangplank as he headed to shore and was ground up by the bucket-line.[105]

  In 1908, carpenter Lester Coffey fell from a Sunnyside mine aerial tram tower and died.[106]

- In April 1878, Rudolph Kleeman, superintendent of the Sunrise mine, fell from a bucket as it was being hoisted to the surface. He struck the other bucket as he fell – the two buckets worked in opposite directions, and were powered by a horse whim. Miner Reese Davis rescued Kleeman from the sump and pulled the injured man into a drift, but he died twenty minutes later from a fractured skull and internal injuries.[107]

  On April 12, 1889, Hugh O'Donnell, a miner employed by the San Francisco Mining Company of Philipsburg, Montana, fell from the collar of the shaft 200 feet to his death.[108]

  Missing his step while boarding a hoisting bucket at the Iowa-Tiger mine near Silverton, miner Stephano Rossi fell 150 feet to his death.[109]

- In March of 1879, miner Thomas Holton, ascending the Homestake No. 2 shaft by windlass, apparently became dizzy as he approached the collar, lost his grip, and fell to the bottom of the 50-foot deep shaft and was impaled on a drill steel. He died a few hours later. Due to this accident – and others, George Hearst and Sam McMaster worked to establish one of the first industrial health services of the day. A rudimentary hospital was established, and a monthly deduction of $1.10 was taken from the employee's pay to pay the physicians.[110] Many miners lost their lives falling into the shaft from the cage due to faintness aggravated by drastic changes in temperature. Their remains were brought to the surface in candle boxes.[111]

Austin, Nevada recognized that open and abandoned shafts should be filled or covered so as to avoid possible fatalities.[112]

- Thomas Ross was riding one horse, and leading another, around the Cleopatra shafts on Bellevue Mountain. The rear horse broke loose, and the scared lead horse and rider fell into the shaft. The rider managed to grab the collar of the shaft and pull himself out. The horse, however, fell 40 feet to the shaft bottom, which was filled with water. It didn't drown because the harness caught on a timber. After being hoisted out, the horse appeared all right, but remained in a sitting position for 6 hours.[113]

In 1889, the *Anaconda Review* told of a mule that fell down a 50-foot shaft and remained at the bottom for a week. After being rescued, it was said that he was "feeling none the worse for his experience," and that "he rather enjoyed the rest which it gave him."[114]

Cave-ins, Rock Falls, Falling Objects, and Hoisting

During the ten years 1893-1902, of the approximately 728 deaths in Colorado metal mines, 166 deaths, or nearly 23%, were caused by rock falls.[115]

It wasn't until 1915 that Bullard began work on a *skull bucket* – a helmet, which could protect miners. A patent for this "hard-boiled hat" was granted in 1919. The original hat was made of steamed canvas, glue, and black paint, and was based on the "doughboy" design used in World War I helmets. Prior to this, the miners wore a felt derby, with a brim of leather reinforced by shellac. Later model hard hats, like the Mine Safety hard hat in figure 28, used phenolic resins to impregnate the fabric.[116]

Figure 28   Author
Mine Safety
"Hard Boiled" Hardhat

While shaft sinking, a timber *pentice* was sometimes erected to protect the miners from falling objects. It consisted of a stout timber platform with a trapdoor, and outfitted with a small air-powered hoist. Another method of protection would be to leave a massive rock pentice (horizontal pillar) in the shaft for protection, which would be removed when the shaft was nearly ready for use.[117]

- In 1891, miner Fred Clark was killed by a rock fall at the Bimetallic mine in the Philipsburg, Montana mining district, and in 1892, W. F. Cover and W. F. Roberts were killed by falling ground in separate incidents at the Granite mine.[118]

- On November 11, 1905, a cave in on a tunnel between Camp Florence and the Ontario shaft in Park City, Utah was finally removed. The water that had been backed up was suddenly released, drowning miner Andrew Nystrom.[119]

- Crampton was stranded in a mine behind a caved-in section of the only access adit for ten days with a group of miners. In his rather chilling narrative he describes the cold, wet conditions as being "cold-boiled."[120]

- In July 1884, at the New Almaden mine, three timbermen were killed when a 100-ton rock fell from the hanging wall that they were bracing.[121] The vibration from rock drills might precipitate rock falls or cave-ins.[122]

- Miner Al Marten, a hydraulic monitor operator at the Malakoff Diggins, was killed by debris propelled by the blast of air generated when the bank he was working on collapsed. The force was so great that it knocked him several feet away from his rubber boots.[123]

- A falling board struck Andrew Haggerdy, working in the sump of the Champion mine in Bodie. The force of the impact was so great that pieces of the collarbone perforated his lungs. He died twenty minutes later.[124]

In 1864 two miners coming off shift were riding the bucket up to the surface. A dog – trying to cross on the partition of the two shafts, fell, killing one miner instantly, and causing the other miner to fall from the bucket to his death.[125]

On August 24, 1894, a fire broke out at the Amethyst mine in Creede. The fire burned through the oil-soaked hoist rope, and the cage, not having any safeties, fell to the sump and killed four of the five men working there.[126] Miner Shelley Dunlap died in August 1897 at Gold Creek, Nevada. His partner, Ed Waters, was lowering a bucket filled with tools, when the rope broke and the bucket hit Dunlap, killing him.[127]

On June 18, 1880, eight men boarded a skip at the 2800-level and awaited being hoisted to the surface of the New Yellow Jacket shaft. A car loaded with drill steels was being hoisted in the adjacent compartment when it was caught by some obstruction, tipped, and spilled its contents. The steels fell and struck the miners below, killing five instantly and injuring the others.[128]

- Josiah Cubbon, a miner working at the Terrible Mine in 1888, was killed while attempting to board a moving cage.[129]

In September of 1880, nine men were killed in the Imperial shaft. The cable hoisting the cage that they were in broke. The safety clutches built into the cage functioned as designed, but the weight of the falling cable piling up on the cage was too great, and the cable, cage, and men went to the bottom.[130]

Overwinding caused the loss of fifteen lives at the Independence mine in Victor, Colorado in 1904.[131]

Mine and Mill Machinery

- In 1910, Arthur Jenkins was killed when a compressed air pipe broke from a sudden burst of pressure and struck him in the head.[132]

Mill employee Mike Vranes, while feeding a crusher, lost his balance and was killed by falling into a flywheel at the Kittimac mill near Eureka, Colorado.[133]

In November 1889, W. S. Henning, an employee at a mill in Anaconda, Montana, was killed when he got caught up in the power distributing shafting as he was oiling it.[134]

In July 1896 at the Revenue Mining Company works, miner Alexander Olivetti was verbally warned not to touch any electric wires. Placards in English, Italian, and Swedish were also posted. Despite this, he reached around a protective barrier on a ventilation fan to "see what it felt like" and was electrocuted.[135]

In 1919 Mr. Kirchen lost his left foot in an accident at the White Cap mill in Manhattan, Nevada.[136]

George Backus, a manager at a mill in Leadville, did what he told his mill workers not to do: he failed to shut off the power to a roll crusher before attempting to break free a rock that had become wedged in it. The iron bar he used was pulled between the rollers and hit his jaw, breaking it.[137]

Frank Crampton had the cuff of his overalls catch on a shaft collar set-screw at a vanadium mill, and would have been torn to pieces had the other millmen not thrown the belt from the drive pulley.[138]

It was reported that explosive gases formed in pans used on the Comstock. One millman "standing on the pan-cover of a pan in the California mill brought his candle near the charging-hole to see if the muller was moving, as he had just put on the tightener; the gas becoming ignited, he was blown, together with the cover, into a settler."[139]

Nature

♦ Some miners succumbed to the hellish conditions found deep in the stopes and drifts of the Comstock. "So when Thomas Wilson," who worked at the Imperial mine "turned a deaf ear to his companions on the 2000-foot level of the same rock furnace, who urged him to go to the cooling station, no one was surprised to see him drop his pick and fall dead at his post, March 2, 1877."[140] About 12% of the accidents reported for the Comstock were heat-related.[141]

Men were not the only ones that succumbed to the heat. In 1878 the temperatures were so high near the working face of the Sutro Tunnel that one mule driver saw his mule drop dead from heat. If a mule was brought out alive, a horse doctor was called to stay with the animal and try to save him. The workmen feared that a mule collapsing from the heat might crush them. One or two mules were dying each day from the heat.[142]

♦ On December 21, 1883, an avalanche killed four men at the Virginius Mine boarding house, located at an elevation of 12,500 feet. A second avalanche then hit the rescuers, killing four more and injuring a dozen men.[143]

In 1902 the snow slides – and there were three: one at 7:30 AM, the second at about 1 PM, and the last at about 4 PM, at the Liberty Bell Mine near Pandora, Colorado, took 16 lives and injured 12 others. It also destroyed the boarding house, part of a bunkhouse, the crusher house, the tram house, and ore bins.[144]

Avalanches and snow slides were of frequent occurrence in Park City, Utah. Four teamsters hauling ore for the Crescent mine were killed on January 30, 1886. Rescuers working to recover the survivors were themselves fortunate to escape injury from three more slides that buried the mine buildings. On January 7, 1888, a slide destroyed the Anchor mine's bunkhouse and half of the boarding house. Another slide that same day damaged the Daly mine's engine room. A slide in 1897 demolished the boiler room of the Silver King mine. A few days later, four men were killed when the Daly mine's boarding house was destroyed by a slide. Four more died a few days later from a slide at the Quincy mine.[145]

♦ Lightning struck the rail of the mine track, killing three men working deep underground at the Liberty Bell mine.[146]

Accident Statistics

Many non-fatal accidents were probably not reported by the miners. The scope of the 1880 census survey is necessarily incomplete. It included 19,147 miners employed in 693 mines. A summary of that information is provided in table 3. For the overall ratio of fatal accidents per man employed in the west, Utah had the highest rate of 1 in 73. For non-fatal accidents, both Utah and Wyoming had a rate of 1 in 18.[147] During the years 1891-1892, Aspen miners died at the rate of about one a month. This translated to a 1 in 200 chance of dying each year – slightly better odds than the average of one in 156 for the census.[148] Between 1894 and 1908, U.S. metal miners annually faced a 1 in 323 chance of being killed by their occupation. In 1910, a hardrock worker was ten times more likely to be killed on the job than his manufacturing counterpart.[149] A listing of metal mine disasters, those killing five or more miners, is listed in table 4.[150]

	Total	Fatal	Non-fatal	Total	Fatal	Non-fatal
Total Number of Accidents Reported	435	123	312			
Ratio of Accidents to No. Employed				44	156	61
Cause	Percentage of Accidents Reported			Chance of Having Accident: *One in…*		
Caving, Fall of roof, etc	31.0	20.3	35.3	142	766	174
Premature explosion	12.6	13.0	12.5	348	1197	491
Falls, unconnected with hoisting	12.2	22.0	8.3	361	709	736
Leading	8.1		11.2	547	19147	548
Falling of cages, buckets, etc	5.5	8.9	4.2	798	1741	1473
Overwinding of cages, buckets, etc	4.4	1.6	5.5	1008	9574	1126
Struck by falling timbers, buckets, etc	3.7	3.3	3.9	1197	4787	1596
Crushed by cages, cars, etc	3.0	5.7	1.9	1473	2735	3191
Falling from cages, buckets, etc	2.8	5.7	1.6	1596	2735	3829
Caught by machinery	2.5		3.5	1741	19147	1741
Fire	2.1	7.3		2127	2127	19147
Carelessness in handling tools	1.8		2.6	2393	19147	2393
Unexploded charges	1.4	1.6	1.2	3191	9574	4787
Suffocation not caused by fire	0.9	3.3		4787	4787	19147
Unclassified	8.1	7.3	8.3	547	2127	736

Table 3   1880 Census Mine Accident Summary

Mine	Location	Year	Deaths	Comment
Kentuck - Yellow Jacket - Crown Point	Gold Hill, NV	1869	37	Fire in timbers
Yellow Jacket	Gold Hill, NV	1873	6	Fire from blacksmith forge, 1300-level
Amador	Amador, CA	1874	5	Cage fell 1640 feet
Tioga	Bodie, CA	1879	6	Cage accident
Bull-Domingo	Silver Cliff, CO	1885	10	Surface fire, men in lower levels killed
Gould & Curry	Virginia City, NV	1887	11	Fire at 1500-level
Old Abe	White Oaks, NM	1895	8	Shaft destroyed by surface fire
Sleepy Hollow - Americus	Central City, CO	1895	14	Flooded
Belgian	Leadville, CO	1895	6	Explosion
Anna Lee	Cripple Creek, CO	1896	8	Cave-in
Virginius	Sneffels, CO	1896	5	Cage fell 1100 feet

Table 4   19th Century Non-Coal Mine Disasters

The Worst Mining Hazard Of All?

In 1915 at Rico, Colorado, miners Lee and Stanley decided to play a joke on fellow miners Nixon and Custuss. They came across their boots while taking a shortcut through the mine one Sunday. The boots were left in their working area, which was very hot and humid.

They decided to leave Limburger cheese in them for their discovery on Monday morning.[151]

Drills And Mills

Endnotes

1 TAGGART1947 page 117
2 BANCROFT1890 page 111
3 MONTANADEQ.36
4 BANCROFT1890 pages 398, 485. Milling in the Gregory district, around 1863, lost up to 75% of the gold. HENDERSON1926 page 9
5 JACKSONW1963 pages 123,175
6 RAYMOND1873 pages 204,205
7 BANCROFT1890 page 587
8 FIELDER1970 pages 25-26, 31, 60, 63, 109, 157, 180, 183
9 IRVING1904 page 62
10 ALLIS1902 pages 66-69
11 TAGGART1947 page 203
12 EISSLER1889 page 104
13 FATOUT1969 pages 77-78, 88
14 EMMONS1885 page 279
15 EMMONS1885 page 279
16 FETCHENHIER1999 page 35
17 CHESTERMAN1986 page 32
18 WEDERTZ1996 pages 181, 183.
19 CHESTERMAN1986 page 33
20 THOMPSON1968 page 26
21 BOUTWELL1912 page 28
22 BOUTWELL1912 page 139
23 DEQUILLE1959 page 433, SMITHG1998 page 159
24 JACKSONW1963 pages 50, 182
25 FATOUT1969 page 99
26 WOLLE1977 pages 306-307
27 WEED1901 pages 411-412, 414-416, 418. MONTANADEQ.79. The author is unsure why both sulfuric acid and lime were introduced into the pan with the ore and salt.
28 BUTLER1920 page 383, ALDER1961 pages 34-37, 41, LENZI1973 page 2,5, BARRICK1997, BUTLER1920 page 384, ROTHWELL1896 page 247.
29 The name *Philipsburg* was chosen because *Deidesheimersburg* was a tongue twister. ☺
30 MONTANADEQ.65, EMMONSW1913 pages 191-192, 213, NEU1996 page 4. MONTANADEQ.85 gives $100,000 for the cost of the Stuart (Hope) mill. NEU1996 spells the name as Di*e*desheimer. The manganese dioxide ores of the Philipsburg area were notably pure, and provided a significant amount of battery-grade ore during the First World War. NEU1996 page 16.
31 TAYLOR01989 pages 16, 83, 147
32 EMMONSW1913 pages 194, 197-198
33 EMMONSW1913 pages 192-193, 202
34 the "Peripheral zone"
35 Typically 60-100m in Butte.
36 WEED1912 pages 18-20, 23, MONTANADEQ.183.
37 BUTLER1913 pages 110-112, 114, 164-166. Charts: 1880, page 112; 1875-1900, page 164, where 1875-1878 is prorated from a single figure, ditto 1879-1881 less that of 1880; dividends page 165.
38 MULLAN2000. Also personal communication of 6/14/2001.
39 A tonne is 1000 kilograms, or about 2205 pounds.
40 300 grams per tonne.
41 About 0.38 ounces gold per ton.
42 FIELDER1970 page 124
43 CRAMPTON1956 page xiv
44 PEELE1966 pages 23-21,22
45 DEQUILLE1959 page 231
46 SAYERS1924 page 6
47 DERICKSON1988 page 54
48 SAYERS1924 page 6, PEELE1966 page 23-21
49 Pardon my poor *German*, but I think you get the message. Thanks, Ardea ☺
50 VOYNICK1984 page 47
51 DEQUILLE1959 page 144
52 LORD1883 page 389
53 CRAMPTON1956 page 22
54 CRAMPTON1956 page 88
55 PEELE1966 page 23-22
56 SAYERS1924 page 7
57 SAYERS1924 page 8, BIRD1986 figure 143
58 VOYNICK1984 page 65
59 Absinthe is a beverage derived from the wormwood plant. It is very intoxicating in moderate doses, and has hallucinogenic properties. It quickly lead to stupor, and as Encyclopedia Britannica put it, "idiocy." According to Webster's, "Its continued use causes nervous derangement."
60 BENNETT1966 page 159
61 EMMONS1885 page 175, SAYERS1924 page 10
62 SCHNEIDER1992 pages 46, 108. In 1893, two entrepreneurs, Pfeffer and Meyer, made a deal with the New Almaden to bottle the carbonic acid gas (carbon dioxide) present in the Santa Isabel shaft, which had previously been dammed on the 1400-level because of the poisonous gas. This was the start of the dry ice industry in the U.S.
63 MONTANADEQ.82
64 WEDERTZ1996 pages 196-197
65 DERICKSON1988 page 32
66 EMMONS1885 page 438
67 DERICKSON1988 page 53
68 BAILEY2002 page 136
69 GREGORYD1996 page 47
70 BAILEY2002 page 34
71 EMMONS1886 page 673
72 BACKUS1969 page 102
73 TAYLOR01989 page 6. *Madisonian*, Virginia City, Montana
74 DERICKSON1988 page 54
75 METSCHER1989 page 27
76 TAYLORJ1964 page 215
77 EMMONS1885 page 266
78 EMMONS1885 page 268
79 FARQUHAR1966
80 FETCHENHIER1999 page 23, VOYNICK1984 page 77, DERICKSON1988 page 44
81 The average age of miners buried in the Silverton cemetery at the turn of the century is 41. FETCHENHIER1999 page 32.
82 DERICKSON1988 pages 39,45,46,48,50,51,52
83 DERICKSON1988 pages 40,42,44
84 TAGGART1947 page 118
85 MANRY1999 page 43,47, JACKSONW1963 page 122, CARPENTER1953 page 59. Delamar is named after Captain Joseph Rafael Delamar.
86 CARPENTER1953 page 59
87 DERICKSON1988 pages 42,45,49
88 DERICKSON1988 page 47
89 DERICKSON1988 page 38
90 CRAMPTON1956 page 216
91 WOLLE1977 pages 38-39
92 MONTANADEQ.65
93 He had experience working on the Hoosac Tunnel.
94 STEWART1962 page 129
95 DEQUILLE1959 page 147
96 GIBBONS1987 page 46
97 DERICKSON1988 page 30
98 JACKSONW1963 page 63
99 WEDERTZ1996 pages 192-195
100 BENHAM1980 pages 38,40
101 DERICKSON1988 page 38
102 DEQUILLE1959 pages 145-151
103 ROHRBOUGH1986 page 197
104 BIRD1986 page 97
105 TURNBULL1962 page 253
106 BIRD1986 page 105
107 DUNCAN1990 pages 53-54
108 TAYLOR01989 page 81
109 DERICKSON1988 page 29
110 FIELDER1970 pages 75-77
111 DEQUILLE1959 pages 145-151
112 TAYLORJ1964 page 237
113 ARGO2000 page 3. This is reprinted from *The Idaho Springs Mining Gazette*, Jan 25, 1912.
114 TAYLOR01989 page 83
115 DERICKSON1988 page 38
116 BULLARD2001, HOPPE2001, YOUNGO1972 page 178
117 PEELE1966 page 7-05
118 MONTANADEQ.65
119 THOMPSON1968 page 134
120 CRAMPTON1956 page 91
121 SCHNEIDER1992 page 76
122 DERICKSON1988 page 30
123 MALAKOFF1993
124 WEDERTZ1996 page 190
125 TAYLORJ1964 page 325. It was possibly in Austin, Nevada.
126 BENNETT1966 page 24
127 HALL1998 page 102
128 SMITHG1998 page 244
129 GREGORYD1996 page 55
130 SMITHG1998 page 244
131 DERICKSON1988 page 34
132 BIRD1986 page 108
133 DERICKSON1988 page 35
134 TAYLOR01989 page 131
135 BENHAM1980 pages 52-53
136 CARPENTER1953 page 142
137 BACKUS1969 pages 247-2488
138 CRAMPTON1956 page 203
139 EMMONS1885 pages 264-265
140 LORD1883 page 398
141 EMMONS1885 page 177
142 STEWART1962 pages 147,148
143 GREGORYD1996 page 43, BENHAM1980 pages 25-29
144 WOLLE1977 pages 306-307
145 THOMPSON1968 pages 72-75
146 BACKUS1969 page 112
147 EMMONS1885 page 175, 177
148 ROHRBOUGH1986 page 197
149 DERICKSON1988 page 37
150 DOL1998 pages 23,24
151 HART1968 page 75

APPENDICES

The Welsh (Swansea) Copper Process

Swansea, Wales was one of the premier metallurgical centers in the world during the 19th century, especially with regards to copper. High-grade ore and concentrates – particularly those carrying copper, were sometimes shipped from the U.S. to Swansea for processing, and very often returned a profit despite a transcontinental and ocean journey. The following is a very simplified outline of the *Welsh (Swansea) Copper Process*.

1) The copper sulfide ore – about three tons of a grade containing 8-10% copper, is roasted in a reverberatory furnace for about twelve hours. The furnace is designed with doors that permit rabbling of the ore, and also for admitting relatively cold air into the furnace. The air sinks beneath the flame generated by the combustion of the coal in the firebox. This provides an oxygen-rich and insulating layer above the ore and prevents the ore from melting. The roasting drives off much of the arsenic and sulfur, and part of the remaining sulfur is converted to sulfate. Most of the iron pyrite present is converted to iron oxide.

2) The roasted ore is then treated in a reverberatory furnace, but at temperatures that promote fusion. Copper carbonate and copper ores carrying silica may also be added at this time. In addition, *metal slag* created from step 4 (below) is added to the furnace. At the temperature used in this step, small amounts of copper oxide created in the first step – and introduced as part of the metal slag from step 4, plus iron sulfide still remaining from the first step, convert to copper sulfide and iron oxide, the latter being carried away in the slag.

   After about three hours a complete fusion is reached, which is accompanied by the violent expulsion of sulfurous gases. The temperature of the furnace is then increased. A half hour later, a tap hole connected to a cavity in the hearth is opened, allowing the molten matte to flow into an iron gutter. It then pours into a cistern full of water whereby granulations of *coarse metal* are formed. The coarse metal contains about ⅓ copper. The slag is run off into sand molds; these glassy ferrous silicate bricks, containing up to about 2% copper (an unavoidable loss for this process), are used for building purposes.

3) Three tons of granulated coarse metal are roasted in a third furnace for 24 hours. Additional sulfur is removed. The result of this roasting is the conversion of much of the iron sulfide to iron oxide.

4) This step is very similar to step 2 (above) except that it is conducted in a smaller furnace. The charge consists of about a ton of roasted coarse metal, and 1200 pounds of a mixture including *roaster slag* (from step 5, below), *refinery slag* (from step 6, below), and ore containing copper oxide or carbonate. The fusion proceeds for about six hours, at which time the matte, called *fine metal*, is tapped and cast into molds. The shape of the casting has a very characteristic shape, and is called a *pig*.

   The fine metal may have anywhere from 60-80% copper, depending on the nature of the ores and slag used thus far. If the fine metal is from 60-70% copper, it is called *blue metal*; 75-78%, *white metal*; above 78%, *pimple metal* (due to the characteristic appearance of the surface caused by escaping sulfurous gases). The *metal-slag* created in this step is recycled back to step 2 (above).

5) About 1.5 tons of the fine metal pigs are introduced into a reverberatory furnace, and subjected to moderate heat for about four hours. The purpose is to convert some of the copper sulfide to copper oxide from the introduction of air during the roasting phase, and to remove additional sulfur. The furnace doors (that admit air) are then closed, and the temperature increased. The mass fuses, and in the absence of excess air (oxygen), and at the elevated temperature, the sulfur of the copper sulfide reacts with the oxygen of the copper oxide, forming metallic copper and sulfur dioxide gas. The molten copper sinks to the bottom of the hearth, and is tapped and cast into pigs. When solidified, this is called *blister copper* due to the appearance of the pigs, which are semi-porous.
   A small amount of *roaster slag* is also produced, and recycled back to step 4 (above). This slag contains silica (from sand casting and the furnace lining), iron oxide, and about 16% copper.

6) The pigs are not pure at this point – they contain impurities in small proportions, depending on the nature of the ores and slag used. This includes sulfur, arsenic, iron, tin, lead, and other elements. About 6-8 tons of blister copper pigs are piled in a furnace that is similar to the one used in step 2 (above). The arrangement of the pigs allows the free circulation of air as the furnace is heated. The porous nature of the pigs permits the oxidizing of a portion of the impurities – and some of the copper, too.

After about six hours of roasting, the temperature is increased and the pigs melted. A thin layer of *refinery slag* - oxidized impurities, forms on the surface and is skimmed off, to be recycled back to step 4 (above). It consists mainly of silica and copper oxide. Crushed charcoal or coal is then spread across the surface of the molten metal. This helps prevent further oxidation of the copper. A wooden pole – typically made from a young birch tree, is used to stir the molten mass. This is called *poling*. The gases created by the destruction of the pole react with copper oxide, drawing the oxygen from the metal. The correct duration of poling leads to *tough-pitch* metal. *Under-poling* leads to *dry* – brittle, copper, and *over-poling* leads to a very brittle copper due to a lack of oxygen counterbalancing the effects of the impurities still present.[1]

Smelting Chemistry

The reactions taking place in a lead smelter are numerous and complex. Emmons outlined 35 lead-related reactions, 8 silver reactions, and 8 iron reactions. Fifteen common reactions involving lead compounds follow: [2]

Lead oxide is…

Partially reduced by iron oxide
$$2PbO + 3Fe_3O_4 \rightarrow Fe_3O_4 + 3Fe_2O_3 + PbO + Pb$$
Reduced by sulfur (sulfur present from sulfides)
$$2PbO + S \rightarrow 2Pb + SO_2$$
Reduced by iron
$$4PbO + 3Fe \rightarrow Fe_3O_4 + 4Pb$$
Reduced by carbon
$$PbO + C \rightarrow Pb + CO$$
Reduced by zinc
$$PbO + Zn \rightarrow Pb + ZnO$$

Lead sulfate is…

Reduced to lead oxide by lead
$$PbSO_4 + Pb \rightarrow 2PbO + SO_2$$
Reduced to lead by iron (common in Leadville)
$$PbSO_4 + 4Fe \rightarrow Fe_3O_4 + FeS + Pb$$
Reduced to lead sulfide by carbon
$$PbSO_4 + 2C \rightarrow PbS + 2CO_2$$
Reduced to lead oxide by lime
$$PbSO_4 + CaO \rightarrow PbO + CaSO_4$$

Lead sulfide (galena) is…

Reduced by lead oxide to lead – *a fundamental reaction*
$$PbS + 2PbO \rightarrow 3Pb + SO_2$$
Reduced to lead by zinc
$$PbS + Zn \rightarrow Pb + ZnS$$
Reduced to lead by lead sulfate
$$PbS + PbSO_4 \rightarrow 2Pb + 2SO_2$$
Reduced to lead by iron – *a very important reaction*
$$PbS + Fe \rightarrow Pb + FeS$$
Reduced to lead by iron oxide and carbon
$$4PbS + 2Fe_2O_3 + 3C \rightarrow 4Pb + 4FeS + 3CO_2$$

Lead carbonate is…

Reduced to lead oxide and carbon dioxide
$$PbCO_3 \rightarrow PbO + CO_2$$

Pelton Wheel Power Output

The power output of a Pelton wheel with a one-inch diameter nozzle and operating at a nominal efficiency of 85% is graphed in chart 1.[3] To convert to other nozzle diameters, simply multiply the looked-up value shown by the square of the nozzle diameter.

For example, suppose a Pelton wheel with a 2.75" diameter nozzle operates under a 500-foot head of water. What would the horsepower and water consumption, in gallons

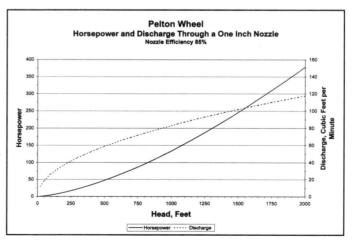

Pelton Wheel
Horsepower and Discharge Through a One Inch Nozzle
Nozzle Efficiency 85%

Chart 1

Drills And Mills

per minute (GPM), be? On the graph, a line drawn vertically from 500 feet intersects the horsepower curve at a value of about 47 HP, and the discharge curve at about 59 cubic feet of water per minute. The diameter of the nozzle (2.75") squared would be about 7.56 (2.75 times 2.75 = 7.56). In round numbers, the power delivered would be about 350 HP (7.56 times 47 HP = 355 HP). The water discharged would be about 446 cubic feet per minute (7.56 times 59 cubic feet per minute = 446 cubic feet per minute). To convert from cubic feet to gallons, multiply by 7.48. 446 cubic feet per minute times 7.48 gallons per cubic foot = 3336 GPM, or in round figures, about 3350 GPM.

Horsepower

A horsepower is the work that a horse does, right? Not exactly. A well-rested horse performs about ⅔ of a horse-power.[4] Then what is a horsepower? The mechanical measure of a horsepower is equivalent to working at a rate of 33,000 foot-pounds per minute, or 550 foot-pounds per second.[5]

If a horse lifts 330 pounds 100 feet up a mine shaft in one minute, that is one horsepower: 330 pounds times 100 feet equals 33,000 foot-pounds, this being performed in one minute, which is the definition of one horsepower.

The Environment

There were – and are, many environmental consequences that came about due to the methods used for mining and milling in the 19th century. It is suggested by the author that the reader not condemn our forefathers for their actions. Their decisions and actions should be evaluated within the context of their time, not ours. The West was a vast, unexplored frontier for the most part. The explorers, settlers, farmers, and Argonauts journeying through the frontier saw abundance and limitless resources in every direction.

The concept of an "environmental consciousness" only existed in an embryonic form. Their actions did lead to devastation at times, and in some cases to an unfortunate legacy that still haunts us today, and will continue to do so for many years to come.

Mining is not the only source of 19th century environmental problems, however. Clearing timber for agriculture and for cordwood made its contributions, as did ranching, railroads, canals, factories, and the Industrial Revolution with its belching stacks. It *was* "Smokestack America," after all.

Only a few facts – plus a few musings and enlightened opinions from others, are presented below. It is left to the reader to place them in a meaningful context.

♦ Estimates of 600 million feet of timber and 2 million cords of wood were used during the heyday of the Comstock Lode.[6] Mountains of sawdust fouled the stream waters around Aspen in the 1880's.[7] For smelting in Eureka, Nevada in 1871, the consumption of charcoal was about 35 bushels per ton. Wood suitable for charcoaling became scarce - at that time it had been cut for a radius of 10 miles from Eureka.[8] According to the *Mining and Scientific Press* in 1879, Virginia City, Nevada – alone, consumed about 300,000 cords of wood a year, and with there being about 30 cords of wood per acre in the Sierras, 10,000 acres were denuded annually.[9]

♦ Regarding the emissions from Butte copper smelters, which were arsenic-laden, Charles Hyde noted in *Copper For America*, "Several Butte physicians argued that smelter smoke served as a disinfectant and thus prevented disease, while W. A. Clark claimed that the arsenic in the air gave the women of Butte attractive complexions."[10]

♦ An 1892 estimate of the mercury consumed by silver mills ranged from 0.5 to 2.5 pounds (typically 1-2 pounds) per ton of ore treated. Gold mills ranged from a low (Homestake, South Dakota) of 0.01 pounds to a high of 0.06 pounds in some California mills.[11] The "consumption" translates to the loss of mercury in tailings and mill wastewater.[12] Considering that the Homestake milled 6,686,370 tons of ore up through 1900[13] that translates to the loss of nearly 67,000 pounds (876 flasks) of mercury. The amount of mercury lost from hydraulic operations in California is estimated at between 3 to 8 million pounds or more.[14] Intact sluice boxes in the Dutch Flat mining district of California still contain mercury in amounts ranging from less than one gram to 26 grams per kilogram of sluice box sediment.[15] In 1998, of 2506 fish and wildlife consumption advisories, 1931 (77%) were for mercury. In 1999,

13 water bodies in California, including the San Francisco bay, had fish consumption advisories due to mercury. Methyl mercury is a potent biotoxin, and is "biomagnified"; that is, the concentration increases with each step up the food chain.[16] It is estimated that 15 million pounds of mercury – nearly 200,000 flasks, were lost into the Carson River drainage system as a result of the milling methods used on the Comstock Lode. Needless to say, the EPA has designated the Carson River a Superfund site. It is estimated that 3 million ounces of gold and 64 million ounces of silver were lost in the tailings along with the mercury. Some remediation plans include recovering these metals to help defray the overall cleanup costs.[17]

♦ In the Pittsburgh, Pennsylvania region during 1920-1921, drainage into the Ohio River basin from 1200 active coal mines was estimated at 450 million tons per year that contained 1,575,000 tons of sulfuric acid. In addition to this was the water draining from thousands of abandoned mines. The Hudson Coal Company estimated that it would cost $39 million for the initial expenditure to neutralize the acid content in the water from their 30 mines, and half that amount annually for ongoing treatment. This would increase the cost of the coal to the consumer by 50 cents per ton. Coal cost $2.89 per ton in 1921.[18]

♦ In the spring, water drains from the Argo Tunnel in Idaho Springs, Colorado at up to 600 gallons per minute (GPM), and during the winter drops to 180 GPM. Clear Creek carries about 90,000 GPM at the point where the Argo drains. Even though the Argo only contributes about 1% of the water, it contributes over ⅓ of the metal load. The Argo Water Treatment Plant – a Superfund site, removes 99.89% of the metals from the water draining from the Argo tunnel. The recovered metals are transported to a solid waste landfill – about 20,000 pounds of sludge per day. The plant cost $4.7 million to build, and $1.1 million per year to operate.[19] Dissolved zinc in the Animas River basin of southwestern Colorado poses an environmental concern. It is interesting to note that the water entering the back of the Old Hundred mine had more dissolved zinc than the water leaving the mine; the net contribution of the mine was negative. Natural mineral sources in the Middle Fork Mineral Creek contribute 90% of the dissolved aluminum and over 60% of the copper, iron, and sulfate, whereas mining related sources contribute about 67% of the zinc.[20]

"The Comstock Lode may truthfully be said to be the tomb of the forests of the Sierras. Millions on millions of feet of lumber are annually buried in the mines, nevermore to be resurrected. When once it is planted in the lower levels it never again sees the light of day. The immense bodies of timber now being entombed along the Comstock will probably be discovered some thousands of years hence by the people to be born in a future age, in the shape of huge beds of coal…"[21]

Dan De Quille (William Wright)

"California has been far too careless in such matters heretofore, and she will regret in the future the vandalism that has left her no relics of a time which grows in interest and in value as it recedes into the past."[22]

Rossiter W. Raymond, 1873

"The original beauty of this little sheet of water has been marred by mining operations, particularly by a partial filling with tailings from the Silver Lake mill."

"A project was at one time set on foot to drain the lake by a tunnel, in order to secure the rich "float" which it was supposed would be found in its bottom. Fortunately for the projectors and for the lovers of the picturesque, this scheme fell through."[23]

Frederick Ransome, 1901, regarding Silver Lake and Lake Como in the San Juan Mountains

---

"When walking in the woods you can see dim trails where the logs once skidded and here and there an old forest monarch who somehow escaped destruction by fire or saw and axe. People who love the handiwork of nature give thanks for the return of the trees, but where are all of the animals who lived in the original woods? The elk, deer, bear and cats are seldom seen anymore. Where are the sassy tufted-eared squirrels who snapped their tails as they ordered you off their property. [sic] Birds too are in short numbers. The power of nature returned the trees, but man destroyed the wild life and only by his acts can it return."[24]

Merle L. Sowell

Wages and the Cost of Living

It is often stated "miners earned three dollars a day." Was this true? Just about. There are, of course, exceptions.

Silverton Railroad employee monthly salaries (daily equivalent in parenthesis) in 1889 were:[25]

Chief Engineer	$175 ($5.76)
Locomotive Engineer	$165 ($5.42)
Superintendent	$150 ($4.93)
Conductor	$125 ($4.11)
Fireman	$100 ($3.29)

During 1873, the Sutro Tunnel paid, per day, Civil Engineer, $26.66, Chief Mechanical Engineer, $10.00, and Chief Miner, $14.00. [26]

Table 1 lists the eastern and western mines used for the minimum, average, and maximum wages in U.S. dollars per day presented in table 2, which is only a *very* small sampling of different mines and locations for different years.[27] The eastern counterparts were paid noticeably less; their cost of living was generally lower. Tables 3 and 4 present location and pay rates for mill employees.[28] The maximum wages for the West generally reflect higher "boom" pay scales. There is a mix of 8, 10, and 12-hour days as well.

Position	Western Wage			Eastern Wage		
	Min	Avg	Max	Min	Avg	Max
Boss	2.95	4.73	6.00	2.00	2.08	2.23
Miner	2.00	3.64	7.00	0.80	1.43	2.75
Driller	2.57	3.82	5.25		1.75	
Mucker	2.03	3.13	4.50	1.00	1.14	1.31
Timberman	2.95	3.78	5.25		1.35	
Carpenter	2.75	4.65	6.50	1.73	1.96	2.31
Hoistman	2.75	4.13	5.00			
Engineer	2.50	4.44	6.00	1.50	2.42	4.00
Blacksmith	1.94	3.95	5.00	1.35	2.42	3.00
Machinist	3.33	4.35	5.50	2.16	2.66	3.50
Topmen	1.75	3.19	4.25	1.10	1.32	1.54
Sorter	1.60	2.59	3.50		1.10	
Trammer	2.00	3.20	4.50	0.50	1.17	1.56
Laborer	1.98	3.14	4.00	0.90	1.36	1.75

Table 2   Mining Wages

Location	State	Year
Nevada City	CA	1851
White Pine	NV	1869
Bannack	MT	1871
Deer Lodge	MT	1871
No Name Mine, Nederland	CO	1874
Sutro Tunnel, Virginia City	NV	1875
Caribou Mine, Nederland	CO	1877
Spanish Mine, Nevada Co.	CA	1877
Comstock Mines	NV	1880
Standard Consolidated, Bodie	CA	1880
New Almaden	CA	1884
Red Mountain	CO	1880s
Aspen	CO	1880s
Wyoming	WY	1889
Hindsdale County	CO	1893
Virginius Mine, Sneffels	CO	1893
Creede	CO	1890s
Bunker Hill & Sullivan, Burke	ID	1895
Sunnyside Mine, Eureka	CO	1897
Camp Bird Mine, Sneffels	CO	1901
Old Hundred Mine, Silverton	CO	1904
Coeur d'Alene district	ID	1904
Goldfield	NV	1908
Newhouse Tunnel, Idaho Springs	CO	1909
Park City	UT	~1910
Ajax Shaft, Cripple Creek	CO	1915
Phoenix Copper Co., Phoenix	MI	1876
Alabama	AL	1876
North Carolina, average	NC	1880
New York	NY	1883
New Jersey	NJ	1884
Continental Mine, Westmoreland Co.	PA	1902
Chisos Mine, Terlingua	TX	1905

Table 1   Mines used for Table 2

Position	Min	Avg	Max
Foreman	2.93	4.72	6.00
Smelter	3.75	4.42	5.00
Helper	3.00	3.70	4.00
Feeder	3.50	4.08	5.00
Blacksmith	2.49	4.75	6.50
Engineer	2.50	4.97	8.00
Fireman	3.00	4.33	6.00
Machinist	1.64	3.55	5.00
Rock handler	1.25	3.58	6.00
Pan man	2.75	3.94	5.50
Amalgamator	4.00	4.56	5.00
Roaster	2.32	3.08	4.00
Laborer	1.73	3.26	4.00

Table 4   Mill Wages

Location	State	Year
Küstel's Estimates		1868
White Pine	NV	1869
Eureka Consolidated Co., Eureka	NV	1871
Deer Lodge	MT	1873
Virginia City	NV	1876
Homestake	SD	1880
Scales & Wagner	ID	1880
Tuscarora	NV	1880
Leadville	CO	1880
Plymouth, Amador Co.	CA	~1880
New Almaden	CA	1884
Stormont Mill, Silver Reef	UT	1880
Spruce Mountain, Jasper	NV	1887

Table 3   Mills used for Table 4

Table 5 is included to help put "three dollars a day" into perspective. A miner on the Comstock in 1881 made about $4.00 a day. This is roughly equivalent to $70 in 2002.[29] Table 6 sketches some of the overall costs per unit for mining,[30] and table 7 for milling.[31]

Location	State	Year	Apx. Age of Camp	Flour	Potatoes	Eggs Dozen	Sugar	Coffee	Tea	Beans	Bacon	Beef	Butter
				Hundred Weight (cwt)						Pound			
California Rush	CA	1849	< 2	$75.00			$1.66		$13.00	$2.00			$2.50
Atlanta	ID	1863	< 2	$30.00			$0.35	$0.50			$0.38		
Austin	NV	1863	< 2	$21.00	$16.50		$0.45	$0.65		$0.20	$0.43		$0.65
Virginia City	MT	1864	< 2	$25.25	$20.00								$0.85
Leesburg	ID	1867	< 2	$22.00	$20.00		$0.60	$0.90		$0.50	$0.60	$0.17	
South Pass	WY	1868	< 2	$30.00	$25.00	$2.00							$1.00
White Pine	NV	1869	< 2	$18.00		$1.17	$0.29	$0.75		$0.10		$0.42	
Park City	UT	1869	< 2	$4.50			$0.10	$0.35			$0.35	$0.25	$0.30
Caribou	CO	1871	< 2	$6.75			$0.18	$0.27					
Bodie	CA	1878	< 2	$7.50	$5.50	$0.75	$0.20	$0.45	$1.00	$0.11	$0.23	$0.18	$0.44
Leadville	CO	1879	< 2	$3.55	$4.50		$0.14	$0.35	$1.00		$0.14	$0.11	
Meadow Lake	CA	1866	2	$7.00	$10.00			$0.50	$1.25		$0.40	$0.16	
Bannack	MT	1865	3	$28.00			$1.00						
Central City	CO	1863	4	$9.00	$6.00	$0.82							$0.42
Butte	MT	1878	4	$5.00	$4.00	$0.40							$0.50
Deadwood	SD	1879	4	$6.00	$1.50	$0.35							$0.35
Silver Reef	UT	1882	6		$2.75	$0.35							$0.37
Central City	CO	1873	14	$4.50	$1.50	$0.40							$0.40
Laramie	WY	1894		$1.50	$1.00		$0.06	$0.25					
Missouri	MO	1863		$3.75			$0.16	$0.50	$2.00				$0.09
Colorado	CO	1868		$8.00	$2.50	$0.55						$0.14	$0.45
Topeka	KS	1886				$0.20	$0.07	$0.13					$0.20
Virginia City	NV	1860	< 2	$75.00				$0.50			$0.40		
Virginia City	NV	1864	5	$9.00	$6.00		$0.27	$0.50	$1.13	$0.13	$0.30	$0.20	$1.25
Virginia City	NV	1871	12	$5.50	$5.50		$0.17	$0.40	$0.87	$0.09	$0.22	$0.19	$1.37
Virginia City	NV	1881	22	$4.13	$2.00		$0.14	$0.25	$0.75	$0.09	$0.20	$0.18	$0.50
2002 Equivalent Prices													
Virginia City	NV	1860	< 2	$1,562.50				$10.42			$8.33		
Virginia City	NV	1864	5	$98.90	$65.93		$2.97	$5.50	$12.42	$1.43	$3.30	$2.20	$13.74
Virginia City	NV	1871	12	$77.47	$77.47		$2.39	$5.63	$12.25	$1.27	$3.10	$2.68	$19.30
Virginia City	NV	1881	22	$70.00	$33.90		$2.37	$4.24	$12.71	$1.53	$3.39	$3.05	$8.48

Table 5   Cost of Living Comparison for Food Items

Mine	State	Year	Operation	Units	Unit Cost	Comment
Eureka Consolidated, Eureka	NV	1871	Silver-Lead	Ton	$3.77	
Briggs, Black Hawk	CO	1879	Gold	Ton	$2.32	
Monarch, Sneffels Mining District	CO	1887	Gold	Ton	$73.35	Mine prep & ore evaluation
Spanish Mine, Nevada Co.	CA	1887	Gold, Open Cut	Ton	$0.37	Chinese labor, includes milling
Portland Mine, Cripple Creek	CO	1903	Gold	Foot	$8.11	896' Drifts, 1229' Xcuts, 112' Raises
Ajax Shaft, Cripple Creek	CO	1915	Shaft Sinking	Foot	$57.28	Machine drills, from 1481'-1983'
Sutro Tunnel, Virginia City	NV	1880	Tunnel	Foot	$38.42	
Newhouse Tunnel, Idaho Springs	CO	1909	Tunnel	Foot	$19.67	8x8', 244'/month
Del Norte & Siskiyou Co.	CA	1885	Gold, Hydraulic	Cu Yd	$0.042	Average of 8 Hydraulic Mines
Dredging, Folsom & Oroville Districts	CA	1912-16	Gold, Dredge	Cu Yd	$0.046	Average of 10 dredges

Table 6   Mining Costs

Mill	State	Year	Operation	Cost Per Ton	Comment
Eureka Consolidated, Eureka	NV	1871	Silver-Lead	$21.86	Smelting
Wagner & Scales	ID	1880	Gold & Silver	$8.70	Arrastra
Homestake	SD	1880	Gold	$0.78	120-stamp
Homestake	SD	1880	Gold	$1.30	80-stamp
Imperial	MT	1873	Gold	$28.33	Chlorination
Plymouth	CA	~1880	Gold	$9.40	Chlorination
Küstel's Estimates		1868	Gold	$14.55	Chlorination
Silver King, Park City	UT	1901	Lead-Silver-Gold	$1.04	Concentration
Barbee & Walker, Silver Reef	UT	1880	Silver	$6.40	Washoe

Table 7   Milling Costs

Annual Metal Production and Average Price

The following figures illustrate the annual U.S. production and average prices of the precious metals gold and silver, of mercury, and of the base metals lead, copper, and zinc. The government fixed the price of gold at $20.67 per ounce during this period. From 1845-1900, 114,348,339 ounces of gold valued at $2,363,580,169 were won.

Silver recovered during this period added 1,338,138,395 ounces worth $1,730,079,131 [at the coinage rate of $1.2929 per ounce] to the Treasury. 1,860,359 76.5-pound flasks of mercury worth $83,868,365 were produced. Lead accounted for 8,892,344,000 pounds valued at $375,525,618. Copper contributed 6,716,521,280 pounds worth $961,316,552. Zinc – a latecomer as far as economic metals and minerals is concerned, accounted for 3,052,295,505 pounds valued at $142,133,420 between 1875-1900. In all, these metals contributed $5,656,503,255 towards the economy of the latter half of the 19th Century. [32]

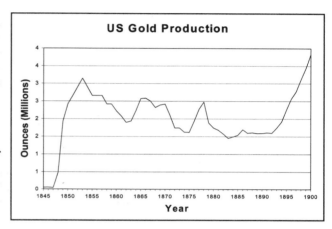

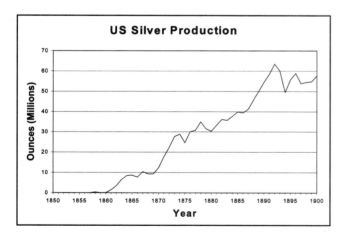

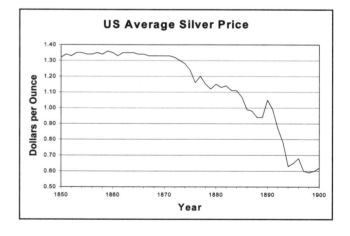

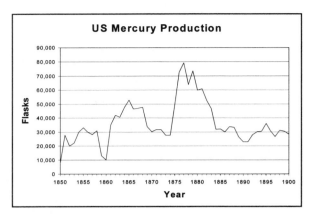

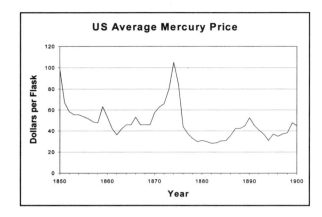

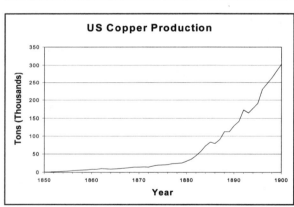

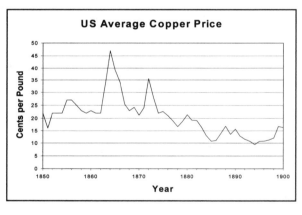

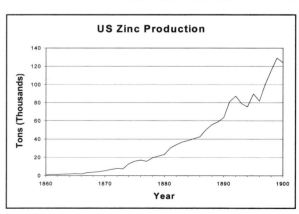

Endnotes

[1] HUTCHISON2003.2

[2] EMMONS1886 pages 732-738

[3] MILLER1906 page 218

[4] James Watt made the arbitrary decision to increase the coal-hoisting ponies' measured rate of 22,000 foot-pound/minutes by 50%.

[5] 1 horsepower = about 746 Watts.

[6] SMITHD1993 pages 12-13

[7] ROHRBOUGH1986 page 112

[8] RAYMOND1873 page 174

[9] BAILEY2002 page 172

[10] HYDE1998 page 91

[11] ROTHWELL1893 page 553

[12] While remodeling the Ontario amalgamating mill in Park City, Utah during 1904, it was discovered that between $3000-$4000 worth of mercury had leaked out of the plant and into the earth. BOUTWELL1912 page 32

[13] IRVING1904 page 62

[14] ALPERS2000

[15] HUNERLACH1999 page 187

[16] ALPERS2000

[17] NG1992

[18] SMITHD1993 page 114, DICICCIO1996 page 137

[19] CDPHE2000. Someday, this landfilled sludge will prove to be a valuable deposit to mine.

[20] USGS1997

[21] DEQUILLE1959 page 174

[22] RAYMOND1873 page 113

[23] RANSOME1901 pages 145, 196

[24] SOWELL1976 page 44

[25] SLOAN1975 page 98

[26] STEWART1962 page 117

[27] In row order:
PAUL1965 page 351
JACKSONW1963 page 118
RAYMOND1873 page 265
RAYMOND1873 page 277
SMITHD1974 page 93
DRINKER1893 pages 345,346
SMITHD1974 page 94
EMMONS1885 page 159
USGS1885 page 535
SMITHP1994 page 107
ROHRBOUGH1986 pages 194,195
DUNCAN1990 page 223
MORSE2000 page 68
GREGORYD1996 page 121
BENNETT1966 page 91
RANSOME1908 page 81
BIRD1986 page 62
BENHAM1980 page 49
FETCHENHIER1999 page 43
RANSOME1908 page 86
RANSOME1909 page 21
PEELE1966 page 6-28
BOUTWELL1912 page 27
PEELE1966 page 7-06
WEEKS1886 page 246
WEEKS1886 page 252
EMMONS1885 page 157
WEEKS1886 page 250
WEEKS1886 page 250
PIONEER2000
RAGSDALE1976 page 40
RICKARD1932 page 63

[28] In row order:
KUSTEL1868 page 250
JACKSONW1963 page 118
RAYMOND1873 page 398
RAYMOND1873 page 280
BANCROFT1890 page 287
EMMONS1885 page 279
EMMONS1885 page 284
EMMONS1885 page 243
EMMONS1886 page 640
EISSLER1889 page 211
USGS1885 page 536
EMMONS1885 page 480
HALL1998 page 243

[29] In row order:
RAYMOND1873 page 112
WELLS2002 pages 62-63
LEWISO1955 page 17
SMITHD1967 page 198
WELLS2002 page 84
SMITHD1967 page 198
JACKSONW1963 pages 117,119
BOUTWELL1912 page 19
SMITHD1974 page 108
WEDERTZ1996 pages 59-60
BLAIR1980 page 65
FATOUT1969 page 162
MOULTON1999 page 288
SMITHD1967 page 198
SMITHD1967 page 198
SMITHD1967 page 198
SMITHD1967 page 198
SMITHD1967 page 198
DUNCAN1990 page 180
MOULTON1999 page 288
BANCROFT1890 page 492
MOULTON1999 page 288
Virginia City (4):
DEQUILLE1959 page 65
LORD1883 page 371
LORD1883 page 371
LORD1883 page 371
2002 prices: CPI2002

[30] RAYMOND1873 page 175
MANRY1999 page 110
GREGORYD1996 page 69
RICKARD1932 pages 63,64
FINLAY1909 page 381
PEELE1966 page 7-26
DRINKER1893 page 346
PEELE1966 page 6-28
EMMONS1885 page
PEELE1966 page 10-589

[31] RAYMOND1873 page 175
EMMONS1885 page 285
EMMONS1885 page 280
EMMONS1885 page 280
RAYMOND1873 page 280
EISSLER1889 page 211
KUSTEL1868 page 250
BOUTWELL1912 page 32
EMMONS1885 page 481

[32] Gold production: USGS1904 page 124-125.
Gold price was fixed at $20.67/ounce until 1934.
Silver production (calculated from the coining value of $1.2929): USGS1904 page 124-125.
Silver prices: USBM1993 page 157.
Mercury production and price: RANSOME1922 page 110.
Lead production: USGS1904 page 206.
Lead prices: 1850-69, USGS2001, 1870-79, NBER2003, 1880-99 RANSOME1901 page 24.
Copper production: USGS1904 page 164-165.
Copper prices: USBM1993 page 51.
Zinc production: BALAZIK2001.
Zinc prices: USBM1993 page 194.

References

1911ENC
The 1911 Edition Encyclopedia
http://3.1911encyclopedia.org

AAA1978
The Mother Lode
Automobile Club of Southern California
1978
Los Angeles, California

AARON1881
Leaching Gold and Silver Ores
Charles Howard Aaron
1881
Barry & Baird, Steam Book and Job Printers, San Francisco

ABBE1985
*Austin and the Reese River Mining District,
Nevada's Forgotten Frontier*
Nevada Studies in History and Political
Science No. 19
Donald R. Abbe
1985
University of Nevada Press, Reno

ACKERLY1997
*An Overview of the Historic Characteristics
of New Mexico's Mines*
Neal W. Ackerly
1997
Dos Rios Consultants, Silver City, New
Mexico

ALDER1961
The Ghost of Mercur
Douglas D. Alder
Volume XXIX, Number 1
January 1961
Utah Historical Quarterly

ALLEN1920
*Handbook of Ore Dressing
Equipment and Practice*
A. W. Allen
1920
McGraw-Hill Book Company, New York

ALLIS1902
Gold and Silver Mills
Catalogue No. 4, 11th Edition
1902
Allis-Chalmers Co., Chicago

ALLIS1903
*Cyanide, Chlorination and Lixiviation
Machinery*
Catalogue No. 14, 2th Edition
1903
Allis-Chalmers Co., Chicago

ALPERS2000
*Mercury Contamination from Historic Gold
Mining in California*
Charles N. Alpers, Michael P. Hunerlach
Fact Sheet FS-061-00
USGS

ANGEL1973

History of Nevada
Myron Angel, Editor
1973
Arno Press, New York
Originally Thompson & West, 1881

ARBITER1964
Milling Methods in the Americas
Nathaniel Arbiter, Editor
1964
Gordon & Breach Science Publishers, New
York

ARGO2000
Argo Tailings
Volume CV, Number 1
2000

ASME.x
http://www.asme.org/history/brochures/
Visited April 2003, where x is:
H084 = *Ten-Stamp Mill, Reed Gold Mine*
Stanfield, North Carolina
Regional Historic Mechanical Engineering
Landmark
1983
H118 = *Grube Samson Silver Mine Reversible Waterwheel and Man-engine*
Sankt Andreasberg, West Germany
An International Historic Mechanical Engineering Landmark
1987
H157 = *Pelton Waterwheel Collection*
Grass Valley, California
International Historic Mechanical Engineering Landmark
1991

BACKUS1969
Tomboy Bride
Harriet Fish Backus
1969
Pruett Publishing Company, Boulder, CO.

BAILEY2002
Shaft Furnaces and Beehive Kilns, A History of Smelting in the Far West, 1863-1900
Lynn R. Bailey
2002
Westernlore Press, Tucson

BAKER1927
History of Colorado
Volume II
James H. Baker and LeRoy R. Hafen
1927
Linderman Co., Inc., Denver

BALAZIK2001
Data courtesy of Ron Balazik
USGS
02/2001

BANCROFT1890
The Works of Hubert Howe Bancroft
Volume XXV
History of Nevada, Colorado, and Wyoming, 1540-1888
1890
The History Company, Publishers, San
Francisco
(No date on reprint, Arno Press and
McGraw-Hill, New York)

BANNACK
Bannack
Park brochure
No date (ca 2002)
The Bannack Association, Dillon, Montana

BARRICK1997
Barrick Mercur Gold Mine
Company brochure
(No date – visited mine 1997)

BEHR1896
Mine Drainage, Pumps, Etc.
Hans C. Behr
Bulletin No. 9
1896
California State Mining Bureau, Sacramento

BENHAM1980
Camp Bird and the Revenue
J. L. Benham
1980
Bear Creek Publishing Company, Ouray,
Colorado

BENNETT1966
Boom Town Boy
In Old Creede, Colorado
Edwin Lewis Bennett
1966
Sage Books, Chicago

BIRD1986
Silverton Gold
The Story of Colorado's Largest Gold Mine
Allan G. Bird
1986
(Self-published?)

BLAIR1980
Leadville: Colorado's Magic City
Edward Blair
1980
Fred Pruett Books, Boulder, Colorado

BODIE2002
Single photocopy of a page 23 from an
unknown document
Provided by Bodie State Park, California

BOUTWELL1912
*Geology and Ore Deposits of the Park City
District, Utah*
John Mason Boutwell
Geological Survey Professional Paper 77
1912
USGS
Government Printing Office

BOYLE2001
Personal Communication
Ray Boyle, Chief Engineer
Mount Morgan Mine
Queensland, Australia
May 2001

BRITANNICA1958
Encyclopedia Britannica
1958
William Benton, Publisher
and also
Explosives

http://208.154.71.60/brit/
Visited 2/21/2001

BULLARD2001
Personal Communication
Jed Bullard, CEO
Bullard, Inc.
Lexington, Kentucky
January 2001

BULLION2001
The Science of Gold Extraction: A Brief South African History
http://www.bullion.org.za/bulza/educatn/AUextrac.htm
Visited 2/22/2001

BUTLER1913
Geology and Ore Deposits of the San Francisco and Adjacent Districts, Utah
B. S. Butler
Geological Survey Professional Paper 80
1913
USGS
Government Printing Office

BUTLER1920
The Ore Deposits of Utah
B. S. Butler, G. F. Loughlin, V. C. Heikes
Geological Survey Professional Paper 111
1920
USGS
Government Printing Office

CARMAN1963
The North Star Power Plant
William E. Carman
Vol. 17, No. 4 – November 1963
Nevada County Historical Society

CARPENTER1953
The History of Fifty Years of Mining at Tonopah 1900-1950
Jay A. Carpenter, Russell R. Elliot, and Byrd F. W. Sawyer
1953
Nevada Bureau of Mines

CDPHE2000
Argo Water Treatment Plant
July 2000
Colorado Department of Public Health and Environment

CERES.x
California State Historical Landmarks
Where 'x' is the Landmark Number
123 = Columbia
269 = Mokelumne Hill
297 = Site of one of the First Discoveries of Quartz Gold in California
537 = Cottonwood Charcoal Kilns
http://ceres.ca.gov/geo_area/counties/lists/landmarks_county.html
Visited 3/2003

CHEMEX2001
Technical Information – Precious Metals Analysis - Gold
Chemex Labs website
http://www.chemex.ca/tech/t-sec42a.htm
Visited 01/10/2001

CHESTERMAN1986
Geology and Ore Deposits of the Bodie Mining District, Mono County, California
Charles W. Chesterman, Rodger H. Chapman, and Clifton H. Gray, Jr.
Bulletin 206
1986
California Department of Conservation
Division of Mines and Geology, Sacramento, California

CORNWALL1968
Cornwall: Its Mines and Miners.
1857
(1968 reprint, Augustus M. Kelley, Publishers, New York)

COUCH1943
Nevada's Metal and Mineral Production (1859-1940, Inclusive)
Bertrand F. Couch and Jay A. Carpenter
University of Nevada Bulletin
Volume XXXVII, No. 4, 1943
Nevada State Bureau of Mines

CPI2002
http://oregonstate.edu/Dept/pol_sci/fac/sahr/sahr.htm
Visited 04/26/2003

CRAMPTON1956
Deep Enough
A Working Stiff in the Western Mining Camps
Frank A. Crampton
1956
University of Oklahoma Press

CSA2001
Historic Mine Report Files Index c.1900 – 1980 at the Colorado State Archives
http://www.archives.state.co.us/hmrfi/home.htm
Visited 4/19/2001

CURTIS1884
Silver-Lead Deposits of Eureka Nevada
Joseph Story Curtis
1884
USGS
Government Printing Office

DAVIS1984
The Chemistry of Powder and Explosives
Tenney L. Davis
1984
Angriff Press, Hollywood, California

DAY1892
Report on Mineral Industries in The United States
Eleventh Census: 1890
David T. Day
1892
Government Printing Office

DEISTER2001
A History of Finding Value Where Others Could Not
Deister Concentrator Company
http://www.deisterconcentrator.com/history.html
Visited 4/06/2001

DENNIS1963
A Hundred Years of Metallurgy
W. H. Dennis
1963
Aldine Publishing Company, Chicago

DERICKSON1988
Workers' Health Workers' Democracy
The Western Miners' Struggle, 1891-1925
Alan Derickson
1988
Cornell University Press, Ithaca

DEQUILLE1959
The Big Bonanza
Dan De Quille (William Wright)
1876 (1959 reprint)
Alfred A. Knopf, New York

DEQUILLE1974
A History of the Comstock Silver Lode & Mines
Dan De Quille
1889 (1974 reprint, Promontory Press, New York)

DICICCIO1996
Coal and Coke In Pennsylvania
Carmen DiCiccio
1996
The Pennsylvania Historical and Museum Commission
Commonwealth of Pennsylvania

DOL1998
Historical Summary of Mine Disasters In the United States
Volume III
Metal and Nonmetal Mines – 1885-1998
1998
Department of Labor

DOUGHTY1989
Bullfrog's Grand Old Man
Nanelia S. Doughty
Central Nevada's Glorious Past
Vol 12, No. 2, November 1989
Central Nevada Historical Society, Tonopah, Nevada

DRINKER1893
Tunneling, Explosive Compounds, and Rock Drills
Henry S. Drinker
1893
John Wiley & Sons, New York

DUNCAN1990
The Medicine Bow Mining Camps
Mel Duncan
1990
Jelm Mountain Publications, Laramie, Wyoming

EGENHOFF1967a
The Cornish Pump
Elisabeth L. Egenhoff
Volume XX Number 6 (Part One - June 1967)
Mineral Information Services
California Division of Mines and Geology

EGENHOFF1967b
The Cornish Pump
Elisabeth L. Egenhoff
Volume XX Number 8 (Part Two – August 1967)
Mineral Information Services
California Division of Mines and Geology

EISSLER1889
The Metallurgy of Gold
A Practical Treatise
M. Eissler
1889
Crosby, Lockwood and Son, London

EKU2001
Commercial High Explosives
http://www.fireandsafety.eku.edu/VFRE-99/Recognition/High/high.htm
Visited 2/21/2001

ELECTRO1904
Extracting Gold and Silver at Wallstreet Mills, Colorado
Volume II, No. 1, January 1, 1904
Electrochemical Industry
Electrochemical Publishing Co., New York

ELLIOTT1973
History of Nevada
Russell R. Elliott
1973
University of Nebraska Press, Lincoln, Nebraska

EMJ1930
Useful Operating Innovations – for mine, mill, and smelter
1930
McGraw-Hill, New York
(A collection of articles reproduced from *Engineering and Mining Journal*)

EMMONS1885
Statistics and Technology of the Precious Metals
S. F. Emmons and G. F. Becker
Department of the Interior
Census Office
1885
Government Printing Office, Washington

EMMONS1886
Geology and Mining Industry of Leadville, Colorado
Samuel Franklin Emmons
1886
USGS
Government Printing Office, Washington

EMMONS1905
Contributions to Economic Geology 1904
S. F. Emmons and C. W. Hayes
1905
USGS
Government Printing Office

EMMONS1927
Geology and Ore Deposits of the Leadville Mining District, Colorado
S. F. Emmons, J. D. Irving, and G. F. Loughlin
Geological Survey Professional Paper 148

1927
USGS
Government Printing Office

EMMONSW1913
Geology and Ore Deposits of the Philipsburg Quadrangle Montana
William Harvey Emmons and Frank Cathcart Calkins
Geological Survey Professional Paper 78
1913
USGS
Government Printing Office

EMMONSW1923
Geology and Ore Deposits of the Creede District, Colorado
William H. Emmons and Esper S. Larsen
Geological Survey Bulletin 718
1923
USGS
Government Printing Office

EUREKA2001
Eureka: Diatoms – Nature's Gems
http://hjs.geol.uib.no/diatoms/Industry/index.html-ssi
Visited 2/16/2001

FARISH1915
History of Arizona
Volume I, Chapter XXII, *Explorations for Wagon Roads – Camels*
Thomas Edwin Farish
1915
State of Arizona
Electronic text version
http://www.library.arizona.edu/swetc/projectsa.html
Visited 3/21/2003

FARQUHAR1966
Excerpts from The Journal of William H. Brewer
The New Idria and The New Almaden Mine
Edited by Francis P. Farquhar
1966
University of California Press
(Excerpted from *Up and Down California in 1860-1864* by William H. Brewer)

FATOUT1969
Meadow Lake Gold Town
Paul Fatout
1969
University of Nebraska Press, Lincoln

FELL1979
Ores to Metals
The Rocky Mountain Smelting Industry
James E. Fell, Jr.
1979
University of Nebraska Press, Lincoln, Nebraska

FETCHENHIER1999
Ghosts and Gold – The History of the Old Hundred Mine
Scott Fetchenhier
1999

FIELDER1970
The Treasure of Homestake Gold

Mildred Fielder
1970
North Plains Press, Aberdeen, South Dakota

FINLAY1909
The Cost of Mining -
An Exhibit of the Results of Important Mines Throughout the World
James Ralph Finlay
1909
McGraw-Hill Book Company, New York

FISHER1977
Silver Mines and Silver Miners in Colonial Peru, 1776-1824
J. R. Fisher
1977
The University of Liverpool

GAGR2001
The Great American Gold Rush
http://www.acusd.edu/~jross/goldrush.html
http://www.acusd.edu/~jross/rocker.html
Visited 5/03/2001

GALLOWAY1947
Early Engineering Works Contributory to the Comstock
John Debo Galloway
1947
Volume XLI, No. 5
University of Nevada Bulletin
University of Nevada, Reno

GARDENER1934
Placer Mining in the Western United States
E. D. Gardener, C. H. Johnson
1934
Circular Number 6786
U. S. Bureau of Mines

GARDINER2002
Mining Among The Clouds
The Mosquito Range and the Origins of Colorado's Silver Boom
Harvey N. Gardiner
2002
Colorado Historical Society, Denver

GARDNER2001
Information courtesy Bob Gardner
North Star Mining Museum
May 25, 2001

GIBBONS1987
In The San Juan Colorado
Sketches
Rev. J. J. Gibbons
1898 (1987 reprint)
St. Daniel's Church

GILBERT1917
Hydraulic-Mining Débris in the Sierra Nevada
Grove Karl Gilbert
Geological Survey Professional Paper 105
1917
USGS
Government Printing Office

GREGORYC1980
A Concise History of Mining
Cedric E. Gregory
1980
Pergamon Press

GREGORYD1996
The Great Revenue and Surrounding Mines When Mining was Booming in the 80's and 90's
Doris H. Gregory
1996
Cascade Publications, Ouray, Colorado

HABASHI1967
Kinetics and Mechanism of Gold and Silver Dissolution in Cyanide Solution
Fathi Habashi
1967
Bulletin 59
State of Montana Bureau of Mines and Geology

HAER01
Historic American Engineering Record
CO-2
Ames Hydroelectric Plant
Donald C. Jackson
HAER, COLO,57-AMES.V,2A-
P&P Online Catalog
Library of Congress, Prints and Photographs Division
Washington, D.C.

HAER02
Historic American Engineering Record
CO-38
San Juan and New York Mining and Smelting Company, Smelter Stack
James A. Caufield
HAER, COLO,33-DUR,1A-
P&P Online Catalog
Library of Congress, Prints and Photographs Division
Washington, D.C.

HALL1998
Old Heart of Nevada
Ghost Towns and Mining Camps of Elko County
Shawn Hall
1998
University of Nevada Press, Reno

HALL2003
Personal communication, Shawn Hall
March 2003

HAMILTON1920
Manual of Cyanidation
E. M. Hamilton
1920
McGraw-Hill Book Company, Inc., New York

HAMILTONP1881
Resources of Arizona
Its Mineral, Farming, and Grazing Lands, Towns, and Mining Camps; Its Rivers, Mountains, Plains, and Mesas; With a Brief Summary of Its Indian Tribes, Early History, Ancient Ruins, Climate, etc. A Manual of Reliable Information Concerning the Territory.
Patrick Hamilton (Compiler)
1881
Prescott, Arizona
Electronic text version
http://www.library.arizona.edu/swetc/projectsa.html
Visited 3/21/2003

HARRIS1987
Column Leach Testing of Gold Ore from the Ortiz gold mine: The effect of surfactant additions to the leaching solution.
Michael J. Harris
1987
Open File Report # 307
New Mexico Bureau of Mines and Mineral Resources, Socorro, NM

HART1968
The Best of HART'S STUFF From Rico
Edited and published by Lawrence and Marilyn Pleasant
1968
Dolores, Colorado

HATCH1895
The Gold Mines of the Rand
Being a Description of the Mining Industry of Witwatersrand South African Republic
Frederick H. Hatch and J. A. Chalmers
1895
MacMillan and Co., London

HAYNES1954
American Chemical Industry, Background and Beginnings
Williams Haynes
1954
D. Van Nostrand Company, Inc., New York

HENDERSON1926
Mining In Colorado, a History of Discovery, Development, and Production
Charles W. Henderson
Professional Paper 138
1926
USGS
Government Printing Office

HOPPE2001
From the Hard-Boiled Hat to Today's Skull Bucket:
A History of Hard Hats
Leslie Hoppe
Bullard
http://www.bullard.com/companyInfo/hardHatHitory.cfm
Visited 1/09/2001

HUNERLACH1999
Mercury Contamination from Hydraulic Placer-Gold Mining in the Dutch Flat Mining District, California
Michael P. Hunerlach, James J. Rytuba, Charles N. Alpers
Report 99-4018B, p.179-189
USGS
http://water.wr.usgs.gov/valley/dutch/wrir994018b.pdf

HUTCHISON2003
Pete's Pages from the Past
http://website.lineone.net/~petehutch/

1 = *Metallurgy*
E. L. Rhead
1939
London
2 = *Metals*
C. L. Bloxam
1882
London

HYDE1998
Copper For America
The United States Copper Industry from Colonial Times to the 1990s
Charles K. Hyde
1998
The University of Arizona Press, Tucson, Arizona

IDL2001
Mines Listing
Idaho Department of Lands
http://gis.idl.state.id.us/GIShtm/static/mines.htm
Visited 4/6/2001

INGERSOLL2001
IR Backgrounder
Ingersoll-Rand
http://www.irco.com/newsroom/03.html
Visited 01/24/2001

IRVING1904
Economic Resources of the Northern Black Hills
J. D. Irving with S. F. Emmons and T. A. Jaggar, Jr.
Professional Paper 26
1904
USGS
Government Printing Office

JACKSOND2001
Historic American Buildings Survey
New Almaden Quicksilver Mine
Donald C. Jackson
HABS No. CA-114
P&P Online Catalog
(No date)
Library of Congress, Prints and Photographs Division
Washington, D.C.

JACKSONW1963
Treasure Hill, Portrait of a Silver Mining Camp
W. Turrentine Jackson
1963
The University of Arizona Press, Tucson

JESSEN1994
Bizarre Colorado
A Legacy of Unusual Events & People
Kenneth Jessen
1994
J. V. Publications, Loveland, CO

JOHNSON1898.x
Getting Gold: A Practical Treatise for Prospectors, Miners, and Students.
J. C. F. Johnson
1898 edition
Charles Griffin & Company, Limited,

Strand, London
Where 'x' is the Chapter Number:
6 = Chapter VI – *Gold Extraction*
7 = Chapter VII – *Gold Extraction – Secondary Processes and Lixiviation*
8 = Chapter VIII – *Calcination or Roasting of Ores*
Electronic text version
http://66.78.12.123/ggbook/ggchp8.html
Visited 12/07/2002

KIROY1961
The Pelton Water Wheel
As Tested and Known by James Hutchinson
Compiled by Elza Kiroy
Vol. 15, No. 2 – April 1961
Nevada County Historical Society

KUSTEL1868
A Treatise on Concentration of All Kinds of Ores:
Including the Chlorination Process
Guido Küstel
1868
Office of the Mining and Scientific Press, San Francisco

LAPOINT1999
The Gold Rush in North Carolina
Dennis J. LaPoint
December 1999
Geotimes

LENZI1973
Geochemical Reconnaissance at Mercur, Utah
G. W. Lenzi
1973
Special Studies 43
Utah Geological and Mineralogical Survey

LESCOHIER1993
The Cyanide Plant
More Gold From The Same Ore
Roger P. Lescohier
1993
Empire Mine Park Association, Grass Valley, CA

LEWIS2003
Personal communications with Wilbur G. Lewis, Saguache, Colorado
January and March 2003

LEWISO1955
The Town that Died Laughing
The story of Austin, Nevada, rambunctious early-day mining camp, and its renowned newspaper, the Reese River Reveille
Oscar Lewis
1955
Little, Brown and Company, Boston

LINCOLN
Lincoln County Driving & Walking Tours
Alamo, Caliente, Panaca, Pioche, Rachel, State Parks & Surrounding Areas
ca 2002
Nevada Commission of Tourism
Wild Rose Press, Pioche, Nevada

LINDGREN1906
Geology and Gold Deposits of the Cripple

Creek District, Colorado
Waldemar Lindrgren and Frederick Leslie Ransome
Geological Survey Professional Paper 54
1906
USGS
Government Printing Office

LOCK1890
Mining and Ore-Dressing Machinery
C. G. Warnford Lock
1890
E. & F. N. Spon, London

LOON1991
Determination of the Precious Metals,
Selected Instrumental Methods
J. C. Van Loon and B. R. Barefoot
1991
John Wiley & Sons

LORD1883
Comstock Mining and Miners
Eliot Lord
1883
USGS
Government Printing Office, Washington

MAB.xxxx-x
Manufacturer and Builder
Western and Company, New York
where xxxx-x is the issue's Year-Month

1871-6   *Stone and Ore-breaking by Machinery*
1871-11   *Annular Diamond-Pointed Rock Drills*
1874-3   *On Fan Blowers*
1874-6   *Trial of Rock Drills*
1874-7   *Percussion Rock Drills*
1878-11   *The Crushing and Pulverizing of Ores*
1880-10   *American Mining Methods*
1882-7   *A Novel Apparatus for Separating Gold*
1882-10   *Precipitation of Gold from Solutions by Charcoal*
1885-5a   *Ingersoll Eclipse Drill*
1885-5b   *Rock Drills Run by Electricity*
1885-10   *An Improvement in Rock Drills*
1887-8   *An Electric Rock Drill*
1887-12   *Rackarock – A New and Safe High Explosive*
1888-2   *The Chemical and Physical Properties of Rackarock*
1891-8   *Electric Percussion Drills*
1892-9   *The Edison Electric Diamond Drill*
1894-3   *Modern Explosives*
1879-8   *Pumping out the Comstock Mines*
1873-2   *The Sturtevant Blower*
1881-5   *The Precious Metals*

MALAKOFF1993
The Malakoff Monitor
(newspaper-like publication reprinting articles from the past)
1993 (copy from 2002)
Malakoff Diggins Park Association, Nevada City, California

MALLICOAT2000

Lighting the Way
Underground 1860's – 1940's
Mark Mallicoat
http://www.memorabliamine.com/lighting_the_way.html
Visited 5/01/2000

MANNIX1913
Mines and Their Story
J. Bernard Mannix
1913
J. B. Lippincott Company, Philadelphia

MANRY1999
Colorado Mines 1859-1879
Boulder and Gilpin Counties
(Originally published as *Colorado, Its Gold and Silver Mines, Farms and Stock Ranges, and Health and Pleasure Resorts – Tourist's Guide to the Rocky Mountains*)
Frank Fossett 1879)
Charles E. Manry
1999
C&M Press, Denver

MCCOMBE2003
An Engine to Kill Men
C. McCombe
The Museum for the Preservation of Elevating History
http://www.theelevatormuseum.org/h/h-3.htm
Visited 2003

MCCORMACK1950
Seventy-Five Years of Rock Drill Progress
M. L. McCormack
Volume 45, Supplement C, 2B
1950
Colorado School of Mines Quarterly

MCKINNEY1995
Four Mining Engineers at New Almaden
Edited by Gage McKinney
1995
New Almaden Quicksilver County Park Association
(Extracts from interviews conducted by T. A. Rickard and
originally appearing in *Interviews With Mining Engineers*.)

MCQUISTON1986
Gold: The Saga of the Empire Mine 1850-1956
F. W. McQuiston, Jr.
1986
Empire Mine Park Association, Grass Valley, CA

METSCHER1989
Accident At Millers
William J. Metscher
Central Nevada's Glorious Past
Vol 12, No. 2, November 1989
Central Nevada Historical Society, Tonopah, Nevada

MILLER1906
Elements of Mining Geology and Metallurgy
G. W. Miller
1906

The Daily Mining Record, Denver

MONAHAN2001
Data courtesy of Kitty Monahan, President
New Almaden Quicksilver County Park
Association
February 2001

MOLINELLI1997
Eureka and its Resources
Lambert Molinelli
1997
University of Nevada Press, Reno, Nevada

MONTANADEQ
Montana Department of Environmental
Quality
State of Montana
http://www.deq.state.mt.us/Rem/mwc/linkd
ocs/techdocs/xxtech.asp where 'xx' is the
mining district number:
2	= Argenta
4	= Bannack
10	= Bryant
30	= Confederate Gulch
36	= Radersburg
41	= Neihart
50	= North Moccasin
51	= Warm Springs
65	= Philipsburg
79	= Elkhorn
82	= Little Pipestone
99	= Lincoln
101	= Missouri River
117B	= Red Bluff
119	= Pony
122	= Rochester
126	= Silver Star
129	= Virginia City
130	= Washington
132	= Castle Mountains
183	= Butte

MORGAN2001
*A Brief Account of the Treatment of Mount
Morgan Ore*
http://www.mountmorgan.com/Treatment.h
tm
Visited 2/22/2001

MORSE2000
*A Brief History of Mining in Hinsdale
County*
Milo Z. Morse and Faye Bielser
2000

MOTTEN1972
Mexican Silver and the Enlightenment
Clement G. Motten
1950 (1972 reprint)
Octagon Books, New York

MOULTON1999
*The Writer's Guide to Everyday Life in the
Wild West from 1840-1900*
Candy Moulton
1999
Writer's Digest Books, Cincinnati, OH

MULLAN2000
Garry Mullan, personal communication,
and
http://www.geocities.com/gold_battery/

MURRAY1972
*Miner's Delight, Investor's Despair
The Ups and Downs of a Sub-Marginal
Mining Camp in Wyoming*
Robert A. Murray
1972
Piney Creek Press, Sheridan, Wyoming

NBER2003
National Bureau of Economic Research
http://www.nber.org/databases/macrohistor
y/contents/chapter04.html
Visited 2003

NEU1996
*A Town Founded on Hope
Philipsburg, Montana A Historic Past A
Certain Future*
Clyde J. Neu
1996
Granite County Museum and Cultural Cen-
ter, Philipsburg, Montana

NG1992
*Mercury Contamination of the Carson
River*
Nevada Geology
1992
http://www.nbmg.unr.edu/nl/nl17a.htm
Visited 1/11/2001

NIEBUR1982
*Arthur Redman Wilfley
Miner, Inventor, and Entrepreneur*
Jay E. Niebur and James E. Fell, Jr.
1982
Colorado Historical Society

NILE1956
Hydraulic Mining in Nevada County
Herbert J Nile
Vol. 10, No. 4 – October 1956
Nevada County Historical Society

NITZE1996
Gold Deposits of North Carolina
Bulletin No. 3
Henry B. C. Nitze and George B. Hanna
1896 (reprint 1996)
North Carolina Geological Survey

NORTHROP1975
*Turquoise and Spanish Mines in New Mex-
ico*
(Excerpted from the book *Minerals of New
Mexico*, 1944)
Stuart A. Northrop
1975
University of New Mexico Press, Albu-
querque

ONEILL1986
Central Nevada's Charcoal Industry
James O'Neill
Central Nevada's Glorious Past
Vol 9, No. 1, May 1986
Central Nevada Historical Society,
Tonopah, Nevada

PAUL1963
*Mining Frontiers of the Far West, 1848-
1880*
Rodman W. Paul
1963
Holt, Rinehart and Winston

PAUL1965
*California Gold
The Beginning of Mining in the Far West*
Rodman W. Paul
1947 (1965 Bison Book edition)

PAULING1988
General Chemistry
Linus Pauling
(1970 W. H. Freeman edition)
1988
Dover Publications, Inc., New York

PEELE1966
Mining Engineers' Handbook
Robert Peele, Editor
3rd Edition
1966
John Wiley & Sons, Inc., New York

PETERSON1997
*James Marshall
California's Gold Discoverer*
Richard H. Peterson
December 1997
Wild West
http://www.thehistorynet.com/WildWest/art
icles/1997/1297_text.htm
Visited 10/11/2000

PHILLIPS1873
*The Explorers', Miners' and Metallurgists'
Companion*
J. S. Phillips, M. E.
Second Edition
1873
Chas. W. Gordon, San Francisco

PIONEER2000
Outside Display
Pioneer Tunnel Coal Mine
Ashland, Pennsylvania
September 2000

POLINIAK1970
*When Coal was King
Mining Pennsylvania's Anthracite*
Louis Poliniak
1970
Applied Arts Publishers, Lebanon, PA

PROCTOR1991
*Silver, Sinners, and Saints
A History of Old Silver Reef, Utah*
Paul Dean Proctor, Morris A. Shirts
1991
Paulmar, Inc.

RAGSDALE1976
*Quicksilver
Terlingua & the Chisos Mining Company*
Kenneth Baxter Ragsdale
1976
Texas A&M University Press

RANSOME1901
*A Report on the Economic Geology of the
Silverton Quadrangle, Colorado*
Frederick Leslie Ransome
Geological Survey Bulletin 102

1901
USGS
Government Printing Office

RANSOME1908
The Geology and Ore Deposits of the Coeur d'Alene District, Idaho
Frederick Leslie Ransome and Frank Cathcart Calkins
Geological Survey Professional Paper 62
1908
USGS
Government Printing Office

RANSOME1909
The Geology and Ore Deposits of Goldfield, Nevada
Frederick Leslie Ransome
Geological Survey Professional Paper 66
1909
USGS
Government Printing Office

RANSOME1922
Quicksilver in 1921
Mineral Resources of the United States – Part I
Frederick. Leslie Ransome
1922
Government Printing Office

RAYMOND1873
Statistics of Mines and Mining in the States and Territories
West of the Rocky Mountains
Rossiter W. Raymond
1873
Government Printing Office

REUNERT1972
Diamonds and Gold in South Africa
Theodore Reunert
[*The Cyanide Process*
John S. MacArthur
Appendix XXI]
1893
Edward Stanford, London
(1972 reprint, Books for Libraries Press, Freeport, New York)

RHYOLITE
Rhyolite, Nevada
Information sheet
No Date
Rhyolite Preservation Society, Beatty, Nevada

RICKARD1897
The Stamp Milling of Gold Ores
T. A. Rickard
Second Edition
1897
The Scientific Publishing Co., New York

RICKARD1932
A History of American Mining
T. A. Rickard
1932
Johnson Reprint Corporation, New York
(reprint of McGraw-Hill edition)

RICHARDS1925
A Text Book of Ore Dressing

Robert H. Richards, Charles E. Locke, John L. Bray
Second Edition
1925
McGraw-Hill Book Company, New York

RINGHOLZ1972
Diggings and Doings in Park City
Raye Carleson Ringholz
1972
Western Epics, Salt Lake City

ROBERTS1982
The Carolina Gold Rush
Bruce Roberts
1982
McNally and Loftin, Charlotte, NC

ROHRBOUGH1986
Aspen
The History Of A Silver Mining Town 1879-1893
Malcolm J. Rohrbough
1986
Oxford University Press, New York / Oxford

ROSENTHAL1970
Gold! Gold! Gold!
The Johannesburg Gold Rush
Eric Rosenthal
1970
Collier-Macmillan Ltd., London

ROSS1953
The Geology and Ore Deposits of the Reese River District, Lander County Nevada
Clyde P. Ross
Geological Survey Bulletin 997
1953
USGS
Government Printing Office

ROTHWELL1893
The Mineral Industry Its Statistics, Technology, and Trade
R. P. Rothwell, C.E., M.E.
1893
The Scientific Publishing Co., New York

ROTHWELL1896
The Mineral Industry Its Statistics, Technology, and Trade
R. P. Rothwell, C.E., M.E.
1896
The Scientific Publishing Co., New York

SANDSTROM1963
Tunnels
Gosta E. Sandstrom
1963
Holt, Rinehart and Winston, New York

SAVORY1970
The Mule
Theodore H. Savory
1970
Scientific American

SAYERS1924
Sanitation in Mines
Miners Circular 28
R. R. Sayers

1924
Bureau of Mines
Government Printing Office, Washington

SCHNEIDER1992
Quicksilver
The Complete History of Santa Clara County's
New Almaden Mine
Jimmie Schneider
1992
Zella Schneider, San Jose, California

SHILLINGBERG1999
Tombstone, A. T.
A History of Early Mining, Milling, and Mayhem
Wm. B. Shillingberg
1999
The Arthur H. Clark Company, Spokane

SLOAN1975
The Rainbow Route
An Illustrated History of the Silverton Railroad, the Silverton Northern Railroad, and the Silverton, Gladstone & Northerly Railroad
Robert E. Sloan and Carl A. Skowronski
Sundance Publication Limited, Denver
1975

SLOANE1970
A Pictorial History of American Mining
Howard N. and Lucille L. Sloane
1970
Crown Publishing, New York

SMITHD1967
Rocky Mountain Mining Camps, The Urban Frontier
Duane A. Smith
1967
Bison Book - University of Nebraska Press, Lincoln

SMITHD1974
Silver Saga
Duane A. Smith
1974
Pruett Publishing Co., Boulder

SMITHD1993
Mining America, the Industry and Environment, 1800-1980
Duane A. Smith
1993
University Press of Colorado

SMITHG1998
The History of the Comstock Lode, 1850-1997
Grant H. Smith, with new material by Joseph V. Tingley
1998
University of Nevada Press

SMITHP1994
Mountains of Silver
The Story of Colorado's Red Mountain Mining District
P. David Smith
1994
Pruett Publishing Company, Boulder CO

SMITHR1932
History of Placer and Quartz Gold Mining in the Coeur D'Alene District
A Thesis
Robert Wayne Smith
1932
(No date on reprint)
Ye Galleon Press, Fairfield, Washington

SOWELL1976
Historical Highlights of Idaho Springs Mining Camp Days
Merle L. Sowell
1976
Historical Society of Idaho Springs, Inc.

SPURR1898
Geology of the Aspen Mining District, Colorado, with Atlas
Josiah Edward Spurr
1898
Government Printing Office

STANIER1998
Mines of Cornwall and Devon
An Historic Photographic Record
Peter Stanier
1998
Twelveheads Press, Truro, Cornwall

STEVEN1965
Geology and Structural Control of Ore Deposition in the Creede District San Juan Mountains Colorado
Thomas Steven and James C. Ratté
Geological Survey Professional Paper 487
1965
USGS
Government Printing Office

STEWART1962
Adolph Sutro, A Biography
Robert E. Stewart, Jr. and Mary Frances Stewart
1962
Howell-North, Berkeley California

TAGGART1947
Seventy-Five Years of Progress in Ore Dressing
Arthur F. Taggart
The Mineral Industry 1871-1946
A. B. Parsons, Editor
1947
The American Institute of Mining and Metallurgical Engineers, New York

TAGGART1954
Handbook of Mineral Dressing Ores and Industrial Minerals
Arthur F. Taggart
1927 (1954 reprint)
John Wiley & Sons, Inc., New York

TAYLOR1989
Montana – 1889
The Centennial News Melange
O. J. Taylor
1989
Self-published, Virginia City, Montana

TAYLORJ1964

Jock Taylor's One Hundred Years Ago In Nevada
Jock Taylor
1964
Western Sales Distributing, Inc.

THOMPSON1968
Treasure Mountain Home
A Centennial History of Park City, Utah
George A. Thompson and Fraser Buck
1968
Deseret Book Company, Salt Lake City, Utah

TINGLEY1990
Salt and Silver
J. V. Tingley
1990
Nevada Geology
http://www.nbmg.unr.edu/n1/n17a.htm
Visited 1/11/2001

TINGLEY1993
Outline of Nevada Mining History
Joseph V. Tingley, Robert C. Horton, Francis C. Lincoln
Special Publication 15
1993
Nevada Bureau of Mines and Geology/Mackay School of Mines, Reno

TRENNERT2001
Riding the High Wire
Aerial Mine Tramways in the West
Robert A. Trennert
2001
University Press of Colorado, Boulder, Colorado

TURNBULL1962
Gold Boats on the Swan
The Story of Ben Stanley Revett, Gold Dredger
Belle Turnbull
Vol. XXXIX Number 4
The Colorado Magazine
1962
The State Historical Society of Colorado

TWAIN1980
Roughing It
Mark Twain
1872 (Signet Classic reprint, 1980)

UAPLAMBECK2000
Introductory University Chemistry
Metals: Industrial Chemical Processes
The Oldest Metals: Gold, Silver, and Lead
http://www.chem.ualberta.ca/courses/plambeck/p102/p02261.htm
Visited 4/19/2000

USBM1993
Metal Prices in the United States Through 1991
By the Branch of Metals and Branch of Industrial Minerals
1993
U. S. Bureau of Mines

USBM1996
Dictionary of Mining, Mineral, and Related Terms

Second Edition (CD-ROM)
1996
U. S. Bureau of Mines

USDA
Beaverhead-Deerlodge National Forests information sign
Elkhorn, Montana

USDL1998
Historical Summary of Mine Disasters in the United States
Volume III
Metal and Nonmetal Mines – 1885-1998
U.S. Department of Labor
1998 (microfiche)

USGS1885
Mineral Resources of the United States Calendar Years 1883 and 1884
1885
USGS
Government Printing Office

USGS1886
Mineral Resources of the United States Calendar Year 1885
1886
USGS
Government Printing Office

USGS1887
Mineral Resources of the United States Calendar Year 1886
1887
USGS
Government Printing Office

USGS1894
Mineral Resources of the United States Calendar Year 1893
1894
USGS
Government Printing Office

USGS1896
Seventeenth Annual Report of the United States
Geological Survey
1895-96
Part II – Economic Geology and Hydrography
1896
Government printing Office, Washington

USGS1897
Eighteenth Annual Report of the United States
Geological Survey
1896-97
Part III – Economic Geology
Government Printing Office, Washington

USGS1902
Mineral Resources of the United States Calendar Year 1901
1902
USGS
Government Printing Office

USGS1904
Mineral Resources of the United States Calendar Year 1902

1904
USGS
Government Printing Office

USGS1909
Mineral Resources of the United States
Calendar Year 1908
1909
USGS
Government Printing Office

USGS1997
Natural and Mining Related Sources of
Dissolved Minerals During Low Flow in
the Upper Animas River Basin,
Southwestern Colorado
Fact Sheet FS-148-97
1997
USGS
Government Printing Office, Washington

USGS2001
USGS Website
http://minerals.usgs.gov/minerals/pubs/com
modity/lead/stat/tbl15.txt
Visited 2/22/2001

UTAH2003
When the fabulous Horn Silver mine caved
in
Miriam B. Murphy
History Blazer, January 1996
Utah History To Go
http://historytogo.utah.gov/hornmine.html
Visited 2/01/2003

VICTOR2000
City of Gold Mines
Wayne R. "Mac" McCormick Mining Arti-
fact Exhibit
Publication of the Victor-Lowell Thomas
Museum
(No date)
Victor, Colorado

VOYNICK1984
Leadville: A Miner's Epic
Stephen M. Voynick
1984
Mountain Press Publishing Company, Mis-
soula

WARD2002
Ward Charcoal Ovens State Historic Park
Park pamphlet
2002
Division of State Parks, Carson City, Ne-
vada

WASHOE2000
Ore Processing
Production of Silver Metal using the Patio
Process
Improvement of the Patio Process (oreproc-
essing5.shtml)
The Washoe Process (oreprocess-
ing6.shtml)
http://library.thinkquest.org/50041/chemistr
y/
oreprocessing3.shtml
Visited 10/22/2000

WASSON1878
Bodie and Esmerelda
Jos. Wasson
1878
Facsimile published by the Friends of
Bodie
Bridgeport, California
No Date

WEDERTZ1996
Bodie 1859-1900
Frank S. Wedertz
1996
Chalfant Press, Bishop, California

WEED1901
Geology and Ore Deposits of the Elkhorn
Mining District, Jefferson County, Montana
Walter Harvey Weed
Twenty-Second Annual Report
Part II – Ore Deposits
1901
USGS
Government Printing Office

WEED1912
Geology and Ore Deposits of the Butte
District, Montana
Walter Harvey Weed
Geological Survey Professional Paper 74
1912
USGS
Government Printing Office

WEEKS1886
Report on the Statistics of Wages in Manu-
facturing Industries
Jos. D. Weeks,
Department of the Interior
Census Office
1886
Government Printing Office, Washington

WELLS2002
Gold Camps & Silver Cities
Nineteenth-Century Mining in Central and
Southern Idaho
Merle W. Wells
2002
University of Idaho Press, Moscow, Idaho

WELLSE1957
Gold Mining and Gold Deposits in New
Mexico
Circular No. 5
E. H. Wells, T. P. Wootton
1957
State Bureau of Mines and Mineral Re-
sources, Socorro, New Mexico

WIER1957
Nevada, A Guide to the Silver State
Sponsored by Dr. Jeanne Elizabeth Wier
1957
Binfords & Mort, Portland, Oregon

WILSON1907
The Chlorination Process
E. B. Wilson
1907
John Wiley & Sons, New York

WOLLE1963
The Bonanza Trail
Ghost Towns and Mining Camps of the
West
Muriel Sibell Wolle
1963
Bonanza Books, New York

WOLLE1977
Timberline Tailings
Tales of Colorado's Ghost Towns and
Mining Camps
Muriel Siebell Wolle
1977
Swallow Press/Ohio University Press,
Athens

WOLVERTON1988
Wolverton Mill
1988
Richfield District
Richfield, Utah
U. S. Department of the Interior

YOUNGG1909
The Ventilating-System at the Comstock
Mines, Nevada
George J. Young
1909
Volume III, No. 4
University of Nevada Bulletin
University of Nevada, Reno

YOUNGO1972
Western Mining
Otis E. Young, Jr., Robert Lenon
1970
University of Oklahoma Press

Index

In addition to text references, underlined entries include charts and tables, **bold** entries include **photographs**. *These graphic and tabular item highlights exclude items in the appendices.*

People

Aaron, Charles Howard, 147
Airis, E. H., 220
Albert, A., 38
Arents, Albert, 168
Ashenfelter, John, 95
Austin, W. Lawrence, 177

Backus, George, 128, 231, 237
Backus, Harriet Fish, 94, 98
Bailey, Louis, 199
Balbach Jr., Edward, 178
Baldwin, F. E., 41
Barba, Alvaro Alonzo, 131
Bartlett, 186
Beach, T. S., 74
Beaumier, Victor, 22
Beemer, George, 216
Behr, Hans C., 66
Bennett, Edwin, 23, 28, 32, 41, 97, 230
Benoist, A. E., 22
Bessel, 128
Betts, Dr. William, 232
Bickford, William, 73
Billing, Gutav, 177
Birkhead, Billy, 198
Bishop, Mr., 100
Blake, Eli Whitney, 201
Bleichert, Adolf, 104
Bokkelen, General J. L. Van, 30
Brannan, Sam, 1
Breevort, Henry, 134
Brewer, William H., 26, 231
Brooks, 78
Brown, Hal W., 220
Brückner, 191, 210
Buckley, William, 82
Bullard, 235
Burleigh, Charles, 78, 79, 80
Burns, "Big Paddy", 233

Cameron Jr., James. C., 114
Campion, John, 176
Carmin, Tom, 23
Carpenter, 128
Chabolla, Luis, 181
Chabot, 9
Clark, Fred, 235
Clark, William Andrew, 223, 224
Cobb, E. F., 109
Coffey, Lester, 234
Colcord, Roswell K., 62
Coley, John, 233
Comstock, Henry Thomas Paige, 193
Cook, Eric, 233
Couch, J. J., 77
Cover, W. F., 235
Crampton, Frank, 29, 35, 36, 228, 229, 233, 235, 237
Crook, Bill, 97
Cubbon, Josiah, 236
Curtis, Allan A., 142

Daly, Marcus, 223
Darby, John C., 233
Davis, Andrew J., 23
Davis, Reese, 234
Davy, 41
De La Mar, Captain J. L., 110, 220, 221
de Medina, Bartolomé, 131
De Quille, Dan, 39, 111, 134, 138, 228, 229, 234
Deidesheimer, Philip, 57, 221
Deister, Emil, 207
Deitken, G. F., 143
Delaney, John, 233
Derby, Lieutenant, 83
Dern, John, 220
Divine, Silas R., 75, 76
Doane, Thomas, 79
Downey, Jerry, 233
Doyle, "Dutch", 98
Doyle, James, 230
Drinker, Henry S., 48
Duffy, Joe, 232, 233
Dugan, Larry, 232
Dunlap, Shelley, 236

Edgar, Henry, 3
Elsner, 154
Emmons, Samuel Franklin, 134, 138
Exeli, Bergrath Adolf, 183

Fairweather, William, 3
Farlin, William L., 223
Foote, Arthur De Wint, 82, 109
Ford, C. S., 108
Forrest, Robert, 154
Forrest, William, 154
Fowle, Joseph, 77, 78, 80
Fowle, Tom, 28
Frue, William, 207

Galloway, James, 44
Galloway, John Debo, 113
Gardner, G. A., 79
Gates, 78
Gibbons, Reverend, 233
Gillespie, R. T., 138
Gregg, Harry M., 58, 228
Gregory, John Hamilton, 216

Haggerdy, Andrew, 236
Haines, J. W. 113
Hallett, S. I., 207
Hallidie, Andrew Smith, 38, 104
Hamilton, Patrick, 140
Harkleroder brothers, 6
Harney, Hank, 216
Hawkes, Samuel, 225
Hawkesworth, Arthur L., 82
Hearst, George, 235
Heffner, 23
Henning, W. S., 236
Hesselmeyer, 109
Hildreth, Dr. Thadeus, 2
Hill, 83
Hill, Professor Nathaniel Peter, 169, 224
Hofmann, O., 153
Holden, Edward, 152
Holt, 80
Holton, Thomas, 234
Horton, Hector, 221
Howland, William H., 134
Hughes, Barney, 3
Humphrey, Isaac, 5

Huson, Charles M., 104
Hutchinson, Jim, 109
Hüttner, H. J., 184

Iler, 86
Ingersoll, Simon, 80

Jackling, Daniel C., 221
Jackson, 85
Jackson, George, 25
Jackson, R. D., 158
Janin, Louis, 182
Jenkins, Arthur, 236
Jenks, L. P., 79
Jones, Richard P., 164
Judson, Egbert, 74

Kearney, W. H., 22
Kelly, Tom, **3**
Keyes, Winfield Scott, 168
King, Wesley F., 22
Kingsley, Clifford W., 98
Kirchen, Mr., 236
Kiss, 153
Kleeman, Rudolph, 234
Knight, George, 22
Koenig, Professor, 151
Küstel, Guido, 141, 153

Langguth, W., 150
Lavin, Samuel, 233
Lean, Captain, 66
Ledford, William, 65
Lee, 238
Leschot, Professor Rodolph, 78
Leyner, J. George, 84, 85, 86
Lord, Elliot, 45, 229

MacArthur, John S., 154, 156
Mahar, Billy, 234
Maloney, 233
Maltman, O., 143
Manuel, Fred, 216
Manuel, Moses, 216
Marshall, James, 1
Marshall, Thomas, 130
Marten, Al, 236
Mason, Alonzo, 233
Matteson, Edward E., 9
McCann, 23
McCoy, Major W. W., 164
McFarlene, Andy, 111
McMaster, Sam, 235
Mears, B. H., M. D., 148
Mears, Otto, 96, 102, 103
Merrill, Charles W., 158
Miller, Mr., 65
Minthorn, D., 82
Montgomery, Bob, 23
Morgan, George, 22
Morgan, Tom, 22
Mullan, Garry & Monika, 226, 227
Murphy, John, 233
Murphy, *Metalliferous*, 123

Nobel, Alfred, 72, 73, 74, 75
Norrbin, J. H., 74
Norton, W. A., 193
Nunn, Lucius L., 110, 220
Nunn, Paul H., 110
Nye, E. W. "Bill", 26
Nystrom, Andrew, 235

O'Donnell, Hugh, 234
Ohlsson, C. J., 74
Olivetti, Alexander, 236
Orr, William, 154
Otto, Theodore, 104
Overton, Captain J. B., 109

Parks, William, 223
Parsons, Mr., 232
Paul, Almarin B., 133
Pearce, Professor Richard, 170
Pelton, Lester A., 108, 109
Penniman, R. S., 75
Percy, 153
Peyton, G. S., 220
Phelps, Lucius J., 84
Pitchford, J. B., 82
Plattner, Karl Friedrich, 143
Pollok, J. H., 146
Porter, John A., 171

Rabitz, Mike "Rabbit", 42
Rand, Addison C., 84
Rand, Albert C., 81
Rand, J. R., 81
Ransome, Frederick, 46, 64
Rasberry, Bennager, 22
Raymond, Rossiter, 168, 197
Red, 191
Reed, Conrad, 1
Reed, David, 231
Reed, John, 1
Revett, Ben Stanley, 13
Richards, Samuel, 233
Rickard, Bob, 113
Rickard, James, 194
Rix, Edward A., 109
Robbins, Colonel G. C., 164
Roberts, W. F., 235
Robinson, 233
Robinson, John, 22
Rogers, Thomas, 233
Roots, Francis M., 165
Roots, P. H., 165
Ross, Thomas
Rossi, Stephano, 234
Rothwell, J. E., 151
Ryan, James, 225

Sample, "Big George", 230
Savory, Theodore H., 93
Scheele, 154
Schneider, Jimmie, 70, 107
Schönbein, Christian Fredrich, 73, 75
Scott, Robert, 184, 185
Sergeant, Henry C., 80, 83
Severance, 80
Shaffner, 74
Shaw, C. H., 84
Shaw, Moses, 73
Sherwood, Rupe, 94
Shifler, Hank, 233
Shoshone Johnny, 23
Sieger, Henry, 177
Simpson, Deputy Sheriff J. B., 115
Singer, Isaac M., 77
Singer, J. A., 77
Smith, Grant, 62, 116
Smith, H. B., 233
Sobrero, Ascanio, 73
Stanley, 238
Stetefeldt, Carl A., 141, 142
Stevens, Colonel Sherman, 114

Stewart, Senator William Morris, 169
Sturtevant, B. F., 165
Sullivan, Michael "Sully", 233
Sunol, Antonio, 181
Sutro, Adolph Heinrich Joseph, 47, 80, 81
Sutter, John, 1
Swickhart, John, 23

Tabor, (Horace), 173
Talcott, William M., 142
Thies, Carl Adolph, 149
Tingley, J. V., 134
Traverdon, M. 84
Tulloch, James, 135
Turner, Col. N. P., 17
Twain, Mark, 123

Vieille, Paul, 75
Von Patera, 153
Voynick, Steven, 229
Vranes, Mike, 236

Walker brothers, 223
Wasson, Jos., 194
Waters, Ed, 236
Waugh, D. S., 84
Wayne, Major Henry C., 100
Whittingham, Wm., 22
Wilfley, Arthur Redman, 205
Willard, J. W., 75
Williams, Henry, 224
Williams Jr., John J., 164
Wilson, John, 96
Wilson, Thomas, 237
Wilson, Tom, 23
Winchester, E. S., 82
Wolle, Muriel Sibell, 93, 98
Wolverton, Edwin Thatcher, 193
Wood, Professor De Volsom, 81
Woods, Daniel, 6

Places

Alamitos Creek, CA, 184
Alder Gulch, MT, 3
Alma district, CO, 94
Amador, CA, 238
American Camp, CA, 2
American River, CA, 1, 12
Ames, CO, **110**
Amusing Placenames, 3
Anaconda, MT, **55**, **86**, 224, 236
Angel's Camp, CA, 22
Animas River, CO, 171
Arizona, 16, 200
Arrastra Gulch, CO, 171
Ashland, PA, **99**
Aspen, CO, 25, 62, 64, 84, 95, 96, 103, 110, 111, 113, 174, 207, 234
Auburn, OR, 96
Aurora, NV, 194
Austin, NV, 101, **134**, 142, 235
Australia, 128, 207, 226
    See *Mount Morgan* Mines and Mills

Bannack, MT, 3, 7, 13, **158**, 198
Bay Horse, ID, 177
Bear River, CA, 12
Bear River, UT, 17
Belgium, 186
Berlin, NV, 28
Bingham Canyon, UT, 25

Bisbee, AZ, **6**
Black Hawk, CO, 107, **111**, 169, 170, 207, 216, 224
Black Hills, SD, 196
Blue River, CO, **14**
Bodie, CA, 69, 71, 72, 106, 198, 218, 230, 234, 236, 238
Boise (Basin), ID, 6, 112
Bonanza, CO, 98, 100
Boulder, CO, **142**
Breckenridge (district), CO, **13**, **14**
Brown University, 169
Brown's Flat, CA, **63**
Burke, ID, 92
Butte, MT, 7, 23, 29, 44, 65, 82, 157, 177, **222**, **223**, **224**, 230, 231, 232, 233

Cabarrus County, NC, 1
California, 5, 6, 8, 14, 15, 16, 17, 153, 195, 204, 233
Calumet, CA, 158
Camp Florence, UT, 235
Camptonville, CA, 108
Cañon City, CO, 186
Canyon Creek, MT, 114
Carbonate Hill, CO, 173,
Caribou, CO, 117, **143**, 232
Carson City, NV, 102, 113, 180
Carson River, NV, 111, **135**, **136**
Central City, CO, 48, 169, 170, 216, 238
Cerro Gordo, CA, 95, 114, 231
Challis, ID, 104, 158
Chattanooga, CO, 103
Chicago, IL, 17, 225
Chihuahua, Mexico, 94, 95
China, 207
Clear Creek (North), CO, 191, 216
Coast Range, CA, 181
Coeur d'Alene, ID, 7, 8, 96, 110, 175, 186, 194, 209
Coeur d'Alene Lake, ID, 92, 96
Coloma, CA, **1**, 6
Colorado, 6, 16, 115, 169, 171, 177, 186
Columbia, CA, 2, **5**
Columbia Gardens, MT, **29**
Comstock Lode
    See *Comstock (Lode)* Mines
Confederate Gulch, MT, 6
Connellsville, PA, 115
Cooper Hill, WY, 22
Corinne, UT, 223
Cornucopia district, NV, 116
Cornwall, 26, 66, 72, 73
Cosumnes River, CA, 194
Coulterville, CA, 26, 194
County
    Boulder, CO, **29**
    Colfax, NM, 16
    Del Norte, CA, 11
    El Dorado, CA, 16
    Gilpin, CO, 169, 196, 197, **205**, 207, 224
    Hindsdale, CO, 25
    Inyo, CA, 16
    Mariposa, CA, 194
    Moffat, CO, **12**, **13**
    Nevada, CA, 9, **10**, 11, 12, 16, 24, 26
    Placer, CA, 10, 12, 14
    Pinal, AZ, **97**
    Siskiyou, CA, 11
    Stanislaus, CA, 11
    Tuolumne, CA, **5**, **63**
    Yuba, CA, 10, 16

Creede, CO, 32, 42, **92**, 97, 99, 116, 186, 203, 236
Cripple Creek, CO, 7, 25, 29, 50, 56, 94, 116, 123, 144, <u>152</u>, 157, 158, 198, 203, 229, 238
Cunningham Gulch, CO, **93**
Cummins City, WY, 26
Curtis Creek, CA, 6

Deadwood, SD, **3**, 158, 216
Delamar, NV, <u>45</u>, **232**
Denver, CO, 84, 96, 103, 170, 175, 177, 186, 220
Devon, 26
Discovery Bar, ID, 2
Dolores River, CO, **17**
Durango, CO, 23, 171
Dutch Flat, CA, 11

Eberhardt, NV, 136, **137**
El Moro, CO, 115
Eldorado Bar, MT, 4
Elizabethtown, NM, 16
Elkhorn, MT, 24, **219**
Elko, NV, 96
Empire, CO, 233
England, 73, 196
Estancia (salt lakes), NM, 94
Eureka, CO, 95, 105, 128, 236
Eureka, NV, 25, **92**, 96, 111, 115, 164, 165, 168, <u>169</u>, 179
Europe, 181

Fairplay, CO, **94**
Feather River, CA, **8**, 12
Fish Creek, NV, 115
Florence, CO, 152
Folsom district, CA, 13, <u>14</u>
Francklyn, UT, 225
Freiberg district, NV, 104
French Corral, CA, **10**
French Creek, CO, **13**
Frisco, UT, 225

Georgetown, CO, 143, 186, 210, 216, 232
Georgia, 1, 4, <u>6</u>, <u>16</u>, 17, 26, 194
Germany, 72, 73, 82
Gila River, AZ, 25
Gillett, CO, 152
Gladstone, CO, 23
Glasgow University, Scotland, 146
Glendale, MT, 114
Gold Creek, NV, 236
Gold Hill, NV, 62, 238
Golden, CO, 177
Goldfield, CO, **122**
Goldfield, NV, 61
Grass Valley, CA, 22, 66, 68, **130**, 141, 155, 209
Grasshopper Creek, MT, 13
Gregory district, CO, 170

Hamilton, NV, 95, 103
Hanging Flume, CO, 17
Hecla, MT, 114
Helena, MT, **16**, 96
Hettstadt, Germany, 171
Hildreth's Diggins, CA, 2
Hilliard, UT, 17
Howardsville, CO, 103, 106
Humbug Gulch, NM, 16
Hungary, 73

Idaho, <u>6</u>, <u>16</u>
Idaho City, ID, 6
Idaho Springs, CO, 25, 43, 48, 84
Illinois Central district, CO, 170
India, 207
Indian Bar, CA, 17
Indianola, TX, 95

Jack Rabbit Spring, CO, **12**
Jarbidge, NV, 199
Jerome, AZ, **170**
Joachimsthal, Czechoslovakia, 153
Joplin, MO, 232, <u>233</u>

Kansas, 186
Karangahake, New Zealand, 154
Kingman, AZ, 116
Klondike, AK, 25

Lake City, CO, 25, 64, 105
Lake Superior region, 180
Lake Tahoe, CA-NV, 113
Lander Hill, NV, 142
Lead, SD, 3, 58
Leadville, CO, **57**, 61, 94, 95, 96, 99, 108, 114, 115, <u>172</u>, <u>173</u>, **175**, <u>176</u>, 177, 186, 231, 237, 238
Leeds, UT, 123
Lehigh, PA, 180
Lincoln district, MT, 14
Little Meadow Creek, 1
Little Pinto, UT, **114**
Livingston, MT, 101
Loon Creek district, ID, 104
Los Angeles, CA, 95

Magdalena, NM, 95
Manhattan, NV, 236
Marble Bar, Australia, 226
Maryland, 223
Marysville, CA, 3
Marysville, MT, 198
Meadow Lake, CA, 24, 25, 119, 128, 218, 219
Mercur, UT, 110, **117**, 154, 158, 220, **221**
Mesa Creek Flats, CO, 17
Mexico, 131, 153, 175
Millers, NV, 231
Milwaukee, WI, 13
Mine Hill, CA, 36
Mineral City, WA, 93
Mokelumne Hill, CA, 24, 116
Mokelumne River, CA, 12
Montana, <u>6</u>, <u>16</u>, 155, 157, 158, 193, 221, 222
Montana Bar, MT, 6
Montrose, CO, 96, 102
Mosquito Gulch, CO, 94
Mother Lode region, CA, 15, 196, 228
Mount
    Aspen. CO, 105
    Bellevue, CO, 235
    Bross, CO, 92
    Engineer, CO, 64
    Galena, CO, 105
    Pancake, NV, 165
    Pennell, UT, 193
Mountains
    Henry, UT, 193
    Klamath-Trinity, CA, 12
    Mosquito, CO, 92
    Pine Valley, UT, 113
    San Juan, CO, **23**, 28, **93**, 105

Sierra Nevada, CA, 12, 95, 98, 103, 111
Uintah, UT, 17, 111

Neihart, MT, 101
Nevada City, CA, 144
Nevadaville (district), CO, 170, 207
New Jersey, 177
New York (City), 64, 73, 84, 172, 173
New Zealand, 13
Newark, NJ, 168, 177
North Carolina, 4, 26, 181

Oatman, AZ, **93**, <u>233</u>
Old Placers, NM, 7
Omaha, NE, 96
Ontario, Canada, 211
Ophir Canyon, UT, 223
Oreana, NV, **164**
Oregon, <u>6</u>, <u>16</u>
Oro Grande, ID, 112
Oroville district, CA, 13, <u>14</u>
Orwigsburg Landing, PA, 46
Ouray, CO, 46, 50, 95, 96, 102, 103, 105, 177, 231, 233, 234
Owens Lake, CA, 114, 231
Owyhee district, ID, 112

Palisade, NV, 168
Panamint, CA, 169
Pandora, CO, 105, 219, 237
Park City, UT, 28, 30, 42, 46, 57, 67, 71, 85, 86, 99, 100, 105, 110, 111, 116, 130, 209, 215, 218, 231, 233, 235, 237
Pennsylvania, 81, 151
Peru, 131
Philadelphia, PA, 77, 148
Philipsburg, MT, 83, 199, 221, 222, 233, 234, 235
Pilbara, Australia, **226**, **227**
Piños Altos district, NM, 193, 194, 203
Pioche, NV, 50, 96, **104**, 117, 123
Placerville, ID, 139
Placerville route, CA, **98**
Pony, MT, 23
Pony Gulch, NV, 142
Portland, ME, 186
Portland, OR, 96
Prichard Creek, ID, 7
Promontory, UT, **91**, **102**
Provo River, UT, 110, 221
Pueblo, CO, 102, 103, 175

Quartzville, CO, 92

Radersburg district, MT, 215
Red Mountain, CO, 22, 25, 30, 31, 38, <u>45</u>, 50, 96, 103
Red Mountain Creek, CO, 64
Red River, NM, 16
Redstone, CO, **115**
Reese River district, NV, 3, 25, 142, <u>143</u>, 198, 199
Reno, NV, 102, 103, 142
Rhodes Marsh, NV, 101
Rhyolite, NV, 3, 23
Rico, CO, 128, 238
Robinson, CO, 177
Rochester district, MT, 71
Rockerville, SD, **9**
Rocky Bar, ID, 96
Rossie Hill, UT, 116
Rossland, B.C., 61

Roubaix, SD, 198
Russell district, CO, 170

Sacramento River, CA, 11, 12
Salt Lake (City, valley), UT, 17, 115, 177, 221, 223, 225, 231
San Francisco, CA, 1, 80, 168, 203
San Francisco district, UT, 114, 225
San Jose, CA, 181
San Miguel River, CO, 17
Sandy, UT, 122, 177
Santa Rita, NM, 95
Scotland, 41, 123, 146
Searchlight, NV, 23
Silesia, Czechoslovakia, 143
Silver City, NV, 158
Silver Cliff, CO, 143, 232, 238
Silver Plume, CO, 80
Silver Reef, UT, 39, 113, 123, 138, 140, 198
Silver Star district, MT, 157
Silverton, CO, 64, 85, 95, 102, **104, 105,** 106, 171, 177, 234
Smartsville, CA, **16**
Snake River, 10
Sneffels, CO, 46, 95, 238
Socorro, NM, 95
Sodaville, NV, 95
South Boise area, ID, 193
South Carolina, 1
South Dakota, 6, 16,
South Pass, WY, **25**
Sparta, OR, 6
St. Joseph, MO, 96
St. Louis, MO, 95
Steven's Wharf, CA, 114
Summit Valley, MT, 7
Sutter's Mill, CA, 1
Swan River, CO, 13, 234
Swansea, Wales, 92, 169, 241
Sweden, 74, 82, 83

Telegraph Hill, CA, 80
Telluride, CO, 50, 94, 98, 105, 110, 231
Terraville, SD, 3, **129, 216**
Tombstone, AZ, 66, 140
Tomichi, CO, 112
Tonopah, NV, 25, 37, 50, 95, 97, 102, 199, 233
Toston, MT, 177
Tourtelotte Park, CO, 103
Trail Creek, ID, 8
Transvaal, South Africa, 154
Treasure City, NV, 112
Treasure Hill, NV, 96
Trinidad, CO, 115
Trout Creek, MT, **16**
Tuolumne River, CA, 12
Tuscarora, NV, 116

University of Pennsylvania, 151

Victor, CO, 7, **31,** 117, **152,** 157, **203,** 236
Virgin River, UT, 140
Virginia, 1
Virginia City, MT, 3
Virginia City, NV, 30, **35, 39,** 44, 61, 62, 68, 95, 101, 102, 111, 116, **133, 139,** 142, 219, 238

Walker Lake, NV, 101
Wallula, OR, 96
Ward, NV, **114**

Wardner, ID, 84
West Willow Creek, CO, 97
White Oaks, NM, 23, 238
White Pine, NV, 25, 29, 41, 81, 95, 96, 97, 104, 112, 136, 137, 164, 165, 166, 216, 219, 232, 233
White Sulphur Springs, MT, 101
Witwatersrand, South Africa, 154
Wood River, ID, 110

Yankee Fork district, ID, 193
Yuba River, CA, 12
Yukon, AK, 25

Mines, Tunnels & Flumes

A. E. Reynolds properties, CO, 23
A. G., CO, **57**
A. M. Holter, MT, 219
Acquisition, MT, 223
Aduddel, CO, 49
Alice, MT, 223
Allegheny Tunnel, PA, 46
Alliance Tunnel, UT, 46
Alta, NV, 69
Amador, CA, 238
Americus, CO, 238
Amethyst, CO, 236
Amie, CO, 173
Amusing Mine Names, 24
Anaconda Silver Mining Co., MT, 224
Anchor, UT, 237
Anna Lee, CO, 238
Argo Tunnel, CO
       See *Newhouse Tunnel* Mines
Aspen, CO, 105
Aspen Mining and Smelting Co., 103
Asteroid, MT, 223
Auburn Canal Co., 96
Auburn Tunnel, PA, **46**

Barbee & Walker Silver Mining Co., 39
Barron, Forbes Co., 36, 181
Belcher, NV, 58, **59,** 108
Belgian, CO, 238
Big Ditch, NM, 16
Bimetallic, MT, 221, 233, 235
Bobtail Tunnel, CO, 107
Bodie, CA, 230
Boss Tweed, MT, 23
Breece, CO, 173
Broadway, MT, 157
Buena Vista, CA, **66,** 69
Bull-Domingo, CO, 238
Bullion, NV, **39,** 44
Burke, NV, 117
Burleigh Tunnel, CO, 80
Burroughs, CO, 49

Cable, MT, **86,** 221
Calhoun, CO, 49
California, CO, 49
California, NV, 45, 59
Camp Bird, CO, 50, 105
Carbonate, CO, 173
Carissa, WY, **25**
Champion, CA, 69, 236
Champion, MT, 71
Charles Dickens, ID, 193
Chollar, 109
Chrysolite, CO, 173

Cleopatra, CO, 235
Climax, CO, 94
Colorado Gold Dredging Co., 13, **14**
Comanche, MT, 221
Combination, NV, 44, 68
Commodore, CO, **92, 99**

Comstock (Lode), 24, 25, 26, 38, 39, 41, 43, 44, 45, 47, 50, 56, 57, 58, 59, **60,** 61, 62, 63, 64, 69, 70, 71, 72, 74, 81, 83, 98, 102, 107, 108, 109, 111, 112, 113, 133, 134, 138, 139, 140, 142, 143, 158, 215, 231, 233, 237

Concrete, CO, 49
Consolidated Virginia, NV, 39, 44, 45, 59, 62, 82, 113, 116
Contention, AZ, 66
Copper Falls Co., MI, 81
Cora Blanca, CA, 70
Crescent, UT, 237
Cresson, CO, 7
Crown Point, NV, 58, **59,** 61, 238

Daly, UT, 42, 46, 237
Daly West, UT, 46, 85, 231
Daly-Judge, UT, 28, 46, 100
Delamar, NV, 45
Dunkin, CO, 173

Eberhardt, NV, 104
Elkhorn, MT, 219, 220
Eureka, CA, 141
Eureka Consolidated, NV, 119
Evening Star, CO, 173

F. Shanly & Co., MA, 81
Forman Combination, NV, 44
Free Silver, CO, 64
Frontenac, CO, 49

Galt, MT, 101
Gem, CO 49
Genessee, CO, 22, 64
Gilpin, CO, 49
Gold Coin, MT, **55**
Gold Hill, CA, 22, 66
Gold Hill, ID, 139
Gold King, CO, 110
Golden Cycle Mining Co., 51, **152**
Golden Gate, CA, **8**
Golden Gate group, UT, 220
Goldfield Consolidated, NV, 61
Gopher, SD, 58
Gould & Curry, NV, **35,** 70, 74, 238
Grand Central, AZ, 66
Granite (Mountain), MT, 221, 233, 235
Grey shaft, CA, 106
Gunnel, CO, 49
Guston, CO, 45, 50, 64

Hale & Norcross, NV, 44, 48, 70, 109, 112
Hanging Flume, CO, **17**
Hecla Consolidated Mining Co., MT, 114
Hector Mining Co., 105
Hell's Gate, NY, 83
Hemlock, CA, 169
Henriett, CO, 176
Henrietta Tunnel, UT, 46
Hidden Treasure, CA, 15
Hilliard Flume and Lumber Co., 17
Hock Hocking, CO, 94
Holy Terror, 24

Homestake, SD, 25, 50, 57, 58, 61, 83, 85, 86, 100, 216, 234
Homestake, NM, 23
Hoosac Tunnel, MA, 46, 74, **78**, 79, 80, 81
Hope, MT, 83, 221
Hope Mining Co., MT, 221
Horn Silver, UT, **62**, 225, 231
Horn Silver Mining Co., UT, 225
Hub Gold Mining Co., 25
Hudson, CO, 50, 96

Ibex, CO, 61
Idaho Co., 96
Illinois and Michigan canal, 77
Imperial (-Empire) shaft, NV, 44, 62, 236, 237
Independence, CO, 105, 236
Iowa-Tiger, CO, 42, 234
Iron Silver, CO, 173

Joker Tunnel, CO, 64, 85
Julia shaft, NV, 44
Jupiter, MT, 230

Kansas, CO, 48, 49
Kendall, MT, 155
Kentuck, NV, 61, 62, 238

Last Chance, ID, 84
Lexington group, MT, 23
Liberty Bell, CO, 50, 219, 237
Little Jonny, CO, 176
Logan, CO, **29**

Maginnis, MT, 198
Maid of Erin, CO, 176
Malakoff (Diggins), CA, 9, 10, **11**, 236
Mammoth, CO, 49
Matchless, CO, 173
Mayflower, CA, 15
Mercur Gold Mining and Milling Co., UT, 154
Mexican, NV, 26
Miner's Delight, WY, 25
Minnie, CO, **57**
Mollie Gibson, CO, 84, 174
Monongahela, CO, **39**
Mont Cenis Tunnel, France, 78
Montana, SD, **21**
Montgomery-Shoshone, NV, 23
Montrose Placer Mining Co., CO, 17
Moose Mine, CO, 92
Moose Mining Co., 92
Morning, ID, 110
Morning Star, CO, 173
Mount Morgan, Australia, **34, 35, 37, 51, 63, 84**
Myrtle Mining Co, ID, **8**

Nellie, CO, 105
New Almaden, CA, 36, 43, 62, **66**, 67, 68, 69, 70, 82, 83, 84, 106, 108, 181, 182, 183, 203, 230, 236
New Idria, CA, 26, 63, 185
New Pittsburgh group, CO, 175
New Yellow Jacket, NV, 63, 71, 236
Newhouse (Argo) Tunnel, CO, 43, 48, **49**, 84
North Bloomfield Mining Co., 12
North Star, CA, 68
North Star Mining Co., **109**

Old Abe, NM, 238
Old Dominion, OR, 22
Old Hundred, CO, 85, 106
Old Town, CO, 49
Ontario, UT, 46, 57, 67, 71, 110, 231, 235
Ophir, NV, 57, 64, 107, 116
Ortiz, NM, 7

Pacific Wood, Lumber, and Fluming Co., 113
Paragon, CA, 15
Parrot, MT, 223
Philadelphia Mining and Smelting Co., 110
Pioneer Tunnel, PA, **99**
Pittsburgh and Idaho Gold and Silver Mining Co., 96
Polar Star, CO, 64
Portland, CO, 50
Pozo, CO, 49
Present Help, CO, 92
Prize, CO, 49

Quartette, NV, 23
Quicksilver Mining Co., 181
Quincy, UT, 237

Rawley Tunnel, CO, 98
Revenue Tunnel (Mining Co.), CO, 46, 64, 100, 109, 110, 233, 236
Robinson, CO, 64

Samson, Germany, **72**
San Francisco Mining Co., MT, 234
San Miguel Flume, CO, **17**
Santa Isabel, CA, 68, 69
Saratoga, CO, 49
Savage, NV, 39, 40, 44, 47, 48, 61
Schuylkill Navigation, 46
Silver Cord, CO, 175
Silver King, UT, 46, 105, 233, 237
Silver Lake, CO, 85
Silver Ledge, CO, 30
Sleepy Hollow, CO, 238
Smuggler (Aspen), CO, 62, 95, 113
Smuggler (Pandora), CO, 105
South Lateral Tunnel (Sutro), NV, 48
Spanish, CA, 51
St. Gothard Tunnel, Alps, 228
St. Lawrence, MT, 65
St. Louis & Montana Mining Co., 221
Standard, CA, 106, 230
Stewart, MT, 44
Sun and Moon, CO, 49
Sunnyside, CO, 95, 105, 234
Sunrise, WY, 234
Sutro Tunnel, NV, 42, 44, **47**, 48, 63, 70, 80, 82, 83, 100, 110, 112, 233, 237

Terrible, CO, 231, 234, 236
Tioga, CA, 238
Tomboy, CO, 94, 98
Tonopah Mining Co., 102
Travona, MT, 223, 224
Treasury Tunnel, CO, 31
Trout Creek Flume, MT, **16**
Tucson, CO, 173

Union, CO, 105
Union, NV, 71

Van Emmons, CA, 10
Vanderbilt, CO, 50, 64
Veteran Tunnel, CO, 110

Virginius, CO, 46, 64, 234, 237, 238

Weed's Point, CA, 10
Wellington, CO, **13**
White Hills, AZ, 116
Widow, ID, 7
Wyoming, CA, 169

Yankee Girl, CO, 22, 64, 95, 96
Yellow Jacket, ID, 104
Yellow Jacket, NV, 47, 61, 81, 108, 238

Mills & Smelters

Alaska Treadwell, AK, 152
American Smelting and Refining Co., 171
American Zinc-Lead Co., 186
Amethyst, CO, 203, 230
Anaconda, MT, 224
Argo (Denver), CO, 170
Argo (Idaho Springs), CO, **49**
Arkansas Valley, CO, 175

Balbach, NJ, 168
Ballou, Napheys & Co., 216
Belcher, NV, 139
Bi-Metallic, CO, 177
Bi-Metallic, MT, 199
Birdie, MT, 193
Black Hills Gold and Extraction Co., SD, 158
Bobtail, CO, 207
Bodie, CA, 198
Boston-Globe Smelting Co., 177
Boston and Colorado Smelting Co., CO, 169, 216, 224
Brunswick, NV, **135, 136**
Buell & Co., NV, 142
Bunker Hill & Sullivan West, ID, 209
Buster, NV, 199

Caledonia, SD, **216**
California, CO, 207
California, NV, 203, 219
Camp Bird, CO, 110
Carson Mint, NV, 180
Cherry Creek, MT, 157
Christy, UT, 138, 198
Colorado, MT, 65
Colorado & Montana Smelting Co., 224
Colorado Smelting & Refining Co., **224**
Comstock, NV, 101
Consolidated Mercur Gold Mines Co., UT, 221
Consolidated Mining Co., UT, 209
Consolidated Virginia, NV, 134, 135, 136, 139, 219
Crown, New Zealand, 154

Dakota, MT, 198
Dall's Freiberg, NV, 143
Daly-Judge, UT, 46
Deadwood Terra No. 2 (and No. 3), SD, **216**
Deloro, Canada, 211
DeSantis, 157
Dexter, MT, 223, 224

Eagle, CO, **122**
East Malarite, 157
Elkhorn, MT, 219, 220

Empire, CA, 155, 156
Enterprise, CA, 219
Eureka, CO, 105, 196
Eureka Consolidated, NV, 164, 165, 166, 168, 169, 201
Excelsior Co., CA, 218

Garrett, Martine & Co., 216
Geddes and Bertrand, NV, 169
Germania Separating and Refining Works, UT, 177, 178
Gilt Edge, MT, 158
Gold King, CO, 23
Gold Recovery Syndicate, 154
Golden Chest Mining Co., ID, 194
Golden Gate, UT, 110, **117, 221**
Golden Reward Gold Mining Co., SD, 150
Golden Star, SD, 198, 216, 218
Gould & Curry, NV, **133, 139**, 143
Greene, CO, 171
Gregory, NV, 194
Gunnar Gold, 157

Haile, SC, 149
Hale & Norcross, NV, 139
Harrison, CO, 175
Hendricks, MT, **158**
Highland, SD, 130
Home, CO, 177
Homestake, SD, 16, 117, 130, 158, 197, 198, 216, 218
Hope, MT, 221
Horn Silver Mining Co., UT, 225
Huepeden & Co., 216
Humphrey, CO, **cover, 127**

Idria, Austria, 183
International, NV, 104, 140, 219

J. R. Nichols Metallurgical Works, UT, 122
James Stewart, MT, 221

Kendrick-Gelder, CO, 177
Kerr Addison, 157
Kilton Chlorination Works, CO, **142**
Kittimac, CO, 236

La Plata, CO, 175
Lebel Oro, 157
Leopard, NV, 116

Manhattan, NV, 134
Manhattan Silver Mining Co., NV, 142, 143
Manning, UT, 154, 220
Marsac, UT, 209
Mayflower, CO, **104, 105**
Mercur Gold Mining & Milling Co., UT, 220
Metallic Extraction Co., CO, 152
Mexican, NV, 143
Midway, CO, 105
Montezuma Silver Works, NV, **164**
Morris Kirkland, 157
Mount Morgan, Australia, **146, 163, 167, 206**

Nevada, NV, 109
New Almaden, CA, **181, 182, 183**, 185
New Idria, CA, 231
North Star, CA, **130**, 199, **209**
Number One Sand Plant, SD, 158

Old Hundred, CO, 218
Omaha and Grant Smelting Co., 171
Ontario, UT, 130, 209, 218
Ophir, NV, 143, 219
Oregon Co., NV, 142

Palmer & Nichols, 216
Parrot, MT, 65, **223**
Pelican, 216
Pioneer Reduction Works, CA, 143, 144
Plymouth, CA, 142

Racine, SD, 216
Revenue, CO, 46, 64, 203
Rickett's Mill, CO, 103
Robinson Gold Mines, South Africa, 154
Rough and Ready, MT, 193

San Juan and New York Mining and Smelting Co., 171
Savage, NV, 139
Scales & Wagner, ID, 193
Silver King, UT, **i, 215**
Sladen Malartic, 157
Smuggler (Aspen), CO, 207
Smuggler (Pandora), CO, 105
Standard, CA, **218**
Stanford, NV, 136, **137**, 138, 140, 216
Stormont, UT, 140
Sunnyside, CO, 128, 196

Taylor & Brunton Sampler, CO, 123
Terra, SD, **129**
Tesora, NV, 142
Tomboy, CO, 231
Tonopah Mining Co., NV, 231, 232

Utica, CA, 158

What Cheer, CO, 216
White Cap, NV, 236
Wolverton, UT, **193**

Yellow Jacket, ID, 158

Miscellaneous

Allis-Chalmers, 157
Allison-Bannan, 82
American Bridge Co., 218
Ames Powerhouse, CO, **110**
Bessie Brady (steamer), 114
Blatchley, 80
Bryer, 83
Bucyrus (dredge), 13, **14**
Burleigh Rock Drill Co., 80
C. H. Shaw Pneumatic Tool Co., 85
Caminetti Act, 12
Cassel Co., 154
Cerro Gordo Freighting Co., 95
Charcoal Burner's Association, 115
Clayton, 83
Cobb and Hesselmeyer, 109
Cottonwood Charcoal Kilns, 114
Cuter (horse), 99
Denver & Rio Grande Railroad, 102, 103, 171
Denver Rock Drill Co., 86
Edison General Electric Co., 84
Findlayson, 105
Fish Creek War, 115

Fulton Engineering, 109
Gardner-Denver Co., 86
Gardner Compressor Co., 86
Giant Powder Co., 74, 234
Graves, Fielding L. (dredge), 13
Hodgson, 104
Iler Rock Drill Co., 85
Ingersoll-Sergeant Rock Drill Co., 84
Ingersoll-Rand, 85
Ingersoll Rock Drill Co., 80
Maudie (burro), 100
Michigan Central Iron Works, 114
Northern Pacific Railroad, 177
Olmstead Generating Plant, 110, 221
Panic of '73, 115
Panic of '93, 176, 224
Prunes (burro), 94
Rae Electric System, 138
Rainbow Route, 102
Rand & Waring Drill and Compressor Co., 81
Rand Drill Co., 83, 84
Rend Rock Powder Corporation, 76
Risdon (dredge), 13
Sawyer Decision, 12
Sergeant & Cullingsworth Co., 80
Sergeant Drill Co., 83
Severance & Holt, 80
Sherman Silver Purchase Act, 175
Siemens & Halske, 85
Silverton Railroad, 102, 103
Sutter's mill, **1**
Swem, 104
Telluride Electric Power Transmission Co., 110
Tonopah Railroad, 102
Union Pacific, **91**
U.S. Fuel, 116
U.S. Railroad, 103
Utah Central Line Railroad, 122
Utah Southern Railroad, 225
Virginia and Truckee Railroad, 102
War Department, 100
Ward Charcoal Kilns, NV, **114**
Wells Fargo & Co., 25, **139**

Rear Cover Photographs

Top down:

1. Placer miners in Routt County, Colorado 1903
   Courtesy USGS

2. Mine crew ca 1900, probably in Butte, Montana
   Courtesy World Museum of Mining, Butte, MT

3. Machine drilling at the Gold Coin mine, near Anaconda, Montana, 1905
   Courtesy World Museum of Mining, Butte, MT

4. Muckers
   Courtesy Mount Morgan Historical Museum, Inc.

5. Dumping Slag
   Courtesy Mount Morgan Historical Museum, Inc.